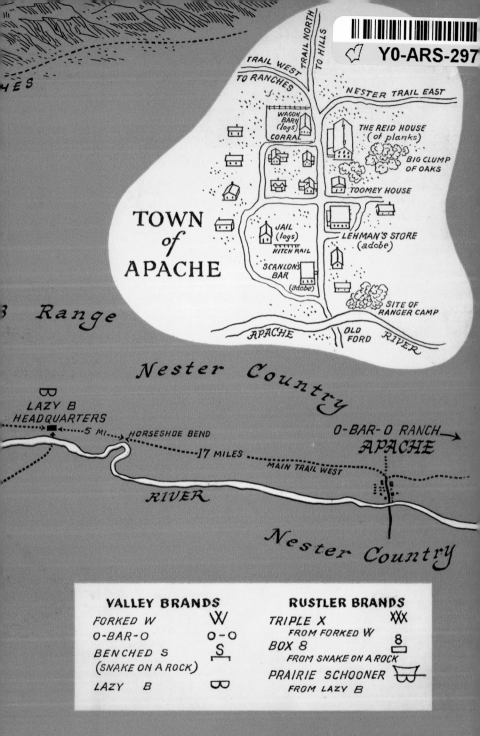

TRAIL NORTH
TO HILLS

TRAIL WEST
TO RANCHES

NESTER TRAIL EAST

WAGON
BARN
(logs)
CORRAL

THE REID HOUSE
(of planks)

BIG CLUMP
OF OAKS

TOOMEY HOUSE

**TOWN
of
APACHE**

JAIL
(logs)
HITCH RAIL

LEHMAN'S STORE
(adobe)

SCANLON'S
BAR
(adobe)

SITE OF
RANGER CAMP

Range

Nester Country

APACHE   OLD   RIVER
            FORD

LAZY B
HEADQUARTERS
◄---- 5 MI ----► HORSESHOE BEND

O-BAR-O RANCH →
APACHE

---- 17 MILES ---- MAIN TRAIL WEST

RIVER

Nester Country

VALLEY BRANDS		RUSTLER BRANDS	
FORKED W	W	TRIPLE X	XXX
O-BAR-O	O-O	FROM FORKED W	
BENCHED S	S	BOX 8	8
(SNAKE ON A ROCK)		FROM SNAKE ON A ROCK	
LAZY B	B	PRAIRIE SCHOONER	
		FROM LAZY B	

SMOKE UP THE VALLEY

Smoke Up the Valley

AN HISTORICAL NOVEL OF TEXAS IN THE '70's

By

MONTE BARRETT

THE BOBBS-MERRILL COMPANY, INC.

Publishers

INDIANAPOLIS   NEW YORK

CONTENTS

SMOKE UP THE VALLEY

Chapter 1 A TWIG IS BENT

OLD CRUMP was bad spooked. The sudden clamor of her bell, mellowed by distance, marked her headlong course across the hill, back toward the cabin. Grady halted the mare, leaned against the plow haft, listened.

The clatter ended as abruptly as it had started. That bothered him. A running cow didn't generally stop that quick. He stood quiet, his ears strained for further sound. There was nothing to hear but the lazy midday whisper of spring, the murmur of leaves astir, the drone of insects on the wing.

Maybe she lost her bell, he thought. It could have been a snake that spooked her so. Still he stood alert, his gray eyes searching the borders of the field and beyond. They were young eyes—he was only thirteen—but their gaze was sharp. He'd learned a heap the past two years, since Pa rode off to fight the Yankees. The men from the border stretches had been early to volunteer and once they were gone the Comanches started sifting back, cautiously at first, then with increasing boldness as they felt the country's weakness. Soon the whole long frontier of Texas was a bloody scar, red with scalps and the flame of blazing cabins.

Grady was canny in the woods. Pa had taught him a lot; the rest he'd picked up himself, lately. These days you learned fast or the Indians lifted your hair. His rifle was tilted against a stump in mid-field. He knew better than to leave it near the fence, where someone might beat him to it. He glanced from it to the field, still only half plowed, and was reluctant to stop, yet prompted to go and investigate. It was nearly two miles back to the house. Pa had come over here to fence a bottom-land field for corn the winter before he left.

Then, far off, he heard it—a gobbling sound, like the racket of excited turkeys, only shriller. The dread cry chilled him as he stooped to loose the trace chains. That was one of the earliest lessons he'd learned—hide the horses when Indians were about. The gobbling still was in his ears as he grabbed his rifle and swung to the mare's back.

He heard two shots—sharp little coughs from this distance—and took heart from the sound. If Ma had reached the house. . . if the girls . . .

Worry downed his caution at first. He headed the mare up the narrow trail, dug his moccasins in her ribs, bent low to dodge the overhanging boughs that choked the path here in the bottom. The brush thinned on the hillside and he swerved to avoid the crest. No sense making a target of himself against the sky. "I can't abide a gun-shy turntail," Pa always said, "but a brash fumble-fist is worse. He just gets hisself kilt without helpin' nobody." It was odd, Grady thought, recollecting things Pa had said at a time like this, almost as if he could hear the slow rumble of his voice, and him dead a year now, at a far-off place called Shiloh. Overflow from the spring birthed a creek, with brush woolly on its flanks. Grady circled to reach this cover about a mile below the house and hid the mare there, fuming at the time it took to tie her. If she'd been a cow pony instead of a work animal a flip of the reins over her head would have tied her to the ground. No yells now. No shots. He gripped his rifle tighter, in fingers slippery with sweat.

The quiet tortured him. If only a gun would slam, to tell him they still held out! He fretted most at the slowness of his gait. Time was slipping by. He wanted to run, but was too wise for such foolishness. He wouldn't be much use dead. He dodged the open fields, used up precious minutes working his way through the scrub, his eyes always busy ahead searching each shadow before he slid to its safety.

The fear that turned him watery wasn't for himself. He couldn't forget Pa's warning to Molly. "Never let the Injuns cotch ye alive, girl," he'd said. "Take a knife to yorself fust."

"She's only fifteen, Pa, still just a child," Ma had protested.

"Growed up enough for red appetites, Ma. It's time she knowed."

Pa had scowled. The words came out slow. You could tell he didn't like the chore of saying it. " 'T ain't no picnic fer a man to be took by Injuns, Molly, but they've got a special hell fer women." He looked to Ma for help but she had turned away. "They'd pass you around, till every buck had his fill of you. Understand what I'm sayin'?"

"Yes, Pa."

"Thar's plenty things wuss than just plain dyin', child. Mind, I don't aim to let nothin' happen, not while I'm hyar, but this is somethin' you had to know."

Off to the right Grady marked where the cow had fallen, two feathered shafts upright in her flank. He stopped, held his breath to listen better. Even the birds had turned still. That was when he smelled the smoke. He forgot some of his caution, moved faster, sure he knew what it meant if the cabin was ablaze.

From the edge of the clearing he could see the smoke, just beginning to sift from the windows, and noticed how its gray wisps curled through the weathered shakes and rolled across the roof. The Indians were gone. He started to run. Closer, he could see Ma, sprawled in the open door. In his haste to reach her, he missed Betty, almost stumbled over her body half hidden by the berry bushes.

It didn't look like Ma. He'd seen scalped bodies before but never one he'd known and loved in life. It wasn't the cruel red wound that shocked him so much as the sag of her face. Severed muscles had let it fall into a blurred mockery of the image he remembered.

"Christ!"

He picked her up tenderly, carried her out under the trees and brought Betty to lie beside her. The child was scalped too, but she was only ten and the knife hadn't altered her face so much. Or maybe he couldn't see her so well. His eyes had grown blurred and he swallowed against the dry choking of his throat.

But Molly? Where was she? He turned and ran back to the house. The flames, a bright wall now, drove him away from the door. If she was in there, he was too late.

"Molly," he called softly. "Molly! Molly!"

The wind was from the south and he could reach the window on that side. The interior of the room was bright but he couldn't see his other sister there. Molly was the oldest, seventeen now and 'most a woman. Again he remembered what Pa had said. She had known what to expect if the Indians caught her. They'd had no warning. The open door told its story of surprise. Still, if Molly'd been away when the Indians struck, maybe she was hiding out. He turned away, called her again, louder this time.

He found her later when he went to the spring to slake the dry ache of his throat. There was an overturned milk pail on the lip of the water. That started him searching there.

He sobbed when he saw her. Pa had been right! This was so much worse. Her dress was torn away. The grass around her was trampled. That and her twisted body told the story of her struggle against her ravishers. The torture had ended with mutilation. One young breast was severed. The same knife had ripped her abdomen. Grady sank to his knees, wrapped her gently in the tatters of her dress.

"Christ!" he moaned. "Christ!"

He looked mighty small, even for thirteen, a-straddlin' a big-boned plow mare, and the old-style muzzle loader looked longer than the boy. Headed west, Tom Williams saw, as if he didn't know he'd left the last settlement behind where he forded the river at Apache. Just a couple of ranches, and them far apart, between here and nothin' but Indian country.

Tom reined in his horse. "Where you headin', son?"

"West."

"Might be yor aimin' for Lazy B headquarters. If you follow the river you can't miss it, 'bout twelve miles on. The Blakes are friends of mine."

"I don't know 'em."

A curious little cuss, Tom thought. Not hostile, exactly, but he sure was stingy with his conversation. Tom's glance sharpened, read the misery in the young eyes and caught the dogged set of his chin. He slowed his horse down to the mare's plodding gait, disturbed by what he saw.

"There's only one other ranch out this way, the Forked W. That's mine. We're sixteen miles beyond Blakes's."

This brought no answer.

"After that, nothin' but Comanches an' hell, son. These are bad times to be ridin' that range."

"I know. That's where I'm headin'."

He didn't get the story of the Indian raid that had wiped out the boy's family all at once. It came little by little, in response to prodding questions. They were several miles farther on their way before the whole grisly picture was complete.

"So you're huntin' yourself some Comanches." He kept his voice matter of fact. He'd already plumbed the youngster's stubbornness.

"I aim to scalp every red bastard I can find." Bitterness and pain, determination and the barest hint of a sob were all choked together in the stormy voice.

"Can't say I blame you. In your boots I'd feel the same way." Tom wanted to tell the kid how hopeless his task was but knew he lacked the words for it. This was a case for his wife. Ma would know how to handle it. Somehow he must find a way to take the boy to the ranch. He turned the problem over in his mind for the space of another mile.

"First thing you need is a good saddle horse," he finally commented. "One that can tote you into trouble and out again. That mare ain't cut out for the job. Your Comanche's a good horseman. To scalp 'em you've got to catch 'em.

"And a new breach-loadin' rifle would be a help, too. Course I'm sure you're right handy with the one you've got, but when you're up agin numbers, you want to be ready for 'em."

Grady stole a glance at Tom's fine mount. "Where'd a body get such things?"

"I reckon I could spare you a bronc. Stop by the ranch an' we'll fix us up a swap."

"Your horse is worth two of mine. I ain't askin' favors."

"Whoa, son. You're gettin' ahead of me. Who said anything 'bout favors? I'm shorthanded. You can stay over with us a spell and work out the difference." He saw the boy eyeing his horse again. "Maybe we could work up the same sort of swap on a new rifle, too. I'd like to see you fitted out proper, where you're goin'.'"

Grady rode on to the Forked W with him that day.

Ma took to him right from the first, just as Tom had. They both cottoned to his sturdy truculence, and the way he rebelled at favors. But it was the tight line of his lips and the hurt, lost look in his eyes that got under their skin.

"I can't tarry long, ma'am," he told Ma right off. "I'm huntin' Indians."

In her wise way, Ma didn't argue. Instead she said: "'T ain't in me to hinder anybody that's huntin' Comanches, Grady, but 't won't harm you none to rest here a spell and put some meat on your bones." Later, when she learned more of his story, she broached the subject in a roundabout way.

"Ever roped a calf, Grady?"

He shook his head. "I'm a good hand with a plow, though."

"Ever rode a bronc?"

Again he shook his head.

"Now me, if I was aimin' to be a cow hand—" Ma sank into a rocker beside him on the porch—"I'd start a-learnin' from the ground up. For ridin', I reckon I'd start with the gentled critters and work up gradual, till I could set any bronc they fetched in. I reckon maybe I'd throw my first rope at a post and then work up to calves till finally I knowed just what I was goin' to catch in my loop before it left my hand. Then I'd be ready for any steer on the range. Nothin' comes too hard if you work up to it, easy. I reckon it's the same way fightin' Indians. First I'd learn all the tricks of it, slow and easy."

"I can shoot with the best," the boy volunteered.

"Sure you can. But 't ain't just shootin'. There's ridin' and' trackin' an' a heap of other knowledge goes into the makin' of a real Indian fighter. What you want to do—just go out an' shoot a Comanche or two, before they get you? I'd rather get me the know-how an' keep on makin' 'em pay for what they've done, year after year. One or two dead Indians won't even up your score. Hell's bells, you ain't ready to tackle all the Comanches in Texas till you've learned a heap."

There was suspicion in Grady's eyes. "You're just tryin' to put me off," he said accusingly.

Ma had a hearty ring to her laugh. "Even Indians won't fool you easy, son. Now you hark to what I'm sayin', 'cause there's no foolishness in it." She tilted the rocker toward him and her voice sank to a confidential murmur. "If anybody ever had cause to go out an' scalp himself a whole damn passle of red-skinned skunks it's you. Standin' in your boots, that's what I'd be hankerin' to do myself. But s'pose you go before you're ready, s'pose you lose your hair before you've evened up the score? That won't help nobody. That's what I'm tryin' to tell you, boy. First learn how to do the job right. When that time comes, hell's bells, I'll stake you to a bag of bullets an' a scalpin' knife. I reckon you're man enough to hear straight talk an' that's what I'm givin' you."

Grady nodded. "That sounds like my Pa. He never could abide a brash fumble-fist. That kind just gets hisself kilt."

Ma wheedled him into staying just a week or two at a time, at first, to learn the needed lessons. There were always new things he must master. She had plenty of help. Every hand on the ranch volunteered after they heard the story, and most of them had something to contribute to such an education. They were shorthanded on account of the war but aside from increasing vigilance against the Indians, there were spells when there was little to do.

"We're just hangin' on, holdin' back the redskins, tryin' to keep the outfit together till better times," was the way Ma explained it. The market for cattle was stifled. Hard money was almost nonexistent. Most

outfits weren't even branding calves. Still the Forked W worked doggedly on, managed to trade a few yearlings to the settlers around Apache,
a few steers to Lehman's Store against the mounting debt for needed
staples. That first winter Tom took them on a buffalo hunt, over near
the Breaks. There was still a market for the hides. Tom had come home
from the army with a bullet through his shoulder. After the wound
mended, the Indian trouble kept him there. Peg Denham had left a leg
at Shiloh, was still awkward on his stump.

"Shiloh?" Grady's eyes widened. "Maybe you knew Henry Scott
there."

"No, can't say I did, son. There was a mighty heap of folks at Shiloh,
all mixed up. Why?"

The light in the young eyes dimmed. "That was my Pa. He was kilt
there."

Old Peg hesitated the barest instant. "Not . . . not *Texas* Henry
Scott? Not *that* Henry Scott?"

"In Terry's Rangers, he was."

"I should have knowed, son." Peg studied his young friend through
narrowed lids. "Yep, I should have guessed it. Why, you favor your Pa,
right smart."

"We never rightly heard what happened to Pa—just the list sayin'
he was kilt. I reckon you wouldn't know?"

Peg took a deep breath. "Know? Why, son, I was right thar. I seed
it with my own two eyes. Your Pa was the God-damnedest soldier in the
whole Secesh army, an' who's got a better right to hear it than you?
'Twas the second day at Shiloh an' things was nip an' tuck. We had
'em runnin' the day before, but now they throwed a new army at us. I
ain't likely to fo'get that day. We was a-holdin' the woods at Shiloh
Church yard an' had just beat off one attack, when all of a suddent all
hell let loose. A regiment of Bluecoats had broke through on our
left an' come up behint us. A lot of the boys was down in that first
volley an' the rest was shook up mighty bad. They had us betwixt an'
between 'em. The line broke. It shore looked like we was headed for a
bad case of scampers. That's when I noticed this here feller—your
Pa. Thar he stood, a-holdin' his ground, a-firin' away as cool as Billy-
be-damned.

"'Come on,' he yells. 'We've run them Yankees in front of us, now
it's time we gave this batch a dose of the same medicine.'

"With that he starts chargin', all by hisself at first. Then he yipped out with the good ol' Rebel yell. Every man jack of us heard him. Even them with feathers in thar heels was shamed by the sight of one lone man, chargin' an army by hisself. We picked up his yell so strong I reckon they thought we was a whole damn army corps, a-tearin' through them woods after your Pa.

"That's how he died, Grady, a-leadin' us through that woods. But we turned them Yankees back, thanks to him. Ol' General Beauregard hisself said so, after the fightin' ended."

Ma heard the story. Later she found Peg alone. "I thought you lost your leg the *first* day at Shiloh," she said.

The grizzled veteran fumbled with his hat brim in confusion. "I wasn't lyin' just for the hell of it, Ma. You know me better'n that. That young'un *needed* to hear somethin' 'bout his folks."

Ma held out her hand. "You're the damnedest liar in Apache County, Peg, but I love you for it. And if you ever tell him different, I'll skin you alive."

Peg wasn't riding again yet, but his skill with a rope was uncanny. He spent hours teaching Grady all his tricks.

Pedro Ramirez was the wrangler. He had a liking for the youngster too, took seriously the responsibility of making him a rider. "I work myself out of a job," he told Ma once. "*Muy pronto,* the *joven* will top all the broncs here by himself. Then you won't need Pedro."

"What's a *joven?*" Grady demanded suspiciously.

"Hell's bells, he ain't callin' you names." Ma laughed. "A *joven* is a youngster."

The lessons that Grady allotted the most time were taught by the taciturn Brazos. If he had another name, no one at the Forked W knew it. Brazos was a waddy.

"What's the difference between a waddy and a ranny, Ma?" Grady wanted to know.

"Well, a ranny is a top hand."

"Brazos is more'n a match for most riders."

"But he ain't steady," Ma pointed out. "He's an extra hand. Every cow outfit needs spare hands come spring. An' for trail herds, too. I reckon that's where the word comes from—waddin'—somethin' to fill in with. Your waddy don't stay hitched long. He's here a spell an' yonder a spell, always driftin' on. But plenty of 'em are top hands, an' no mistake."

Brazos didn't fit into the close-knit family spirit that marked the

Forked W outfit. Both Ma and Tom were responsible for it. The biggest horses in the *remuda* were always set aside for Tom because of his size, and his strength equaled his bulk. It was the unspoken pride of the outfit that no man could match him. There was flint in him, a compelling drive that knew no obstacles. A man of flabby temper couldn't have built a one-horse shirttail outfit into a spread like the Forked W on this frontier. But the hard core of him was smoothed over with gentleness. He spoke in a slow drawl and usually it was "Let's do this" rather than "Go do that." Men liked to ride with Tom Williams, took pride in the outfit.

Ma was their friend. She patched their britches, shared their grub, wrote letters when necessary. When they were sick she nursed them along like dogies, and there was tenderness in her hands. They took their troubles to her, too. But there were no frills to Ma. She swore like a man and rode like one. When they were shorthanded she spent as many hours in the saddle each day as any of them. Then she wore britches and boots, like everybody else, but come sundown, she was always in a dress.

Two big cottonwoods sheltered the main house but there was seldom time to use their shade by day. After supper, though, this was the gathering spot. Ma had a hickory rocker there and when evenings were long, there was usually some mending in her lap that kept her fingers busy until the light faded. The rest lounged on the ground to swap their yarns. "Kickin' up corral dust," Ma called it, when the tales were biggity.

They all looked forward to Sundays. Ma spent that morning in the kitchen, baking something special to add to the cook's fare, "just to let the boys know they ain't eatin' at the chuck wagon."

This homey flavor was strange to Brazos. He was the tight-lipped, cat-eyed kind, who kept his past to himself. No one ever asked where he was from. In easier times he wouldn't have stayed on the pay roll long, but he was competent and, whatever his troubles elsewhere, he'd washed off his war paint here. He wasn't quarrelsome.

One day, watching Grady's patient aim with a rifle, he whipped out his six gun and let three bullets go into the tree the boy was using for a target. There was awe in Grady's eyes.

"But I was aimin' at that knothole."

"Listen, kid, when you're fightin' Indians, each bullet counts whether you hit 'em in the eye or in the belly. I didn't miss the tree, did I?"

It was the speed of it that captured the youngster's imagination. One instant the pistol was in Brazos' holster; a second later it was spitting in his hand and the bullets found their mark.

"That's something I'd better learn," he said.

Brazos spilled the bullets from the gun into his palm. "It'll take a heap of practice before you're ready for any shootin'," he warned. "You'll probably get tired and quit before I trust you with lead."

They started with a single roll. "Best practice there is," Brazos commented. "It limbers up your fingers, gets you used to the feel of your weapons, and once you've learned it, your pistol will always come out cocked."

He demonstrated, fast at first, and the pistol flashed in the sun; then slowly, so that Grady could follow the movement. It began with the weapon in firing position, the forefinger in the trigger guard. The spinning movement, or roll, was forward. The butt flipped upward as it was released, described a full circle, end over end, his finger as the axis. The trick was in catching the hammer with extended thumb, so that the pistol was cocked by its own weight at the end of the maneuver. Nor would he demonstrate anything else until Grady had practiced the roll to his satisfaction. That took some days.

Tom had a spare six gun that he let Grady use. Even in the last notch the belt sagged around the boy's thin hips and the cartridge loops prevented piercing another hole to tighten it. Brazos laughed when he saw its droop. "A holster's got to fit, kid, right down to the width of the last hair if you want to be good. That's more than half your speed in a draw."

Tom gave indulgent consent when appealed to, and the belt was shortened by cutting out a section in the back. The sliced ends were laced together with a thong. "So you can let it out as you grow," Brazos explained. "Mind what I say! You've always got to know exactly where to touch that butt. There's no time to grope or guess in a draw. If it's hung too low, you've got to reach. That wastes time. If it's too high, your muzzle will catch on the holster top. That's even worse."

He draped the belt expertly, so that Grady's hand fell naturally to the gun butt, with the elbow only slightly crooked. Another change was necessary. Tom's holster had the usual flap. This had to be cut away. "You'd catch a hidefull of arrows whilst you was fumblin' with that fool thing," Brazos grumbled.

Practice started in earnest then. Always they began in the same way, Grady's arms hanging loosely at his sides. A snap of Brazos' fingers was the signal. Grady's hand whipped to the pistol butt, the forefinger slid into the trigger guard, outstretched thumb spread over the hammer.

Hours spent learning the roll made sense now. The thumb cocked the hammer as tightening fingers pulled the weapon free. The pistol muzzle traveled only inches, barely enough to bring the barrel level, before the trigger was snapped from the hip. There were niceties about this. Body balance was important. This was best achieved with legs slightly spread, weight evenly distributed on the balls of the feet. Movement was hastened by starting with the arm hanging free, but steadiness of aim was gained by clamping the upper arm tight against the body in the split second when the fingers first reached their grip.

Always they worked with an empty weapon. When Grady complained of this Brazos sometimes varied the lesson by showing him tricks. One was the Road Agent's draw. In effect, it was the reverse of the single roll, although much more deceptive. It started with the pistol extended as if in surrender, butt foremost, but the forefinger was hooked through the trigger guard, as always. The spin was backward, started with a slight upward jerk of the hand. "There's always a moment when your opponent relaxes his guard, when he's reaching for your gun," said Brazos. "That's the instant for this. As with any draw, it's all a matter of timing." Added speed was acquired by pulling the trigger back in firing position the instant thumb pressure reached the hammer. Shooting was simply a matter of lifting the thumb as the gun reached the horizontal. It was very fast.

One lesson Brazos stressed constantly. "Never go for a gun unless you mean to use it, kid. That's one big advantage a lead slinger always has. He ain't bothered 'bout what he aims to do. He knows, and shoots while the other feller's makin' up his mind."

Occasionally Grady was allowed to try shooting from the hip, but a month passed and still he practiced his draw with an empty gun. He chafed under the restraint, eager to try his progress. One night he "borrowed" some cartridges from Tom's belt. Generally he did his shooting out behind the big corral and as a rule Brazos went with him. Next morning he slipped off alone, before breakfast, determined to put his skill to a real test. Here was a gnarled oak, already scarred from his marksmanship. He squared away, feet slightly spread and weight nicely balanced; he gave himself the word and went for his gun. He was too eager, let fly before he'd leveled the barrel and the bullet kicked up dust at his feet.

He was disgusted. Next time it would be different. Again he took his stance.

Brazos had heard the first shot. He came stampeding around the corral. Huddled against the rails were half a dozen dogies that had been herded in the day before. They spooked up at his approach, scattered running, just as Grady drew the second time. His bullet drilled one of the racing calves.

He was standing there, bewilderment on his face, when Brazos reached him and yanked the smoking six gun from his hand.

"Didn't I tell you you wasn't ready for that?" he growled. "If you won't pay me any heed, I've a good mind to call these lessons off."

"I reckon we can stand some veal for supper," was Tom's only comment, but Ma was plumb vexed and made no secret of it.

"I call to mind once when I tried to raise some chickens," she said. "We had an onery hound that was plumb set agin it, I reckon. Any rate, every time I turned my back, that dog killed another pullet. Hell's bells, I never saw the like! We tried every way to break him. Whipping didn't seem to do no good.

"Finally, one of the boys came up with an idee. Next time a chicken was killed, we tied it around that houn' dog's neck. He didn't like it a speck, tried ever' way he could figger to get rid o' that carcass. He'd paw at it, he'd roll—Lord, he even tried to run from it, racin' all over the place till he was plumb give out. I never set eyes on a critter so sick of anything in my life.

"An' you know what? That cured him. Seemed like he was so plumb wore out with that one carcass, he lost his taste for chicken, from then on."

She eyed Grady sternly. "I'm wonderin' if maybe that wouldn't work with you? Maybe tyin' that calf around your neck might cure you of this hankerin' for gun play."

"It's a purty hefty calf for that, Ma," Tom put in.

"Well then, we might try the hide. It's time we took some kind of steps."

Grady had never seen Ma so put out. He half expected her to carry out the threat.

The trouble was, Ma was uneasy about those six-gun lessons. "What are we runnin' here, a school for killers?" she demanded. "How'm I goin' to gentle this boy down with the whole damn outfit agin me? I don't like it. You want him to grow up to be like Brazos?"

"He won't," Tom promised. "'T ain't in him. It's Injuns he's got stuck in his craw, Ma. These are just some more of those lessons you promised him."

Just the same he gave Brazos his time the following month. Work slacked up in the fall and he made an excuse of that.

Brazos taught Grady one final lesson. Up to then, nothing had been said of his impending departure. They were riding in from a day hunting calves.

"Still bent on learning a fast draw, kid?"

Grady nodded.

"Then mind what I'm tellin' you. Pretty good ain't enough. The second-best man in a draw gen'rally winds up in a pine box. You've got to practice and keep on practicin'. Don't fo'get to roll your gun plenty. Nothin' beats it for timin' and keepin' your fingers limber. Now I'm going to show you a new wrinkle."

He dismounted, emptied the shells from his gun and drew a poker chip from his pocket. This he placed on the back of his right hand, extended before him, shoulder high. His movement was deliberate, at first; the arm twisted slowly, the chip slid off. Then his arm flashed, faster than the eye could follow. Before the chip hit the ground, his six gun was out, cocked, leveled, and had clicked three times.

Brazos grinned his satisfaction. "Three shots is tolable fast. Any time you can shoot three times before the chip lands, you'll know you're doin' all right. It's an easy way to check up on yourself. If you can't do it, don't start no fights."

Grady learned the poker-chip draw. Brazos left the chip with him when he rode away.

About once a month a wagon was sent the thirty-eight miles to town to freight back supplies. Apache was still a town with the hair on and Ma, who seldom interfered, made one hard-and-fast rule about these trips. Any hand who took Grady into Scanlon's Saloon would have her to reckon with. Since they all were fond of the kid—and feared Ma's wrath—her wishes were respected. There was little else there, except Lehman's General Store, and after one or two dull trips, the youngster avoided the town. It failed to interest him, even when he grew older and there was none to stop him if he visited Scanlon's. He seldom went to town once in a year. He was a stranger there.

Most supplies came out by the barrel or gunny sack—flour, beans, molasses, salt pork, potatoes. There were few delicacies available and nothing perishable could outlast the long trip. Once a barrel of dried apples was unloaded at the ranch for use in Ma's special Sunday baking. They would keep indefinitely. This was something new to Grady. Ma gave him some to munch and he found them so tasty that later, unnoticed, he slipped back into the kitchen and helped himself to a hatful. Tom had bought him a new, high-crowned hat that held fully a couple of quarts.

All afternoon he gorged himself. This created an almost unquenchable thirst. He made several trips to the spring, was as free with the water as he had been with the dried fruit.

Then the pain began. Air was what he thought he needed and he made his way to the corral—where the water trough was handy. The sickness came in dizzy waves. His belt was about to cut him in two. He loosened it with fumbling fingers. That relief was only temporary. His britches were unbearably tight in the waist. He loosened them, too, and stared with dizzy, horrified eyes at his protruding stomach, frightened by what he saw, yet too ill to care much. "I reckon I've got the bloat," he told himself. Dimly he remembered hearing, back in the old days, of a neighbor's cow that had died that way. He laid down, closed his eyes, sure that he would share the same fate.

Pedro found him there, face up to the sky and green around the gills. One look at that bulging belly sent the *vaquero* running for Ma.

"What's wrong with him?" she asked, reaching for the medicine shelf. With one hand she grabbed the liniment bottle, the other closed over the calomel box. "Hell's bells, Pedro, can't you talk?"

"Señora, I don't know for sure," he answered reluctantly. "But if *he* was a *she*——" He brandished both arms over his abdomen in a fat arc.

Ma grunted, and chose the paregoric. She knew the swelling power of dried fruit in water. "Don't you go namin' no babies yet, Pedro," she advised, as she hurried off.

Ma's medicine worked, but it took Grady a long time to live down the bunkhouse jokes about his whelping. Every time someone found a motherless dogie and brought it in, he could count on being asked if it was his.

Profanity was commonplace around the ranch. It was mostly clean swearing, ran largely to hells and damns. There was a clear-cut line drawn between this and filth, however. Throughout the ranch country, certain words were not tolerated, could bring on gun play. Grady was quick to learn the common vocabulary. One day Ma heard him trying to corral some stubborn mossy-horns, wily old steers that had eluded too many roundups. While he was turning one back, others would scatter.

His patience wore thin and he swore like a bone-seasoned waddy. "God damn you to hell" was his favorite, overworked expression.

Ma scowled but she said nothing to him in front of the other hands. Later, at the house, she brought up the subject.

"But there can't be any harm in it, Ma," he protested.

"Why can't there?"

"Well, you swear, don't you?"

Ma frowned, studied the smoke curling blue from the end of her cigarette. "I reckon maybe I've been ridin' a man's range too long to act much like a lady," she answered slowly. "Anyhow, I s'pose it's what's in your heart that matters most to God. Just the same, let's you an' me leave Him out of it an' stick to a little plain cussin'. I will if you will. What do you say?"

"I didn't know you felt that way about it, Ma. I reckon I'd try to do most anything you asked."

She held out her hand and they shook on it. "We'll both try. Hell's bells, I'll bet I've bitten off a bigger job than you have, son."

They both kept their word. Occasionally, when Grady slipped, he'd look up to see Ma's eyes on him, but after a time this occurred only rarely.

Ma was right. It was harder for her. She put her mind to the problem, after she discovered its difficulty, decided to center on one expression, to the exclusion of all else. That was hell's bells.

Once a new hand called her "Ol' Hell's Bells." He meant no harm by it but that didn't spare him from Peg's wrath. "Lucky for you the other boys didn't hear that," she warned. "There'd be a shootin'. And if you ever do it again, I'll draw on you myself."

Sometimes Ma thought Grady had forgotten his determination to go off hunting Comanches. He quit talking of it. The storm was gone from his eyes. But there was still a stubborn set to his chin and tight little lines at the corners of his mouth, for all he was so young. When Curly Stark got back from the army, the boy became his shadow. Curly was *segundo* at the ranch, Tom's right hand, an old-timer whose memory stretched back across many an Indian fight. No one in the valley could read the sign of a trail as he could. Cow-camp logic had earned him his name. His head was as slick as a peeled onion. Years of sun squint had left a crisscross of trails on his face; some of these had worn into deeper gullies, like the game paths around a water hole. Curly taught him trackin' and Indian ways. Grady had a good start. He was soundless in the woods. Curly gave him the same stealth on the plains, each lesson punctuated by the story of how and where it was learned, often at the cost of a life.

The first mule Grady ever saw was ridden by Loose Joe. There was nothing but horses in the valley. Joe was as black as a blizzardy night, had been a slave before the war, over in the East Texas plantation country around Hempstead. He'd spent the days since freedom in aimless wandering, stopping in one place only long enough to earn his way with chores, the mule his single possession.

There was a story in his coming. Peg Denham and Link Tatum had driven to town to freight out supplies and had taken advantage of their rare visit to celebrate at Scanlon's Saloon. On such occasions, Peg was loquacious and always insisted on telling the same story—with a few embellishments—of how he lost his leg at Shiloh. This was a particularly fine opportunity. Most Forked W riders had tired of the yarn but Link was a new hand. He listened patiently while the tide of Shiloh rose and fell, its greatest drama reserved for the point where Peg's leg was lost.

"You know, my real name's Harry," Peg confided in conclusion, "but ever since then I've been known as Ol' Peg Denham."

Link murmured his sympathy and called for another drink, thinking the subject finally ended, but Peg now realized he had opened a new avenue of conversation.

"You've got a nickname, too, Link." The excitement of discovery was on him. "Tell me about it. What's your real name?"

Tatum scowled. "What difference does it make?"

"A heap of diff'rence, maybe."

"Well, I'd rather not say."

Peg's dignity was offended. "Didn't I tell you how I come to be called Peg? Didn't I?"

Link Tatum normally was cautious on this subject. He was a Confederate veteran. So was every other hand on the ranch who'd been old enough to go. But firewater had loosened his tongue, too. He leaned across the table, confidentially.

" 'T ain't ever'body I'd tell," he confessed. "My real name's Lincoln—Lincoln Tatum."

Peg gasped.

When Link saw the effect of his indiscretion he glared angrily at his companion. "Don't fo'get, I'm a Confederate soldier, too," he snarled. "If you want to make somethin' of this . . ."

Fortunately for their friendship, Peg only thought it was funny. He let out a whoop and started to laugh. This mollified Link, but he decided he'd better get Peg out of there, before he spread the shameful cause of his mirth. They reached the street, reeling, but with the secret still sacred to the two of them. There was no one about at this hour but Joe, who was dozing at a corner of the building.

He lifted one sleepy eye at the disturbance.

Peg saw him. "Looky here, boy. You know who this is?"

Link tried unsuccessfully to shush him but he wouldn't be stopped. "This is Lincoln, that's who it is—Lincoln hisself."

There was magic in this name for black Joe. He was wide-awake now, stared from one ranny to the other in obvious bewilderment. He fixed his wide stare on Link. "Is yo name really Mistuh Lincoln, suh?"

"Course it is," Peg roared. "This is Ol' Lincoln hisself."

They made their way back to the wagon yard without further event. Long after they'd bedded down in their blankets, Peg kept chuckling and saying, "Lincoln."

When they awoke next morning, a mule was tethered to their wagon wheel and Joe was curled up, snoring, under a tree at a respectful distance. Link tried hard to drive the Negro away, with no success. He merely retreated a safe distance and waited.

"What you want of me?" Link's patience was in shreds.

"Nothin', Mistuh Lincoln."

"Don't call me that!"

"Yassuh, Mistuh Lincoln. Just as you says, suh."

Peg chuckled and watched. When they left town, Joe and his mule plodded after them at a safe distance. He was still at their heels when they reached the ranch, thirty-eight miles later, in spite of Link's impotent threats.

"If he wasn't just plain daft I'd shoot him," he stormed once.

"No you wouldn't." Peg grinned at him. "The pore ol' devil ain't even got a gun. You can't draw on him." Range law was Joe's protection.

Joe's devotion to Mistuh Lincoln provided merriment for all hands at the Forked W for a week. That was as long as Link Tatum could stand it. He disappeared one night, without even asking Tom for his time.

Joe stayed on. Whatever his disappointment in Mistuh Lincoln, he had found a place that suited him. No one ever went hungry here. First Tom, then Ma, tried unsuccessfully to find a useful place where he might fit in. For half an hour, on each new task, he was diligence personified. Then he lost interest. If found at all, he would be asleep in some corner. Usually he just vanished—until the next mealtime. Finally he was given a single chore, to keep the wood boxes full, given sternly to understand that if he failed in this there would be no food. Either he took the threat seriously or the task suited him. Half an hour's effort was sufficient in summer. In winter it was too chilly to nap in the corral anyway. The wood boxes stayed full.

Shiftless or not, he was a general favorite, full of good nature and an exhaustless stock of memories. When he couldn't find a word to fit his thought he coined it. One evening he was reminiscing about slavery times with unmistakable nostalgia.

"You sound as if you liked those days, Joe," Grady observed.

"Oh, yassuh. Them was *good* days."

"You got plenty of good food?"

"Oh, yassuh. Marse Tallant, he looked aftuh us mighty good. Victuals mighty tasty then, better'n they ever been since."

"What about your house, Joe? Did you have a comfortable place to live? Good clothes to wear?"

"Yassuh. We-uns war fixed up mighty comf'table them days. I ain't nevuh seed the like, since freedom."

"But I guess they worked you mighty hard?"

"Well, suh, co'se we-uns worked, but them was good times, suh. Take Sat'days, now. Marse Tallant always give the black folks a steer fo' theyselves, come Sat'day. An' no work that aftuhnoon, neither. Well, suh, we roast that steer, an' you nevuh clopped eyes on such feastin' an' singin' an' dancin' as we had, come Sat'day. Yassuh, them war *good* days."

They all had fallen silent, listening. There seemed to be a wistful note in Joe's descriptions.

"Better food, better cabins, better clothes and all that singin' and dancin'," Grady counted off the advantages. "Sounds to me like you liked those days best, Joe."

"Nosuh, I cain't rightly say that." Joe shook his head vigorously. "Them war good days, sho 'nuff, but thar's a kind of *looseness* 'bout this freedom that I's larned to like."

"Maybe Joe's earned a little looseness," Ma would say after that, if she occasionally found the wood box low. From then on, they called him Loose Joe.

All Grady's lessons weren't learned outdoors. When Ma discovered he'd never been to school she took him in hand. "You've got to know letters an' numbers," she decided. "Hell's bells, I aim for you to get somewhere, son."

Secretly he felt this a useless chore. For what he planned the other school had more value, but he wanted to please Ma and he tried hard. These lamplight sessions were trying on them both. After wearing days in the saddle, sunup to sundown, they had to fight sleep as well as the lessons, but Ma's mind was sternly set. There was no flexibility in her, once she'd started something. Each night's task lasted its full hour until, after two years, she decided she'd given him all she could. He read with facility now. His clear script surpassed the ability of her work-worn hands. It was different with numbers, though, and she hugged this little pride to herself. When it came to "calculatin'" her mind was swift and unerring. He reached the right answers; that satisfied her, but she wasn't able to give him her flair for quick, self-taught short cuts.

His stay remained on a temporary basis for a long time. The eventful days never quite crowded the vengeance out of him. This was home now. Time had blurred many of his memories but every stark detail of the Indian raid still was cruel in his mind. Sometimes he'd wake at night with Molly's butchered body in front of his eyes, or his mother's face sagging from the wound of a scalping knife.

Ma waited, was fairly sure of her ground before she broached what was on her mind. "Tom an' me, we've always wished we had a boy of our own" was the way she started. The evening's lesson had been late. Off yonder in the bunkhouse the windows had turned black. Tom was still sitting up, a new lariat stretched on the table, his fingers busy splicing in a honda for his loop. He didn't look up but his hands turned quiet.

"There's a heap of comfort, watchin' a son grow up, seein' him turn into the kind of man you'd like him to be. It's a natural hankerin' folks have for—for love." The word didn't come out easy for her and she turned brusque. "Hell's bells, even a coyote will fight for its whelps. There's nothin' strange 'bout it.

"Now Tom an' me—" her voice lost its bristle—"we know what we'd like in a boy. We've known for quite a spell he'd be a heap like you, Grady."

He understood what she was aiming at—wished he could tell her how it felt to be wanted by someone. There was a glad, warm glow, deep inside you, at the thought of having folks of your own again. Somehow he couldn't get the words out. His throat had gone tight on him. All he could do was swallow.

"How would that strike you, son?"

He tried again to say something, couldn't manage it, nodded his head instead. He was shamed by the way his eyes misted. It worried him. They wouldn't want him if he cut loose and bawled like a spooked calf. Not at his age, not real top folks like Ma and Tom. He had reckoned them the finest people living, a long time ago.

The nod was enough for Ma. Her understanding eyes had read his trouble more easily because they, too, were a little blurred. When she rounded the table, she ruffled his hair back gently, kissed him on the forehead.

He found his voice then. They didn't seem to notice how it quavered. "He-hell's bells, Ma!"

She tousled his hair again. "That has a right good sound comin' from you, son."

The awkwardness was gone. They all were laughing.

Tom wasn't much of a hand with words. "I like this fine, son" was all he said, but his arm was tight about Grady's shoulders. It was enough. They both understood.

Ma brought up the subject of his vengeance not long after that. The new understanding made it easier for them to talk.

"I used to fret a lot, Grady, never knowin' when you might light out after the Comanches."

His chin set stubbornly. "I'm still goin'. It's a job that's been ahead of me for a long time."

"Just wait for the proper time," she urged. "You're most a man now, but what good's one rifle against a thousand tomahawks? I'm not askin' you to forget, Grady, nor change your purpose. You wouldn't be who you are, if you could. All I say is, wait till the proper time. Sooner or later we've got to have a showdown with these red devils. Then you'll have company. You won't just be throwin' yourself away."

He nodded slowly. "You talked that much sense into me a long time ago, Ma. But when the right day comes, I'm goin'."

Times grew easier, after the war. There was a market, far north, for beef, and the ranges were loaded with herds that hadn't been thinned out in years. Money, almost unknown for so long, began to trickle back to the frontier. Tom sent a herd up the trail to Kansas along with the

Lazy B outfit. The hard cash it brought went a long way toward paying the notes that had been accumulating so long at August Lehman's store. He determined to trail his own herd up the following spring. There were nine hundred steers, fours and better, in the bunch they threw together. Grady was anxious to go. He knew the toil of it, the grinding months of sweat, but trail driving had the glamour of far places, the tang of adventure.

Tom shook his head when the boy asked to go, and said, "Who's goin' to look after the ranch? We'll be shorthanded here. I'll need Curly, but mostly I aim to hire trail hands for the trip. I'm countin' on you to run the outfit while I'm gone, son."

Grady couldn't argue. Tom was countin' on him. That settled it. He was disappointed, but he tried hard not to show it.

Indian trouble continued bad. The frontier was bitter. There were plenty of troops in Texas but they wore blue uniforms, came as conquerors to enforce Yankee law on a defeated people, and were garrisoned in central, populous areas where the dread Comanche cry hadn't been heard in years. Each border community fought its isolated battle to survive. The frontier asked for Rangers, organized companies of veteran Indian fighters who could carry the war to the red man. Their appeals went unheeded. Confederate veterans must not even vote, let alone be armed for fighting.

"We're just Rebels" was Peg's stormy comment when he heard this news. "The more of us gets kilt the better it suits these blue-bellied carpetbaggers."

Word of the newly organized state police reached them about a month late. Indians were particularly bad that summer—it was in '70—and Tom had sent Curly and Pedro to town with Peg to freight out supplies. They came home jubilant with the news.

"I've half a mind to jine up myself." Curly had a hankering gleam in his eye until he saw Ma's scowl. "Leastwise I would ifn you and Tom warn't so shorthanded." The damage had been done. Grady had heard and he wanted to go.

"It's just like you always said, Ma. Sooner or later the right time would come for me to go. This is it."

Tom looked uneasy. "I reckon you'd better talk this over with Ma, son."

Ma shook her head. "Nothin' to talk over," she declared. "I asked him to wait an' he waited. Hell's bells! I don't want to see you go, Grady, but I reckon you're right. This is the time. If you're goin', go in good company."

Before he left, Tom gave him a Sharp's rifle and the six gun and holster with which he'd practiced for so long. He was given his pick of the ranch horses. And both Tom and Ma rode with him as far as Apache.

"Remember we'll be waitin' for you, son," she said at their parting. "This is home. It won't be the same till you get back. I'm not keepin' you from the job you've got to do, but as soon as the score is settled, come back to us."

Grady stooped to kiss her on the cheek, a little awkwardly. Reserve was natural to them both; it was hard to break the seal on this tenderness.

Five days later he reached Austin. There was an urgency in him, now that he was on his way. He had ridden hard, and bitter memories were with him. He was sure the day of his reckoning with the Comanches was near.

The bustle of the capital confused him. Its streets were wide and there were almost as many carriages as horsemen. The frontier rode astride or in wagons; there was only one buggy in all of Apache Valley. The splendor of these vehicles amazed him. Many had two seats, bow tops, gaily painted wheels. Coachmen drove the more elaborate and these were pulled by glossy teams. Most confusing of all, their occupants often were Negroes in tall, shiny beavers. Not counting the blue-coated soldiers—they seemed to be everywhere—there were more blacks than whites on the street.

Presently he sighted a man who looked like homefolks. He wore a cowman's wide-brimmed hat and his pants were tucked into his boots. Grady reined up at the curb. "I can't make heads or tails of this place, mister," he confessed. "Maybe you can help me."

The stranger smiled. "Maybe. I will if I can."

"Where do I go to enlist in the state police?"

"The *what?*"

"I aim to join up. If you can tell me——"

"That's something I don't know." The smile had faded and the voice had lost its friendliness. "Better ask one of the Bluecoats."

The man turned away. Grady stared after him in perplexity.

"Just another Reb. Don't pay him no mind, pardner." A soldier had stopped to listen. He stepped forward, indicated the direction with a jerk of his thumb. "There's a recruiting office one block down, tother side of the street. You'll see the sign—you can't miss it."

"Thanks." Grady looked after the man who had turned so rude at his question, was tempted to follow and ask him more. This had a queer, uneasy ring to it that filled him with disquiet. No matter. He was on his way to fight Indians. This had the odor of carpetbagger trouble. He'd best stay clear of things he didn't understand.

His qualms returned when he entered the recruiting office. He didn't like the looks of what he saw. The long, narrow room was crowded. Smoke clouded the air; the stench of sweat and unwashed bodies hit him in a nauseous wave as he stepped through the door. He wondered first if these were prisoners. Many of them were recently freed Negroes. As he edged his way toward the desk at the rear, he decided he liked the black men better than the surly, unkempt whites who were gathered here. He hadn't glimpsed a real fighting man in the whole scurvy crew. The lieutenant at the desk was no exception. An unkempt beard smudged his face and a brown stain dribbled from a corner of his mouth. He took in the six gun at Grady's belt and the rifle on his arm with approval.

"You aim to jine up?"

Grady had grown cautious. "Maybe. First, I want to find out more about the state police. Where do I go for that?"

The officer threw out his chest, his manner grew pompous. "I is Looten'nt Hawkins of the state police an' I asks the questions hyar. Ifn you pleases me, maybe I let you jine up."

Grady's eyes narrowed; harsh brackets tightened at the corners of his mouth.

"Now le's see." Lieutenant Hawkins twisted his head back arrogantly, looked him over from head to foot through bloodshot eyes. "Fust I got to know is you reli'ble. Any Rebels in yo fambly?"

"What's that got to do with fighting Indians?"

"Injuns, he says!" The lieutenant's cackle attracted an audience. It echoed his scorn. "Whar you think you is, boy? We's the state police. Gov'nor Davis, he ain't lost no Injuns. I reckon he got his hands full with these damn Rebels. Now answer my questions. You got any Rebs in yo fambly?"

"Plenty." There was smoke in Grady's voice. He'd learned all he wanted to know of the state police and he couldn't still his anger. "All my folks were in the army. My father died at Shiloh, if you want to know." He stared around him at the motley recruits who had surged forward to listen, and he made no effort to hide his contempt. "You'd better get you some fightin' men for the job you're planning. This bunch of mavericks can't handle it."

"Why, he's a Reb hisself!" The lieutenant pushed back from the desk. "You can't talk to me that-a-way."

There was a warning in the crowd's growl. They had the confidence of numbers. Someone grabbed at Grady's elbow. He snapped it back sharply, felt the slap of it against flesh, and the hold was broken. The crowd at his back was what worried him. He slid around the desk in a swift stride, shifted his rifle from his right arm to his left. A six gun was better in these close quarters.

"Drop that gun!" the lieutenant barked, but he made no move to rise from his chair.

Grady backed slowly toward the rear wall. His right arm hung loosely at his side, elbow slightly crooked, the way Brazos had taught him. The crowd edged forward, surly, growling.

"Don't let him git away. He's a Reb and a bad un!" The lieutenant pointed at the open, rear door. "He's aimin' to git out that-a-way."

The mob surged forward, stopped just as abruptly, its snarl dying in its throat. Grady's hand flashed. It was no longer empty. A six gun was leveled from his hip.

"Don't move!" he called.

The speed of his draw was warning of his skill. The lieutenant and his recruits watched silently as Grady backed out the door and none ventured to follow him into the alley.

GRADY had only one thought when he slid out the back door of the recruiting office. He wanted to quit the town, rid himself of the reasty smell of that room. "The stink of carpetbaggers," he called it.

He'd left his horse out front, half expected trouble when he went for it but that was unavoidable. He saw no crowd when he turned the corner. He suspected a trap but he had to reach that horse. His six gun was holstered now but his hand was at his side, ready, when he approached the building.

It proved surprisingly easy. There was shrill excitement in the recruiting office but the crowd was massed in the back where he'd left them. He had swung into the saddle before a hoarse shout informed him that he'd been recognized. He dug in his spurs, started at a gallop, was fifty yards away when the mob boiled into the street, roaring its anger. The babble outdistanced him. Warned by it, two blue-coated soldiers ran into the street, tried to stop him with outstretched arms. The first lost his nerve, dodged when Grady headed straight for him. The second had stouter courage. He grabbed for the bridle but he didn't know cow ponies. By a quick shift of weight, Grady swerved his mount, laughed when he glanced back to see the soldier sprawled in the dust. No one else tried to stop him.

Ma recognized his tall figure in the saddle from a distance and was waiting for him at the corral when he swung to the ground. The gladness of her greeting was held back; her eyes were searching. There was something here she didn't understand. He'd barely had time for the ride to Austin and back. "It didn't take long, son." She yearned to ask him more but that wasn't her way.

"These state police aren't my kind of folks, Ma." He had never outgrown the stubborn set of his chin. "They're after the wrong kind of scalps—white scalps. I don't want any part of that outfit." He told her what had happened.

"We won't get much help against the Indians from them" was Ma's grim comment.

"We probably won't even see 'em out here," Grady answered soberly. "And it will be a bad day for us if we do."

"Maybe we're lucky out here—nothin' but Injuns to fight" was Curly's bleak verdict on the new state police.

The Forked W had had its share of Indian troubles. Once, in the early days when Curly and Peg had been the only hands, they'd withstood a three-day siege until Curly had slipped past the encircling enemy at night and fetched help from the Lazy B. Remembering that fight, Ma always insisted that water buckets be kept full against such an emergency. Water had run low that time. During the full of the moon, when Indians were most likely to prowl, Pedro always penned up the headquarters' *remuda* in the corral at night, and Tom insisted that his rannies ride in pairs when they were far from home. Several times over the years lone riders had failed to make it back. Game was plentiful, Indians didn't bother cattle much unless they found a herd rounded up. Then they'd stampede it for sheer deviltry. It was different with horses—they were Comanche bait. But vigilance never relaxed. Partly because of that, partly because of the outfit's strength, the red men usually gave it a wide berth. Isolated cabins were easier prey. Indian sign was common, though. There were occasional brushes with them, particularly on the far range to the north and west. The Forked W was the last ranch in the valley. About eighteen miles beyond, the hills converged in a rugged jumble of flinty hills and scrubby valleys, called the Scalp Creek Breaks. The Indian travel west led through here and in bad times the place was infested with Comanches. This natural barrier marked the limits of Forked W range in that direction.

While they were building the trail herd for Kansas, every hand on the place was busy. Tom wanted big, rangy steers, four-year-olds and better, for the long drive, beeves that could stand the trip, get there with some meat on their bones. Even Loose Joe saddled up his mule and joined the riders. He wasn't much help, many ways, but he could comb the draws for likely critters, drive them out for others to handle. He'd found a job he liked, for once, in spite of long hours in the saddle. The men worked in teams and he was proud of this partnership. "'Sides, this is white man's work. I jest sets still an' lets de mule do de runnin'."

One day he rode with Curly and Grady when they were working the far range, out near the Breaks. There were plenty of gullies for him to explore in this rough country. Often he would disappear in them, be gone the better part of an hour before he'd lope back, tailing a mossy-horn or two, his teeth flashing over the accomplishment.

"Whar you reckon Joe's got to now?" Curly demanded, during one of these absences.

Grady shrugged. "You know Joe. He's probably crawled under a bush to take a snooze."

"I ain't so shore." Curly squinted back toward the draw where he'd last seen the Negro. Too many Comanches came through here to suit him. Often, returning from raids farther east, they made a highway of the valley, hugging its northern fringe where the hills offered cover, until they reached the Breaks. "I warned him agin Injuns but he don't know 'nuff 'bout 'em to take heed. Reckon I'd best keep an eye on him."

They rode back together. Curly checked his horse short of the hill's crown so, by standing in his stirrups, he could peer over into the dingle beyond without being seen. He slid off his horse, beckoned to Grady, waiting behind. Together they stretched in the grass while Curly's gnarled finger pointed out the still body stretched below. There was no sign of the mule.

Grady's impulse was to hurry down. Curly stopped him.

"Nothin' would suit the Injuns better if thar still round. Like as not they are."

His eyes searched the whole horizon carefully, lingered on each rock and shrub, worried along the outline of each hill before he was satisfied. Then he led the way back to the horses.

"'Pears to me this is the chance you've been a-lookin' for, Grady. 'T ain't a strong party or they'd have waited for us. I reckon thar a-headin' for the Breaks."

"What about Joe?"

"He'll still be thar when we get back. Fust we'll settle his account."

He turned his horse west, toward the broken country, picked a wind-ing course in the shelter of the valleys, rode hard, with Grady at his heels. He held the pace for nearly an hour and the horses were blowing hard before he stopped. "Reckon we've passed 'em by now, son. Let's have a look."

They were in the lee of a tall hill and they climbed it afoot, scrambling fast, saved their caution until they neared the top. There they crawled, careful of silhouettes against the sky.

"They'll be off that-a-way." Curly indicated a ridge they had skirted with a sweep of his arm.

Grady's younger eyes picked them up first—three mounted men driving a mule before them. They were about a mile away, Curly guessed. He studied their path, pointed out a narrow valley ahead. "That's whar we'll meet 'em," he decided. "Come on. It's time we was movin'."

He led the way back to the horses. They rode slowly now, their roundabout path picked for its cover. They checked their weapons on the way, halted their horses short of their destination and scurried the last hundred yards afoot. Where the hill merged off into the level grass of the valley they edged up its shoulder. Grady watched Curly pull several handfuls of grass, thrust them in his hat band, and copied the trick. They kept low. When they peered over, only two green hummocks were apparent from below.

Curly nudged Grady. "Part of a war party," he whispered. The Indians were closer now. Paint streaked their faces and there were scalps dangling from their belts. The leader had three. Grady saw them and swallowed hard. His mouth had turned dry, there was an ache in his throat and across the years he could hear the crackling flames of a blazing cabin. His vision blurred. He no longer saw the approaching Indians, but his mother's face, withered from the stroke of a scalping knife. He shut his teeth and brushed a sleeve across his eyes.

They were within forty yards when Curly leveled his rifle.

"You take the first one, kid. I'll take the second. We'll jine hands on tother'n."

They fired together. Both bullets found their mark. The last Indian tried to escape, turned and raced for shelter. Grady shot first, but too fast. He knocked the horse down. The rider went sprawling over its head, rolled a few yards, regained his feet and started to run. Curly's rifle flattened him.

Grady forgot his promise to Ma, swore as he counted the scalps. There were seven of them, still sticky with blood, and three had belonged to women. "The red bastards!" he kept snarling. That long hair reminded him of Molly's hacked body.

He drew his Bowie knife, knelt over his victim, worried at the scalp with his blade but he was clumsy at it.

"Here, let me show you, son." Curly twisted the fingers of his left hand into the oily hair and held it taut, punctured the skin with the point of his knife, then slid in the blade with a swift circular motion.

Grady wasn't prepared for the squashy sound of it. The scalp came free with a plop. "It just takes practice," Curly explained. "I've had aplenty of it."

It was a messy business. He wiped his hands on the grass, dried them on his pants. When he looked around, Grady's hands still were red and he was staring at them.

"What's the matter? Feel squeamish?"

"No. That's Comanche blood. I've waited a long time for this and I don't want to wipe it off. This is just the beginning, Curly."

"Thar's two more for you." The veteran indicated the other bodies with a sweep of his hand.

Grady shook his head. "Those are yours. I don't want any I didn't earn myself. They don't count."

The old Indian fighter lifted the other scalps. "There's somethin' 'bout losin' their hair that goes agin the grain with Injuns, son. Never neglect it. They seem to figger it's a sign o' weakness if you don't take scalps. Never let 'em get that idee."

He noted with satisfaction that Grady wore his scalp in his belt.

Normally the winters were mild in the valley, but there was a sleet storm that February. It began with a bitter wind out of the north. The temperature dropped twenty degrees between noon and sundown. The rain began about dark, hard-driven and cold.

About fifteen hundred big steers, gathered early for the spring drive, had been thrown on the home range west of headquarters. They weren't close-herded; they had a wide range there, but in weather such as this they'd bunch and drift. The whole outfit took to the saddle, Ma included. They couldn't stop the herd's movement; they didn't try. Their aim was to slow it down, give it direction, keep it out of trouble. No steer would face the storm. It was brute nature for them to move with it.

About midnight the sleet began, its needles sharp in the sobbing wind. The riders copied the cattle, sat hunched in their saddles, backs to the wind, hatbrims pulled low, faces hooded in bandannas against the sting of the storm. The temperature continued to drop, sodden clothes turned stiff with ice. The herd bunched badly, plodded steadily southward. Some of the old hands sang at first to quiet them. That stopped. Their voices were lost in the wind's mutter.

The Apache River was the ranch's south boundary. Its thickets offered some protection. The first fringe of the herd would have halted here but inexorable pressure from the rear pushed them on. Tom tried to string the critters out, scatter them into a thin line that would hold at the barrier, without success. The wind drove the herd on its set course.

Ice coated the river but it was thin. Again the front ranks tried to halt. The pressure from behind was too great. Some of the leaders went down in the icy current. The herd surged over them, kept moving. The half-frozen riders stuck doggedly with them. Once, shortly after the river crossing, Grady encountered Ma.

"Let's get down and walk a stretch," he suggested. "It might warm us up some."

"I thought of that but, hell's bells, I think I'm froze to this damned saddle!"

She dismounted stiffly and they trudged for half an hour, stomping, swinging their arms to restore circulation. It was risky. They were tailing the herd now and there were only stragglers here, but anything that went down in the path of the steers was sure to be trampled.

The sleet continued through the next day, covered the grass with a white crust. There was no barrier here short of the hills far south. The herd kept plodding. It was breaking up some, too. The cattle took the line of least resistance, always with the wind. Small slopes were ignored. They swept over them. Occasionally rougher hills or patches of scrub rose from the valley floor. At these the current of animals would eddy and part. Sometimes considerable segments of the herd would be split off in this way. The outfit split up too. Each hand stuck to the bunch he was tailing.

The sting of the icy pellets ended before the day wore itself out. A whining wind still stampeded the clouds; men and beasts stumbled before it. The sun died but there was no night, only eerie twilight. The endless sheet of white didn't lose its luster. The men walked most of the time now. Walking helped fight off the chill and rest the exhausted, floundering horses. They'd turned tender-footed, too. At each step they crunched through the sharp crust. There was blood on their fetlocks.

Blood in the sky, too, Grady thought dully, until he realized it was the new day's sun, burning in the east. Its fire spread swiftly across the sheet of ice, turned the whole world red. For a few minutes he forgot the ache of his weariness to wonder.

The wind had finally died. Grady found himself following a herd that had dwindled to about two hundred gaunt steers. The crimson faded, and as the sky brightened he could see other bunches like his own, black splotches on the white sheet that hid the familiar plains. The cattle would handle now. Gradually, the bunches were worked together, headed back north. It was slow toil. The crust was sharp where the herd broke through. There was no grass and the animals were uneasy with thirst. They had to be moved carefully. All hands were accounted for, but the herd had dwindled badly. About half of it was missing, dead at the river crossing or lost in the storm.

Ma and Peg rode ahead, met the outfit with a chuck wagon when they reached the river. Steaming pots of coffee were ready, on the fire. They could smell it long before they reached camp. They waited for dawn to cross the river but that night they dozed by warm fires, the nightmare ended. What was left of the herd was nursed home the following day.

Their troubles weren't ended. All over the range the grass was covered by ice, starving the herds.

"Back in the war years, when you couldn't hardly give steers away, the range was crowded with fat ones," Peg growled. "Now they fetch hard money an' they're starvin' to death."

"A Longhorn's an ornery brute but thank God he's tough," Ma replied. "He don't starve easy." Fortunately it turned warm and a thaw set in.

August Lehman arrived in his mud-splattered buggy a few days after the storm. In spite of the hard journey he still looked dapper when he clambered out. He was plump and pink. His neat store clothes didn't match his surroundings and two heavy gold seals dangled over his paunch. His mustache was the color of butter, curled tightly at the corners, and a pint-sized goatee dripped from his chin as if the buttery whiskers had started to run. With him, at the reins, was his son Carl, a slim youngster of fifteen who had his father's china-blue eyes and yellow hair.

"You're a long way from the store, August." Tom hurried out to greet him.

"An' that's a bad trail to travel, just you two," Ma added.

"I think the Comanches don't like the storm any more than we do. I wass safe enough." The pudgy German merchant spoke without accent except for the exaggeration of his s's. His stare quested from Ma to Tom. "Are you hurt bad? When there iss trouble iss when you need friends."

August Lehman was more than a merchant. His general store supplied the wants of the whole valley, but in times of stress he was both banker and friend as well. Only since the cattle drives had Tom been able to make substantial payment on the credit advanced through the lean war years.

"We haven't got the old debt squared up yet," Tom pointed out.

"Am I complaining? If there iss another rancher like Tom Williams around just show him to me and I will give him what credit he needs. I wish all my money wass as safe. There iss plenty of gold in Kansas, Tom. You can bring it home if you drive the beef up to market. But if you've lost your cattle you must buy more. That iss where I come in." His head bobbed with his earnestness. "If you've lost cattle, buy more. The price will go up if the supply iss down. Buy. Buy all you can handle. I will back you with all the credit you need."

"I won't know how we stand till we get out on the range," Tom answered slowly.

"Don't wait too long," the merchant cautioned. "If you have to buy, buy soon."

After supper he gave them the gossip of the valley. "Thiss storm will hurt the O-bar-O worst of all," he said. "Already they've had too much trouble."

"Why don't they buy cattle like you suggest?" Grady had hung back till then. He didn't know August Lehman, had seen him in the store a time or two.

The bright blue of the merchant's eyes clouded. His plump hands fluttered when he shrugged. "Not with my money," he snapped. "It iss better if the O-bar-O leaves the valley. Killers! Maybe then we'll have peace."

The O-bar-O was Luke Nesbit's spread, east of Apache where the hills retreated farther and the valley floor was a wide, flat plain. There had been ten thousand Longhorns on that range, but old Luke had run into nester trouble. He was a thorny man, bone-seasoned on the frontier. He'd been master of the lower valley too long to truckle under to nesters. He met their invasion with stubborn truculence. They had retaliated, with the result that a fierce, unrelenting war of survival had flared on the O-bar-O range.

Grady had heard rumors of the struggle. It was hard for him to understand. There were no nesters here. The land seemed so limitless, he couldn't see why men should be fighting over a few scrubby acres. His earliest memories were of a farm. He saw no conflict between that and his present life. "I still don't see why nesters and cowmen can't get along," he said. "Seems to me there's room here for everyone."

Young Carl Lehman had been quiet until now. This fitted his views. He leaned forward eagerly, found his tongue. "Why should Luke Nesbit who has a million acres try to crowd out a little man who only has a hundred in his homestead? What's fair about that?"

They were in the big room. Half a dozen of the hands had drifted in, attracted by the visitors. A hostile silence followed the youngster's question.

"Shucks, I wish 'twas that simple, Carl." Ma's friendly tone eased the strain. "Trouble is, nesters need water same as cattle. The fence around a hundred-acre farm doesn't bother anybody unless it shuts in water. I don't care how high your grass is, it ain't much 'count if your stock can't get a drink. I reckon there was just such a heap of free land nobody ever gave it much thought. It was here for the takin'. It didn't seem to make much sense settlin' up papers for a little passel of ground here an' yonder. Folks just took what they needed an' that was that.

"When the nesters came it was different. They took out papers on their land, easy enough to do 'cause they didn't want much, an' of course they strung out along the streams, built fences around their fields. Old Luke didn't start fightin' right off. He didn't pay much attention to it till he woke up one mornin' an' discovered his stock bawlin' for water an' no way to get to it. That's when he started tearin' down fences to let his herds through. Those cattle could stomp down a year's crops in an hour. Sure, the nester fought back. It was his land, he'd settled on it, everything legal. But it had been O-bar-O land for years before. Without that water a million acres of grass wouldn't do Luke Nesbit much good."

"An' mind, Luke was thar fust," Curly added. "He fought the Injuns offn it. If it hadn't been for him and others like him, the nesters wouldn't dast be hyar. I don't hold with all Luke's done but he's fightin' for his life. No water, no ranch."

"The farmers are fighting for their lives, too," Carl persisted.

His father rose abruptly, placed a restraining hand on his shoulder. Worry puckered his pink face. "Enough, Carl. There iss right and wrong on both sides. Just to argue doesn't settle anything." His perplexed eyes turned to Williams. "Still there should be some way to settle it, Tom. If you and other cowmen could talk some sense into Nesbit. . . . If I could make my German settlers see both sides. . . . You can't and I can't. I don't know where it will end. Alwayss trouble seems worse here in the valley than anywhere else."

"It's hell with the hide off when it starts," Tom agreed grimly.

"It's because the nesters are German and cowmen don't like Germans," Carl blurted out.

"Your Pa is a German an' we never had a better friend," Ma commented. "Still there's somethin' in what you say. It's nesters we mistrust first, but here they happen to be Germans. Trouble is, havin' two languages makes the misunderstandin' worse. An' then I reckon it's only natural the Germans should stick together like they do. But that makes our folks suspicious."

"And the war made it worse," said Tom. "We were Texans and we fought for Texas, but the Germans were on the other side of the fence. They didn't hold with Secession, stayed at home while we were off fightin'. Our folks called them Dutch Yankees and they called us Rebels. All that didn't help."

Lehman bobbed his head in agreement. "The Indian troubles made it worse," he added. "It didn't take the Comanches long to learn the country wass stripped of fighting men. Just a few old men and boys left to hold them back, most places."

"An' women," Ma added grimly. "Whilst the menfolks were off fightin' Yankees the womenfolks were home fightin' Indians. Some places whole neighborhoods were wiped out. But the German settlements weren't bothered much. Their men were still home. Folks couldn't help noticin'.

"Hate's like weeds," she added. "Give it a start an' it's hard to dig out."

"Alwayss it iss something to keep us apart." Lehman shrugged pudgy shoulders. "Now it iss Reconstruction. If a man wore a gray uniform he can't vote, but the German communities can. They were Loyalists. It classes them with the carpetbaggers and that makes more bitterness. More bitterness!" He shook his head. "Alwayss it iss something to keep the trouble alive."

There had been no nester trouble at the Forked W. It was too remote from the settlements, too exposed. After Lehman's visit Tom and Ma decided upon a way to protect themselves from such encroachment. Water was the key to it. Every hand in the outfit was encouraged to file on a tract of land along the river. "I'll buy it from you once it's yours," Tom promised. It was the same with the scattered waterholes across the upper range. They scraped the bottom of the barrel for resources, stretched their credit with August Lehman, bought what they could outright. They didn't bother with the endless miles of grassland. No nester would squat there.

"Thar's still a heap of riverland left," Curly pointed out.

"We can't buy it all. I ain't worried" was Tom's reply. "I've got nothin' agin these little fellers. I sort of admire their grit. They can come here, and welcome, as long as they don't crowd me out. I reckon August Lehman's right. There ought to be room here for all of us."

The cattle weathered the blizzard better than they'd expected, although losses had been heavy. For a week they worked hard with skinning knives, retrieving the marketable hides. The herds were thinned out, the animals were gaunt, but the range still had the makings of a trail herd. As Ma had said, Longhorns were hard to kill.

Spring broke fast. Damaging as the storm had been, the melting ice greened up the grass early. Spring roundup started and as soon as the last maverick was branded they set to work cutting out the trail herd. No she's were taken, since they were needed to replenish the range. The young stuff was turned back, too. But every far cranny of the ranch was combed for big steers that could take the trail. At the job's end they had eleven hundred beeves ready to go, fewer than they'd planned but still a sizable herd.

This time Grady was to go along with Tom and Curly. The rest of the trail outfit was new. Tom had hired nine extra hands for the job. The ranch couldn't be stripped of riders during their absence. Even the chuck wagon was new, its bed carefully calked in readiness for the streams they'd have to swim. It was a trail-wise spread. Grady was the only hand who hadn't made the journey before, and they shook down into the routine quickly. Curly and Red Yarnell rode the points, their responsibility was to guide the herd, watch for Indians, be on hand to nurse the leaders into the water at river crossings. They rode some distance apart, abreast of the lead steers, let them choose their gait and only changed the herd's direction by pressure on the flanks. This was a post for seasoned hands. The swing riders worked in pairs, too—one on either side of the plodding herd. The flank riders followed them, while the dragmen, bandannas over their faces to shut out the dust, brought up the rear and nursed along the laggards. This was the most unpleasant task. Except for his pointmen, Tom switched the other riders day by day, each eating his share of trail dust. There was a definite technique to handling a herd on the move. The men forced the pace the first two days, until the home range was well behind and the herd had become accustomed to its new discipline. Tired cattle were less likely to stampede. At the first day's end they milled them for an hour, turned the herd into a tight circle until the leaders were tailing the stragglers.

"You've got to wear 'em down at the start," Tom explained to Grady. "We don't want 'em headin' for home before daylight."

Once they were trail-broken the pace slackened. Ten or twelve miles a day was a good average. The animals grazed their way along, reached their bedding grounds with full bellies, kept in condition. Each morning the herd moved out before breakfast was ended at the chuck wagon. The cook took his time, cleaned up the dishes, usually started about an hour later. He circled the herd during the day, rode ahead to the next camp, had coffee hot when the outfit rode in. Tom usually went ahead to join him in the late afternoon to select a site for bedding down the herd, near water if possible, although there were many stretches where it wasn't. "I always try to find a place that's open and flat where they won't feel crowded," he explained. "The sort of spot they'd choose themselves out on the range."

There were about fifty horses in the *remuda*, with the wrangler in charge. Each rider had his own string, his top horse reserved for night work. The *remuda* was grazed along separately.

Night was the time to be alert. Except for river crossings or during storms, the daylight journeys were generally uneventful. Stampedes usually came after dark. The men stood watch in turns, two at a time, circling the bedded-down animals, often singing the "Texas Lullaby," whose chant soothed uneasy beasts. Even when rolled in his blankets, each hand kept his night horse saddled and tied close at hand in case of trouble. Always, a big pot of coffee simmered in the ashes of the cook's fire for the hands who were to mount the next shift.

They had their first run one night on the Upper Canadian. There was storm in the air. The sun had died in a red haze. The night turned breathless and black, except for the flicker of heat lightning off west. Grady was riding herd, didn't like the feel of things, occasionally stopped in his round to listen before picking up his song again. Thunder began to mutter, still far off. The lightning flashes were nearer, more frequent. By their light Grady saw old Wrinkle lift his head, climb slowly to his feet. Wrinkle was one of the lead steers—"old enough to vote," Curly said—a big roan animal whose wrinkled horns betrayed his age and gave him his name. Other steers began to rise. Grady raised his voice to a louder croon, kept his eye on Wrinkle during the fitful flashes. The heat had turned stifling; the thunder rolled closer. Thirty or forty steers were on their feet, all silent, all turned toward the west watchfully.

Then as Grady watched, a pale, phosphorescent glow spread across the herd. There seemed to be a ball of fire on the tip of every horn. He'd heard stories of St. Elmo's fire—fox fire rannies usually called it—during electrical storms but had never seen it before. The herd began an uneasy movement. Every animal was on its feet now, walking slowly, but the riders kept them milling in a circle. The "Texas Lullaby," soothing, plaintive, quavered across the herd. He dared not cease his singing now. Once he glanced toward the chuck wagon, hoped to see other riders astir, but the fire had died out yonder. He couldn't see anything, dared not quit his post to arouse them. The steers had increased their gait, were walking faster now.

The storm broke with a climactic crash of thunder. Lightning tore the black sky apart, loosed the rain in a sudden torrent.

The thunder found its echo in a sudden roar of hoofs. Every animal in the herd was running and they were headed his way. Grady leaned low in the saddle, dug in his spurs, gave the horse his head. There was death for anyone caught in that avalanche of horns. At first he rode blindly, all his trust in his mount. Gradually, as he began to gain distance, he veered slowly toward the right to escape the dangerous path. When he risked a glance backward the fox fire still pointed every horn. The ghostly light spread wide across the prairie like a sea of blue-and-yellow waves.

The camp had been aroused; the whole outfit sprang to the saddle when the stampede began. Once he was able to angle out of the herd's path, Grady slowed up to breathe his horse. Then he could hear the men shouting above the clamor. Curly raced past. "Turn 'em! Turn 'em!" he shouted. Grady followed. When he reached a point abreast the leaders, Curly used his six shooter, fired into air to wheel the fear-crazed animals. The whole outfit began to string out along the flank. "Hi! Hi! Hi!" they shouted and Grady joined the chorus. Gradually the herd swerved, slowly at first. Then, yielding to the constant pressure, it began to wind itself into a circle.

"Hi! Hi! Hi!" the waddies chorused. No effort was made now to calm the crazed animals—they were past that. The only hope was to twist them into a knot. As the circle tightened, the beasts began to mill.

Gradually they churned into a slowly ebbing whirlpool, the leaders trapped in the center. The stampede had been stopped.

"That was a lucky one," said Curly. "If we hadn't got 'em millin', they'd have run till tomorrow and we'd have been days gatherin' 'em up."

The herd stampeded for three nights running. The overworked outfit was on edge. Tom questioned Grady carefully about the first run's start, decided old Wrinkle was the troublemaker. "If he wasn't such a good lead steer, I'd shoot him right off," he declared. "Maybe I can handle him differently."

That night when they bedded down he and Curly cut Wrinkle out from the herd, roped and tied him down a safe distance away. The hours till dawn passed peacefully. Tying Wrinkle down became a nightly chore after that and their stampede troubles were ended.

They went through storms, and there were troublesome river crossings, but this was what Curly called a "lucky herd." They reached Dodge City in just over two months, near record time for the distance. The extra hands took their pay there. Tom was determined to bring the new chuck wagon home. Curly and Grady came with him. They took turns driving the wagon, the others ranging alongside in the saddle, the spare horses tethered behind. They traveled faster now and were watchful. The herd had brought a big price; there was enough gold in the wagon to pay off the account at Lehman's in full with some to spare. The outfit's strength had dwindled. It wasn't just the journey across the Indian country that made them cautious. Dodge City was a hairy town. Its ready money attracted many of the wild bunch, hard-eyed men who'd know about that gold. Many of them had notched their guns for less. Everyone in the outfit kept a sharp watch on the back trail. Three days out they came to a creek with a stony floor, where their wheels would leave no tracks. They turned down it for a mile or more before striking out on a new path of their own and headed due south across the grass, relaxing their caution a little now that they'd left the beaten trail.

Several dawns later Tom was awakened by Grady's muttering. It was jumbled talk about Comanches and his own mother and the finding of Molly's body, so disconnected Tom wouldn't have known its meaning had he not been familiar with the story. Grady's face was flushed with fever and he didn't recognize the two friends who bent over him anxiously. Tom wasn't too worried at first. "He'll throw this off in a day or two," he promised. "Shucks, he's tough as whang leather."

They stayed three days in camp, but Grady didn't improve. Fever loosened his tongue. Constantly he prattled and always of the Indian raid that had wiped out his family.

"It's typhoid," Curly said. "I saw aplenty of it in the army."

"I wish Ma was here." Tom was uneasy. "She'd know what to do."

The third day Grady was definitely worse. His two companions did their best to make him comfortable, with awkward tenderness, but they lacked medicine and knowledge. A feeling of helplessness contributed to Tom's worry. Finally at sundown he made his decision. "Hitch up the team, Curly. We're headin' for home."

"But he ain't fittin' to travel. We must be three-four hundred miles from Apache. You want to kill him?"

"He'll die waitin' here. We ain't helpin' him none. If I can just get him to Ma, she'll fetch him out of this."

While Curly readied the outfit, Tom gathered the long-stemmed grass by the armful, heaped it in the bottom of the chuck wagon to soften its jolts. They moved out at dusk, their cow horses tethered behind, and always headed south, with the scrabble of Grady's delirium hoarse against the rattle of the wagon. Mostly they journeyed by night, since darkness was kinder to their fevered patient, but their hitches were long. They were on the trail before sunset, and were still plodding long after day had come again. They'd have driven longer but the team had grown gaunt and must be nursed along now. One night rain inked out the sky and the familiar stars by which they set their course. They dared not stop. Tom took to the saddle, felt his way ahead. A dreary dawn found them bedraggled and dripping but their patient was snug under his tarpaulin and apparently a little better. The storm had cooled him somewhat. It didn't last—by night he was worse.

Their starting point was eleven camps back. The country had grown familiar, but the tired team was lagging. Curly Stark was driving. His whip cracked as he hustled the jaded horses. When he peered around, the leather of his face was seamed with worry. "What's he sayin', now?"

"He's still fightin' Injuns." Tom adjusted the wet towel across the fevered face again. "That's been ten years and it's still fresh as yesterday in his mind."

"I ain't surprised. Some things a man can't fo'get."

Tom looked down at his patient and his answer came slowly. "This was somethin' a man shouldn't have to face but once, Curly. But he's been livin' it over, day after day, ever since the fever took him."

Grady opened his eyes. He recognized Tom bending over him and frowned with the effort to reconcile this familiar face with his anguish over Molly. They were in a wagon, he could tell that. The wheels jolted over the rough prairie and he could hear the jingle of harness. Dusty canvas stretched across the bows overhead and near by water sloshed in a bucket. Tom leaned down with a wet cloth for his forehead and saw the recognition in his eyes.

"How long you been awake, Grady?"

"Just now. The Indians . . ." His voice trailed off.

"Always the same dream, ain't it, son?"

He wanted to tell Tom it wasn't a dream. Ma's dead face, so horribly relaxed . . . Molly's mangled body beside the spring . . . But the effort was too great. His head throbbed, and there was an insistent roaring in his ears, like wind driving rain. . . . "This will drift the cattle bad," he said, before he closed his eyes to consciousness again.

Tom stretched out a hand for the reins. "I'll take over, Curly. I want you to ride ahead and fetch Ma. You can make the ranch come dawn but there ain't much bottom left in the team. We're still a day out this way."

Curly hesitated. "Maybe it'd come better from you. I can stay with the team."

"No. I don't aim to leave Grady. Now you get goin' and ride fast."

Curly needed no urging. He took the best horse. Tom listened to the fast drum of flying hoofs until they were lost in the night. Grady was muttering again. He leaned back to slosh a cloth in the water pail and stretch it across the burning forehead. Tom wasn't much for words, but his anxiety was in the tenderness of his hand. This boy was like a son to him. Boy? He glanced back at the bulk of him. He was plumb growed now, twenty-three, and outmatched any hand on the ranch, except maybe Tom himself. It was hard to realize it was ten years since he'd fetched him home, just a green nubbin of a man then.

His whip popped. The team lunged into the collars, settled into a slow jog. Mighty slow, it seemed to Tom. The horses had no spring left in 'em. He sat hunched in the seat, nothing to occupy him but to keep the team moving, let his thoughts backtrack to the day he'd first set eyes on Grady Scott.

The sky over east was barely streaked with red when he headed the worn team through the last gap in the hills. Apache Valley was stretched out in front of him. He watched the sun spread across its grass, each of its rolling hills throwing a long blue shadow ahead of it in the slanting light. Off west, still dwarfed by distance, a couple of riders approached. He squinted at them as they grew. He hoped it might be Ma but you couldn't be sure at this distance. He reached back for his rifle, held it ready across his knees until, as the space narrowed, he could distinguish the wide-brimmed hats. At least they were white folks. It was the horses he recognized first, and his face broke into a grin. That could be only Ma ridin' old Baldy and course it was Curly with her.

"How is he?" she asked as she swung from the horse. There was no time for greetings now. There was work to do.

"Can't see no change in him, Ma."

She clambered into the wagon. There was an incredible gentleness in her work-roughened hands.

A fresh team was on the way to hurry them in but Ma hadn't waited for that. Grady still was unconscious when they reached the ranch. When eventually he began to mend, he remembered only vague, puzzling scenes from his illness. He couldn't tell at first which of these memories were real and which were images from the delirium that had tortured him for so long.

"It's hard to straighten things out," he told Ma. "I went to sleep up in Indian territory and woke up back home in the valley. Don't that beat thunder?"

Some of those images stayed with him, however—the awakened memories of his family, the vengeance he had come here to find so long ago. He often fell silent during the lazy days, when he still was wobbly on his legs and Ma kept him abed. "Seems like I never did have so much time to think before," he told her.

He was up and in the saddle again when news of the election reached them that fall. The hands celebrated by whooping and letting off their six guns. Tom called it a holiday and Ma cooked supper herself—a whopping, Sunday meal, topped off with dried apple pie. All over Texas, grim-faced veterans had trooped to the polls, seized control from the carpetbaggers, voted Richard Coke into the governor's chair, and with him a legislature of Texans, too. Reconstruction was past. The hated state police had been abolished.

"The war's finally over for us," said Tom. "Now we'll get somewhere."

"An' high time!" Ma grunted. "Hell's bells, most places it ended in 1865. Here 't is, the close of '73, an' peace just reachin' Texas."

In the spring they had more good news. The frontier was to be protected at last. The Texas Rangers were to be reorganized and a Frontier

Battalion had been authorized, with six companies of seventy-five men each under Major John B. Jones. Here was a Texan of prominence who had won great reputation in the Confederate Army where he'd started as a private in Terry's Texas Rangers and within a month had become Adjutant of the 15th Texas Infantry. At the war's end he had been adjutant of a brigade with the rank of captain and he'd been recommended for further promotion.

"Rangers!" There was a light in Grady's eyes. "My time really has come, Ma. I've waited a long time but this is it. I reckon you know I'll have to go."

"Yes, son, I've always known sooner or later you'd do what you set out to do. The only thing is, I didn't want you goin' too soon."

"I know. You were right, Ma. I'd just have got myself scalped if it hadn't been for you and Tom. Now I'm twenty-four and I've learned a heap. I've got to hustle. You want me to sit around here until Jones has got his companies filled up and there won't be any place for me?"

A week later Grady rode away, headed for Austin and enlistment in the Frontier Battalion.

Chapter 3 A MAN OF AUTHORITY

LUKE NESBIT drew rein at the lip of the draw, squinted down across the valley where hundreds of cattle wearing his O-bar-O brand milled uneasily and bawled their thirst. There was a loop in the river here, and a trail which his herds followed to water. A newly built brush fence barred it. With an impatient gesture he shoved back the wide-brimmed hat. When it was tilted so, he had the fierce look of a hawk—angry eyes, curved beak and once fiery, close-cropped thatch, now faded to a roan. "When was that built?" he growled. "I thought we'd cleaned the nesters out of hyar."

There were four riders with him, saddle-toughened, leathery.

"That's the Pakebusch place," one volunteered.

Old Luke snorted. "Since when? That's been O-bar-O range for twenty years. I was hyar fust and I aim to stay." He headed his horse down the grassy slope and the others followed. The cattle weren't grazing, he noticed. They were uneasy with thirst and noisy. Their bellows stirred his anger more. This squatter had been warned; that fence had been torn down once.

" 'T ain't much of a fence," Salty Leech offered. " 'T wouldn't take much to throw this herd plumb through it."

Luke measured the brush through slit eyes, shook his head. He didn't like the look of it, wanted to inspect it closer and growled when he saw the sharpened stakes that reinforced the boughs. "Pakebusch figgered we'd try to stampede through like we did before an' reckoned he'd pile up a heap of dead cattle hyar. Two of you boys get down an' help me make a gap. Salty, you an' Bob gather up the herd, be ready to run through hyar a-stompin' quick as we're ready."

They worked rapidly. The brush was easy to scatter. It was the stakes which gave them trouble. They were planted in a double row, one upright as a core for the barrier, the other tilted forward at an angle, a

51

line of sharpened teeth that the greenery had concealed. The ground was dry, not tamped too solid. Once loosened, it was an easy matter to snake them out, one by one, with a horse and a rope. As each post came free Nesbit swore. The cunning of this trap frayed his temper worse than the thirsty bawling of his cattle. If the herd had been stampeded into it, those sharpened points would be dripping and red now.

The gap slowly widened. Luke Nesbit straightened from his task, measured the destruction with his eyes. Salty and his partner had the herd bunched now and waiting. He signaled them, waved them on with a wide sweep of his hat.

Off to the right, where the brush barrier remained untouched, a gun coughed. The bullet's slap staggered Luke, spun him half around. He braced himself spraddle-legged, clawed at his holster flap but his fingers fumbled. A spreading stain darkened his shirt. One O-bar-O rider managed to draw but the blast of his six gun was lost in the growing din of musketry. Nesbit crumpled over and fell. One of his men already was down. The other tried to reach cover. The air was filled with the shrill snarl of lead. He staggered only a few steps, then went slack, sprawled in the grass. At the first volley, Salty Leech abandoned the herd and came riding in, his companion at his heels. They made easy targets. One saddle emptied quickly. Salty tried to turn. His horse fell, pitched him headlong. Before he could reach his feet, other bullets found him. Even then the shooting didn't stop. All along the ambuscade guns stuttered their hysteria and the fallen bodies quivered under the leaden hail.

Word of the massacre quickly spread the length of the valley. Nesters, for the most part, received it joyfully at first. With old Luke Nesbit dead the long and thorny O-bar-O war was ended. Others, more somber than their neighbors, shook their heads. The circumstances invited trouble. What if the cowmen should strike back? The worry grew. Soon the grassy ruts leading into Apache were clogged with plodding men. They were afoot mostly, wore homespun and the coarse boots of farmers, and there was trouble in their faces. They carried scatter-guns in their plow-roughened hands—farm weapons, but grisly at close range. August Lehman stood in the door of his store and watched them gather, his face puckered with worry.

The cowmen met at the Blake brothers' Lazy B headquarters twenty-two miles west of town. For the most part they had stayed clear of the nester struggle, their range too distant from the town to cause them trouble. But they had known and liked Luke Nesbit and they were stirred by the sound of what had happened.

"They war dry-gulched, I tell you." One of three O-bar-O riders present repeated the story. "Old Luke didn't even have a chancet to draw his six gun. It war still in his holster." He described the scene as he and other searchers had come upon it later.

There were three cattle spreads in the western end of the valley and all were represented here. Tom Williams of the Forked W had brought five riders. Counting the two Blakes, there were twelve Lazy B men. Biggest of all was the Benched S outfit—the "Snake on a Rock" brand, valley folks called it. John Soames had sixteen hands with him. With the O-bar-O men they counted thirty-eight riders when they strung out along the trail for Apache.

Lehman was sure the cowmen would come and he had gauged the determination in the faces of the nesters who crowded the town. Unless something was done, the long-feared showdown between the two factions was at hand. He started in search of old man Sparks without much hope. Sparks had been a top hand for the O-bar-O once, before rheumatism stove him up. Everybody liked the old fellow. Making him sheriff had been Nesbit's idea and nobody in the valley had objected. There hadn't been much for a sheriff to do in the old days. That was before the nesters came. The new settlers had seen no reason to make a change. The sheriff was a likable old codger who divided his time between the wagon barn and Scanlon's Saloon, gossiping about the "old days" with all who had time to listen. He had grown to be a favorite with the German settlers. The merchant headed for the saloon first and there he found the sheriff. His hope thinned as a quick glance took in the old man's condition. Already he had drunk too much. His faded eyes were bleary and his hands trembled so that the whisky slopped from his glass as he raised it.

"Better you had come with me, Sparks." The merchant's voice was crisp. "There iss work for you today. You'll need a clear head."

Sparks set down the glass, frowned with an effort at concentration. "Work?" he repeated dully. "What kind of work?" Then he recognized his visitor. He tried to rise but midway in the effort collapsed back into the chair. "Can't work today, Mr. Lehman—not today. Ain't you heard? My old friend Luke Nesbit's dead."

Lehman gripped him by the shoulders. "You're going to lose a lot more friends if you don't pull yourself together." In his anxiety the merchant's voise rose. "What you need iss some good strong coffee. Come over to the store with me and I'll see that you get it."

The sheriff made an effort. He swayed to his feet but when he tried to walk his legs were unequal to the task. He lurched heavily against Lehman, would have fallen had not another arm caught him.

"Sorry, sir, but I don't think he can make it. You'd better leave him here."

"But he's got to make it." Lehman turned, recognized the man who was easing the sheriff back into his chair. It was Rowden, the newcomer from Mississippi, apparently a moneyed man who had come here in quest of ranch land. He was tall; the ease with which he handled Sparks revealed a strength that his slender elegance belied. His frock coat and white linen had a strange flavor in these frontier surroundings and had excited comment. The merchant knew the explanation. He was a planter, discouraged by carpetbag rule and the collapse of the old plantation economy, seeking a new start here. The story was that he'd heard of Luke Nesbit's trouble, had offered him cash for the O-bar-O, but nothing had come of it.

"There will be fighting in the streets if something iss not done. It's the Nesbit shooting. The cowmen are on their way and I know the nesters. They're ready for trouble. They won't budge."

"What do you think we could do?"

"He iss sheriff—the only law there iss here."

Rowden shrugged. "A determined man might stop it but——"

"Me, I got determination." The little German merchant drew himself erect. "Do you think I want to stand by and watch the valley shoot itself to pieces? But what can I do?" He pointed at the sheriff slumped in his chair. "There iss the only authority here and it——Bah!"

"Let me get this straight." Rowden's indifference was gone, he was brusque now. "You really think we're headed for a street battle between the cowmen and the nesters?"

"I'm sure of it."

"Then we'll find the authority and I'll know how to use it. Mr. Lehman, I'm your man." He raised his voice. "Oh, Frank! Frank Toomey! Here, lend me a hand."

A burly man with a wide drooping mustache shouldered his way through the crowd. "Comin'."

Lehman knew Toomey by sight. He was one of several riders in the

Mississippian's pay. He'd brought the makings of a cow outfit with him.

Rowden flicked a finger toward old man Sparks. "Get Pete Falkner to help you. Bring the sheriff along to Mr. Lehman's store. Carry him if you have to but don't waste any time."

He explained his purpose to Lehman on the way. "Even sober, I'm afraid Sparks wouldn't be equal to this situation but he can delegate his authority. He doesn't know it yet but I'm going to be his chief deputy. There isn't going to be any fight here."

Even the strong coffee that August Lehman brewed failed to clear old man Sparks's fog. He remained fuddled but pliable. Toomey and Falkner brought him over, propped between them. On their way they'd picked up the third of Rowden's men, Charlie Springer. They slid the sheriff into a chair, stood silently by while the merchant tried to revive him. Two cups of the strong mixture had no visible effect.

"It iss no use," said Lehman. "He iss too far gone. We're losing time."

"Let me handle him, señors." Falkner stepped forward. "I have a way with *borrachos*."

He was a slender man, a little undersized. Leaning forward, he grasped the sheriff by the coat, pulled him erect with surprising ease, shook him gently. His voice was deceptively mild, too. "Listen to me, *amigo*. You're going to wake up *pronto*. You hear?"

His fingers stung the old man's cheek sharply.

The German merchant found a curious resemblance between Falkner and his employer. He was small, Rowden was large, and he wore the familiar garb of the frontier with two guns swung low from his belt, the holster flaps cut away. But there was a certain elegance about his equipment and the way he wore it that matched Rowden's white linen. His quick eyes, black as midnight, were intent on the sheriff now.

"Hear me, *borracho*! Wake up!" Again he slapped Sparks with his open palm, harder now.

The old man opened his eyes.

"He is listening now, señors," Falkner announced. "What do you want of him?"

Rowden had procured a pen and paper. He wrote swiftly. "Here, tell him to sign this."

They thrust the pen into the old man's hand, guided it as he scrawled his signature. The document commissioned Will Rowden to act as the sheriff's chief deputy.

"That's enough. Now I have the authority to make you all deputies. You too, Mr. Lehman. You have influence here." Rowden reasoned swiftly. "I could get a dozen more men from among the nesters but that might invite trouble. I want just one more. Who's the nester with the most influence—someone like yourself who commands respect here?" He directed the question at the merchant.

"That would be Jacob Pflueger."

"Find him and bring him here quick. We've already wasted too much time on Sparks."

Pflueger shared Lehman's determination to halt the threatened outbreak. When the merchant explained his errand he accompanied him eagerly. They found Rowden's preparations complete when they reached the store. Horses were saddled and ready.

Pflueger and Rowden hadn't met before. Each measured the other swiftly. The farmer was a bulky, rough-grained man. His grizzled whiskers gave him a stubborn look.

"Has Mr. Lehman told you what we aim to do?"

"Ja."

"And you're not afraid?"

"Ja. I'm scared a liddle but I vill help chust der same."

"Good. You're now a deputy sheriff, Mr. Pflueger."

Neither of the Germans was armed but August Lehman had six guns in stock. Rowden helped himself to a pair, loaded them and thrust one in each man's belt where it would show. "Don't try using this unless there's a general melee," he advised. "If there's any gunplay, leave that to us."

They mounted in front of the store. The sheriff had gone to sleep but he was aroused and lifted into the saddle. "Just to show our authority," Rowden explained, and placed the two Germans on either side of him. "He's spent half his life on a horse but we're not taking any chances. Keep an eye on him and leave the rest to me."

The little posse was seven strong as it moved out, Rowden in front, followed by his own three riders, with the sheriff and the two prominent Germans in the rear. Rowden didn't dismount when he reached Scanlon's. Instead, he fired two quick shots into the air and when the nesters came boiling out, each ready with his scatter-gun, the new deputy sent for Scanlon himself.

The barkeeper came reluctantly. "What's wrong? Who wants me? Can't you see I'm busy?"

"This is the sheriff's posse, Scanlon. We're closing up the town. You have just five minutes to lock your doors."

"With all these people here?"

Rowden pulled out his watch. "Five minutes. Those are orders."

"Where'd you get all this authority?" Scanlon demanded truculently. The crowd's angry murmur gave him courage.

"There's your sheriff. He's sworn us in as deputies. You all know Lehman and Pflueger, too. Sheriff Sparks has been careful to see that every element in the valley is represented in this posse."

The town was seldom so crowded. Scanlon didn't relish passing up such profits. "There ain't any law says you can do this to me," he protested.

The nesters around him had grown quiet, awed for the moment by this show of authority. That line of horsemen seemed to share Rowden's confidence.

"Three minutes," said Rowden.

Scanlon glanced around him uneasily, seeking help from the crowd. Its quiet offered no support. "How long do you aim to keep me locked up?"

"Just until the danger of trouble is over. We'll let you know."

Scanlon shrugged, made a virtue of yielding. "You know me. I don't want trouble. If it'll help I'll close up." He slid inside, banged the door after him. The scrape of the lock was audible in the silence.

August Lehman smiled his satisfaction, but Rowden's face remained expressionless as he stared about the expectant crowd. His tone was matter-of-fact when he finally spoke. "As you see, the law's in charge here now. There isn't going to be any trouble. You won't need those scatter-guns. Just stack them there against the hitch rack."

No one moved. The nesters were sullen and suspicious. The presence of August Lehman and Jacob Pflueger among the deputies did much to reassure them, but it was Rowden's calm confidence which had the most weight. Adolph Blucher was the first to yield. He shuffled forward, propped his shotgun against the rail. Heinrich Unger followed him. This was surprising. They had been two of the noisiest troublemakers.

"If Rowden says dere ain't goin' to be trouble dere von't be no trouble," said Unger. "Dat's goot enough for me."

That broke the tension. Others stepped forward. As the stack of weapons against the hitch rail grew the crowd's mood changed. Farmers jostled one another good-naturedly. The hush of expectancy ended; they grew noisy again.

Having left Charlie Springer to guard the shotguns, Rowden turned his posse toward the wagon yard at the other end of the street. It was another gathering place for nesters. There were still plenty of scatter-guns up there.

Hallelujah was fat. When she hurried she waddled. Her flesh was quaking now, her black face shining with excitement as she burst into the room. "Dey ain't a-goin' to be no fightin', Miss Letty. Trouble's done ended. De law's took over."

"What law, Hallie?"

"De sheriff man! He done took over."

Letitia Reid looked at Clebourne Soames. Both girls frowned in per-plexity. They knew the sheriff. This didn't sound reasonable.

"I hope she's right." There was doubt in Letty's voice.

"That I'd have to see." Clee shook her head. "It doesn't sound like old man Sparks."

The clatter of hoofs outside caught their attention. They crowded the same window. Letty, blue-eyed, with dark hair curling around her face and making her skin look even whiter, was fairer than her companion despite Clee's blondness. Clebourne had wide-set tawny eyes. There was sun mellowed in her skin, its smooth tan picking up the gold glint of her hair.

Rowden was passing the hotel, astride a deep-chested dun. The horse's pale color dramatized the elegance of the man's somber black broadcloth. On either side of him rode Pete Falkner and Frank Toomey. Behind, in a tight knot, August Lehman and Jake Pflueger flanked the swaying sheriff.

"So that's it!" Letty measured the scene shrewdly. "La! I knew old Sparks didn't have it in him. This begins to make sense now."

"Who is he?" Clee demanded. "Did you ever see a more beautiful horse? I've got to have it."

"Right now I'm more interested in the rider. It looks as if Will Rowden is considerable man," Letty retorted.

"I don't care what it costs, I've got to have that horse."

There was an amused gleam in Letty's blue eyes. "Too bad, Clee. I doubt if even your Pa has money enough for that. They say Rowden has more money than he needs and he sets a heap of store by that animal."

Rumors of what happened at Scanlon's already had reached the nesters gathered at the wagon yard. They crowded out to watch the horsemen approach. Rowden left himself elbowroom, drew rein in the middle of the road, repeated his announcement that the law had taken over control of the town. "So you won't need those scatter-guns now. Just pile 'em against the tongue of that wagon yonder." Several men obeyed with alacrity. A precedent already had been set. It seemed as if this would be easier than before.

Hans Schlager didn't like the sound of this. He was a stubborn man when sober and he was far from that now. He clutched his weapon tighter. "Den vat happens? If der cowmen come und we got no guns—— Not me, I keep mine." He thwacked the stock of his weapon with a horny palm, glared fiercely around at his companions. Several hesitated.

"What's his name?" Rowden's voice was quiet.

"Schlager," Lehman replied. "Watch out for him. He iss a tough one to handle."

Rowden dismounted, handed his reins to Toomey. As he passed Falkner his voice was so low that no one else heard. "He's your man, Pete, but don't draw unless you have to. I've got to have that gun."

From their window across the street the girls watched his deliberate advance. If he was disturbed he didn't show it. His pistol remained unseen beneath his coat and he made no move to free it. Behind him, though, Pete Falkner had dropped his reins around the saddle horn, stood straight in his stirrups.

"We're disarming the whole town, Schlager," Rowden said. "That means you too. Hand over your weapon."

"Na. I von't do it. Keep back, I tell you." The nester retreated a few steps for better clearance, moved as if to raise his weapon. "I tell you— keep back."

Rowden didn't hesitate. He continued his steady pace, one hand outstretched. Only his tone changed. It crackled with authority now. "Drop your gun, Schlager!"

The nester took another step back, raised his weapon. One hand slid toward the trigger.

That was the hand Pete Falkner was watching. He bent slightly forward, his elbow jerked and a six gun smoked in fingers that had been empty a second before. There was just one bullet. It ripped Schlager's right wrist, sent his gun clattering to the ground. Rowden stooped swiftly, possessed it before Schlager's stunned neighbors recovered from their shock.

"Anyone else undecided about giving up his gun?" Rowden glanced about him sharply, right and left. He was surrounded by nesters now.

Those who had been slow hurried to add their weapons to the growing stack in front of the wagon.

At last Clee Soames's interest had strayed from the coveted dun horse. She was watching its rider now as he tossed Schlager's weapon on the heap with the others. "That's *muy hombre,*" she said. "Were you watching, Letty? Did you see it? Why haven't I met him?"

"You will," Letitia promised. "He's just what we've been needing here. I think you're going to see and hear a good deal of Will Rowden from now on."

4 WITH LOVE

BEFORE Rowden's appearance Clee had been contemptuous of Letty's fears. "I'm not afraid. These German clodhoppers wouldn't dare touch Clebourne Soames. They know the Snake on a Rock. If one of them so much as looked at me Jack would take him apart."

"Luke Nesbit wasn't exactly a tenderfoot," Letty retorted sharply. "The O-bar-O was a big spread. That didn't stop them. Look!" She pointed at the nesters milling below, each gripping his scatter-gun. "They're ripe for trouble and you're cattle folks, Clee. You've got to stay. I can't let you leave till this blows over."

Letitia Reid was only a year the elder but she carried a man's burden on her slender shoulders. She was nineteen when her father died, three years ago. Since then she had operated the Reid House with only Hallelujah's doubtful help.

John Soames approved of Letty. No foolishness about her. The Reid House was cowman's headquarters in town, and he had known her since she wore pigtails. Clee could visit there whenever she pleased. He wasn't always generous in his judgments where his motherless daughter was concerned. There was jaundice in his eye when he looked past the boundaries of his own range. Ranch people were fine, but there were no women folks at the Lazy B nor the O-bar-O. Of course, there was Ma Williams at the Forked W. Clee could go there if she pleased, but Ma usually had her hands full of some man's chore. He viewed all nesters with suspicion and this feeling embraced most townfolk as well. Letty was an exception and she was about Clee's age.

He was proud of Clee and indulged her in all the small ways. This made his harsher demands all the more difficult for her to understand. It hadn't always been this way. There'd been openhearted affection between them when she was a child, with no reservations to mar their companionship. She called him Jack, as her mother had before her; he delighted in that—no one else dared use the nickname—and he pampered her extravagantly, kept her beside him whenever possible. He didn't know when and how this good intimacy had been lost. Often he brooded over it, wanted to bridge the gap, but couldn't find the way. Part of this was due to his possessiveness. He had the same conceit about his ranch. The Snake on a Rock had the widest horizons in the valley. It was his and there was none to compare with it. He yearned to dominate his daughter just as he did his range and was uneasily aware that there were reaches of her mind where he no longer ruled. But worry was at the root of his restrictions too. Clee was grown now, 't wasn't fit for her to roam the range like some unbridled filly. He didn't aim for her to take up with the first ranny who came riding in with his hair greased down and a guitar under his arm. He hadn't set eyes on a man who was good enough for her yet.

Time was when he'd enjoyed a little music around headquarters, but that was before Larry White came. Larry was the first boy who attracted Clee seriously. He had been a handsome ranny who'd ridden for the Snake on a Rock two years before, ready with laughter, and with a talent for wringing music from a battered old guitar. John Soames had rather liked it when the youngster had fallen into the habit of drifting over to the big house after supper. It had a homey sound when Clee chimed in on the old songs. One summer twilight the singing had stopped and Soames, rounding the house, had discovered Larry kissing Clee. He had broken the guitar, thrashed the boy, paid him off and sent him riding. After that he lost his taste for music and his perception sharpened where his daughter was concerned. He didn't like his Snake on a Rock riders too young any more. Democracy was the easygoing habit of the country. One rider was as good as another whether he owned his own brand or not. But at the Snake on a Rock a tradition had grown up—hands off the boss's daughter. She had matured in an indulgent world where every whim was gratified but no close friendships ripened. She knew why, and didn't try to penetrate the wall of exaggerated courtesy which hedged her in. Her father had drawn a ring around her. No one ventured to cross it.

Often she regretted the freedom of younger days when, as a cotton-topped youngster, she'd shared ranch chores with the men in unquestioned camaraderie. Sometimes she rode with them yet when her father was present but it wasn't the same. She felt it. Discontent marred her full lips, made them petulant. Because the normal outlets of a healthy curiosity were closed to her, her appetite was whetted. Men and love were mysterious riddles. She read of them avidly, fed her mind on the distorted images derived from a few worn books. The men in the world around her didn't match these pictures. They wore the rough clothes of the range, often were dusty and sweat-streaked from hours in the saddle, didn't know the stilted phrases of the fiction heroes. Sometimes she questioned Letty. Surely the Reid House offered peculiar advantages for observation. Had she ever been in love?

"La! I've seen too much of men." Letty was contemptuous. "Time a ranny hits town he's usually carrying a thirst he's been storing up for a couple of months. And the only woman he's got in mind is the sort of floosey he'd find at Scanlon's Saloon. Not for me."

"But they can't all be like that."

"N-no." Letty looked thoughtful. "I guess I just see more than my share of hell-raisers. Take August Lehman for instance. I can't imagine him ever starting out to take the town apart."

"But he's old. And he's a *storekeeper!*" Clee's lip curled at the very thought of a merchant. "What I want is the sort of man you read about in books. You know, a gentleman with wonderful manners and wearing fine clothes like—like an officer or a planter or someone like that."

"La! You'll play hob finding him here." Letty tossed her head. "We're sitting on the wrong stump. You won't see that sort riding up Apache Valley."

Letty wasn't so skeptical as she sounded though. She had her dreams. "I reckon my man will be bowlegged from straddlin' a cow pony and maybe he'll have saddle sores. He won't know a thing about fine clothes and he'll probably look like he'd been left out in the weather to rust. But he'll have plenty of gumption.

"I reckon he won't be so different from your storybook man at that— not underneath," she added.

As Clee watched Will Rowden disarm the nesters her curiosity was whetted. It was his magnificent horse which first had attracted her attention. Now it was the man. He was too far from her to distinguish his face, but the elegance of his clothes didn't escape her. Heretofore frock coats and immaculate linen only had existed for her in books. His behavior in the face of danger stirred her, too. Her eyes had been on him when the nester raised his gun. He hadn't faltered in his sure, deliberate step. She liked the authority of him, and his coolness. Her racing mind built a picture about Rowden. It made her reluctant to meet him. He probably wouldn't fit it at all. What if he were as old as her father, with pouches beneath his eyes and thinning hair?

"How old is Will Rowden?" She hoped the inquiry sounded casual.

"I've no idea." Letty guessed the direction of the question, her eyes sparkled. "He's not a boy if that's what you had in mind."

"Oh, I wasn't interested that way." The denial was quick. "I just wondered."

So he was old! Clee was surprised at the sharpness of her disappointment. Now that her hope was destroyed she didn't want to see him. It would be better if she went on home. The danger was over, there was nothing to stop her now.

"He won't have that easy a time disarming the cowmen," she promised. "He'll be dealing with a different breed of cats when they come in."

"He won't have to," Letty pointed out. "It takes two sides to make a fight. The ranch folks aren't going to shoot down unarmed men."

Clee recognized the truth of that. The crisis was passed. She would miss nothing if she left now. She announced her determination to start back.

"But it's fifty miles," her hostess protested. "You'd better wait till morning now."

"All the more reason I should get started. I told Jack I'd leave today. Besides, I'm riding my black mare. There's nothing around here can touch her when it comes to covering the ground unless—" her thought reverted to Rowden's magnificent animal—"maybe that stranger might give me a race. No, I'm starting now. I'll ford the river south of town and cut straight for the Snake on a Rock. I'll be on our own range long before sundown and at headquarters by moonrise."

Her father brought her news of what had happened when he rode in next day. Letty's prediction proved right. The cowmen had been reluctant to turn back until Rowden showed them the stacked arms he'd taken from the nesters. That clinched it. They couldn't fight unarmed men.

"But what about the Luke Nesbit killing? This still leaves that unsettled," Clee persisted. She wanted to hear more about Rowden, yet was reluctant to mention his name.

"Rowden promised to stay on as deputy sheriff until that was investigated," her father explained. "I don't put much stock in old man Sparks but this stranger has a way of getting things done, seems like. Leastways, we decided to give him a chance. Now then we'll see what happens."

They had no word for a week. Then it was Rowden himself who brought the news. Clee saw him coming, recognized his mount far out on the prairie, long before the rider was distinguishable. A quickened sense warned her that if her father realized her interest it might affect the stranger's reception. "There's someone riding in from town, Jack."

Soames shielded his eyes against the sun. "It's Rowden. I know his horse."

There was time to appraise the animal further before Rowden reached hailing distance.

"I've got to have that horse, Jack. It beats my black mare. And look at the color of it! Almost a match for my hair, isn't it?"

Soames chuckled, threw his arm across her shoulders. "If you turn out as good a judge of men as you are of horse flesh, I'll never worry about you, Clee. This may take some doin'. I hear he brought this animal all the way from Mississippi with him. But don't fret. If you want it you'll have it, no matter what it costs. Only don't act too eager or this stranger'll drive a hard bargain."

It was near dusk and Rowden was tired; the dust of fifty miles powdered his coat but he straightened in the saddle, conscious of the eyes that were on him as he rode in. He didn't stop at the bunkhouse where a dozen hands lounged, but headed straight for the big rambling dwelling fifty yards beyond, where Soames stood on the steps, hand raised. Behind him Rowden glimpsed a vivid splotch of color—yellow, bright in the porch's shadow. He'd heard that the ranchman was a widower who rode herd on an only daughter. There was a hand waiting to take his reins as he swung from the saddle. Soames's welcome was crisp.

"Come in—come in," he urged hospitably. "You're just in time for supper. This here's my daughter Clee."

Rowden's hat swept off with a flourish. She had bad manners, he thought—cold. She didn't say anything, merely nodded. But the dying sun was in her hair. Why didn't someone tell me what she was like? he thought. This was worth every mile of that ride.

Clee was too surprised to say anything. From what Letty had said she'd expected a much older man. Of course he wasn't a boy. Much better than that! He was mature without betraying a hint of his age. She tried to guess it, failed. He had the assurance of her father's years, yet he might have passed for thirty. There was a sort of elegance about him that matched his clothes. She watched as he peeled off his gloves.

She'd never seen skin so white except on a woman. His eyes were dark, features regular and sharply chiseled. When his teeth flashed tiny wrinkles puckered the corners of his eyes. They were the only trace of years she could find on his face. She liked them, thought they softened what might have been a stern look. All her first admiration for him returned. He was straight from the pages of her well-thumbed books, she thought.

"I have bad news," Rowden announced, once they were in the house and the lamps were lighted.

"No trace of Nesbit's murderers, eh?" Soames scowled. "You should have let me and my boys handle that."

"No, that isn't it. I found them all right. One nester even left a scatter-gun behind at the spot where they dry-gulched the O-bar-O riders. We picked up the trail there. I had some good men with me, so it wasn't difficult. There were four in the gang. We tracked them to a squatter's cabin, not three miles from there. They tried to stand us off but we got every one of them."

"Well, what's bad about that?"

"Sheriff Sparks was killed in the fight. He was the only man we lost." Rowden shook his head. "Too bad. I liked the old man. We brought him back and buried him in Apache."

He told the story of the battle simply. The sheriff's death dramatized its danger for Cleé. The slain nesters were unknown to her, criminals who had invited this grim justice. The kindly, bumbling sheriff had been a landmark in her own life. It was hard to picture him dying so heroically. It brought the smell of powder, the roar of guns close. It was different with Rowden. She'd watched his calm when he faced the armed nesters in Apache. The smell of battle fitted him, she thought.

"What about the nesters? How have they taken this?" Soames demanded.

Rowden shrugged. "This was the law. All you've needed to stamp out the trouble here was a resolute officer."

The rancher held out his hand. "Someone like you. I didn't think anyone could settle this short of open war. What are your plans, Rowden? I heard you wanted to buy the O-bar-O spread. That shouldn't be hard to do now with Nesbit gone."

"I know better now. That wouldn't work. I'd have to buy up all the nesters to protect the water. It's too late—there are too many of them. Nesbit could fight; he was there first. But now the boot's on the other foot. I am the newcomer. No, there's nothing for me here in the valley. Guess I'll have to look farther."

"You're our kind of folks. We'd hate to lose you."

"I can't see anything for me here."

"We need a sheriff."

Rowden smiled thinly. "Hardly my kind of job, Mr. Soames. Not permanently. Someone had to step in to prevent civil war. I just did what was necessary. Now things are straightened out."

"Trouble is, they're not." The rancher thrust his plate aside, leaned forward, arms spread on the table. "The job's just begun. If you'd stay awhile——"

Rowden raised his hands in protest. Clee noticed how long and white his fingers were. Capable, she thought them.

"No—wait!" Soames urged. "It's worth something to all of us to have peace here. We'd make it worth your while to stay, at least till things settled down again. I can speak for all the cowmen."

Again the visitor's hands protested. "That wouldn't be enough," he said. "Your sheriff will have to represent the nesters too, to get the job done."

"You had Lehman and Pflueger in your posse the other day. They're the best in the lot. With them on your side, you'll have the nesters."

Soames continued his urging. By the time they quit the table he had half persuaded his guest to remain as sheriff "at least until things settled down."

Rowden liked the way things were going. Soames had the reputation of being a thorny man to handle, yet it had been easy to guide the conversation into carefully mapped channels. Things were falling nicely into place. It suited Rowden when men fitted into his schemes. He had a vanity about it. His was the mind which forecast the pattern of the puzzle. His nimble fingers pulled the strings which guided the men he meant to use. This seed was well planted. He turned his attention to the girl. Most blonde women lacked color, he thought. She was different. Her hair was bronze where it picked up the lamp's light and her eyes were amber to match. Even her skin had the sun's warmth in it. Everything about her, the dress included, seemed to blend into some rich golden tone. She fascinated him but he'd heard of the rancher's watchfulness where his daughter was concerned. He kept his eyes away from her. Yet his talk drifted to far places, was subtly baited for her ears. He spoke glibly of New Orleans, Memphis, St. Louis and the river packets that churned up and down the Mississippi.

Soon Clee was asking questions. What were these far cities like? What did the women wear? How did they live? Each answer opened up breathless vistas of finery and extravagance, encouraged new questions. Sometimes his tongue was sharp when he lampooned the foibles of that distant world he seemed to know so well. That drew chuckles from Soames, kept him included in the conversation. Clee saw through the trick, was delighted by it. For Clee, the way he captured her father's interest when it flagged was a warm secret between them, and his fluent knowledge linked him more surely than ever to a world she'd known only through books.

Long after she went to bed that night Clee lay sleepless, and the petulance was gone from her lips.

Will Rowden was wakeful, too. It had amused him at first to capture the girl's interest under her father's alert eye. The adroitness with which he had drawn her into the petty conspiracy against her father had appealed to him. It was like a game in which he alone knew all the moves. Gradually he had lost this sense of planning. An amusing game had turned serious. The child he'd set out to dazzle had, in turn, charmed him. Before the evening ended he had the uneasy feeling that the scene had slipped out of his hands, that now it was the girl who gave it its direction. That made him unsure of himself. He didn't like that.

He didn't have her fitted into his plans. He had thought out each step of the near future, knew just where each careful move led. Then, he'd never seen Clee Soames. It annoyed him that she should matter so. He scowled, brushed his hand across his eyes as if to sweep away the memory of the lamplight in her hair. He was no boy, to be haunted by the full curve of willful lips.

And yet why not? What plan couldn't be changed? Fool! he thought. Fool, to let a girl change everything! His life already was planned. By morning even Clee would look different. She was not for him.

He couldn't shut out the vision of her though. He thought of many ways his schemes might be changed before he finally drifted off to sleep.

He laughed at himself in the morning. Those midnight arguments seemed silly. Astonishing, how lamplight and golden hair could mesmerize a man! He found his way to the kitchen, procured a mug of hot water from the cook, and all through his shaving jeered at himself in the mirror over last night's spell. Why, she's just a chit of a girl, hardly out of her teens! Clever little minx though, no doubt of that.

He knew it wasn't merely cleverness as soon as he saw her. She was waiting breakfast for him. Soames already had left for the bunkhouse. The sun was streaming in the window behind her and he stopped at the door, caught his breath at the tricks it played with her hair.

She had changed her dress, of course, to something crisp and white, sprigged with green flowers. Each detail of her face had been sharp in his memory last night, yet he couldn't have told whether she was tall or short. Thought of her youth annoyed him. Had he lost his head over some scrawny, flat-chested child? Watching as she crossed the room, he smiled in quick relief. This was no child.

"Jack usually has an early snack out at the bunkhouse with the boys," she explained. "He'll be in directly."

"I have a confession to make," he said. His eyes were watchful, he was ready to turn the conversation should it develop the wrong way. "I thought you were very young when I first met you, Clee. That must have been because you're so lovely. I know better now. You're a mature woman. Why, I'm surprised you're not already married."

"You mean you thought I was too young for you?"

Her directness caught him off-guard. "Why no—I hadn't thought of it in just that way."

"I'd heard you were old." She continued in the same straightforward way. "I don't know where Letty ever got such an idea. I think it's the way you have with older men. They listen to you."

"I am old, Clee—much older than you. Just in years. When it comes to experience——"

She smiled. "You're not just a boy. I wouldn't like you so well if you were."

The scrape of Soames's boots sounded on the steps. Clee turned away with a quick, startled movement. Rowden glanced over his shoulder guiltily. Like children caught in some mischief, he thought, and was impatient with himself.

Rowden's horse was saddled and waiting when they stepped out the door. Clee, her mind busy with the man, had forgotten her desire to own the animal. Soames hadn't. He lost his bluntness when he sidled into a trade. Actually he wasn't close-fisted—the cost didn't bother him. Bargaining was a challenge; vanity demanded that he make the best of a deal and he enjoyed the verbal maneuvering. Not a subtle man, his efforts at cunning usually were heavy-handed and overplayed. Just now his face was screwed up in consternation. Fleetingly, Clee thought he was in pain.

"Hell 'n' damnation! They've throwed a saddle on this dun for you, Rowden."

"Why not? He's mine."

Soames's pain seemed to grow more acute. "But you rode him yesterday. Folks'll think the Snake on a Rock's lost its neighborliness." His arm swept toward the corral. "Just help yourself to a fresh horse."

Rowden smiled. "This one will get me there."

The cowman shook his head. "Fifty miles yesterday—fifty miles today. 'T ain't my way to send a man off on a tuckered-out animal. Just take your choice of anything in the *remuda* yonder. You can pick up your dun next time you're by this way."

Rowden glanced across at the girl, hesitated. He had recognized the signals. He had no thought of trading but this might offer an excuse for a speedy return.

Soames bobbed his head solemnly. "I know. You're not used to our ways. You're just set agin ridin' another man's horse. This is the custom out here, Rowden. But tell you what I'll do. I'll make it a swap. Just sling your saddle over anything you like and it's yours. I can't let you leave here without a fresh mount."

Now Rowden let the smile behind his face creep out to the corners of his mouth. "I like this horse of mine pretty well, sir. I don't want to trade him."

The rancher seemed to see the dun for the first time. He pursed his lips judiciously, squinted his eye. "Matter of fact, I hadn't paid your horse much mind. It was you I was thinking of. H'm—not ba-a-ad! Off-color, of course, but I won't hold that agin him. You're like me. You like a big mount with plenty of bottom. Better take a look at that big chestnut yonder with the blaze face."

"No, I guess I'll worry along with what I have. He suits me."

Soames glanced at his daughter uneasily. His exasperation was beginning to show slightly around the edges. "I'd hate to have folks say I sent you off on a jaded mount." Impatience tinged the injury in his voice.

"They won't," Rowden assured him. And then because he wanted this man's friendship he thawed. "I just don't want to trade, Mr. Soames. I spent a lot of time finding this horse. I want to keep him."

"Hell, I've got the biggest *remuda* in the valley. 'T ain't as if I needed a horse."

Rowden nodded in smiling agreement. "Of course not. Let's just forget the trade."

"How much will you want to boot?"

"Not anything. I'm not trading."

"I've never seen a horse that didn't have a price."

"You're looking at one now, my friend."

Soames stood spraddle-legged, hands on hips, his chin jutting truculently. "Damn it, Clee!" he exploded. "This fellow's as stubborn as I am." He slapped his thigh and joined in their laughter.

"This was Clee's doing," he explained. "She had her heart set on ownin' this dun. He's a heap of animal all right and she knows horseflesh. But it was the color that got her—it sort of matches her hair."

Rowden, careless of her father's watchfulness, stared at Clee. All last night's misgivings were forgotten; he knew no plan would be complete without her now. He handed her the reins and the gesture was simple. He hadn't planned it, thought out its effect in advance as he did so often. "He's your horse, Miss Clee."

Fool! he thought when he realized what he'd said. Fool! Have you completely lost your mind over this little baggage? But in another part of his mind he was glad he'd done it and he didn't let the conflict show on his face.

She was silent with astonishment.

"Just name your price, Rowden. I ain't the man to haggle after you've met me halfway."

Rowden was staring at Clee. He didn't turn. "There's no price to name," he said. "I've given him to Clee. She's right. His color will match her hair."

"Now see here!" The cowman's voice turned angry. "My girl don't take presents like that. Set a price on the horse and I'll pay it."

The temper of Soames's voice warned Rowden. "I didn't mean any offense," he explained. "There isn't any price on the animal. But since you mentioned it, I see what a fine match he'd be for Miss Clee. I'd like to give him to her."

"Well, damn it, man—name your figure!"

It was Clee who resolved the stalemate. Reluctantly she handed back the reins. "It was generous of you to make the offer but I can't accept."

She saw the change in Rowden's eyes. Where before the warmth of the man had shown through they had turned hard and cold. Now they shut her out. Her hand was soft as she pressed the reins into his palm. She let it linger there, eager for understanding. "Don't you see? I'm not refusing the gift. The horse really belongs to you. With me it was just a whim. What I really want is to see you ride him."

His eyes grew gentle again.

Soames was uneasy over things that baffled him. He felt that way about Rowden. Clee's sudden change of mind disturbed him, too. She's as hard to figure as he is, he thought. What's got into her this morning? He felt relief when Rowden cantered away. "There goes our new sheriff," he told his daughter. "He's a strange one. I'm not sure whether I like him or not, but he's already shown what he can do. He'll get the job done."

When Rowden was in the saddle his coattails flapped, revealing a silk lining, Clee noticed. It was a detail she remembered long after he was gone. She thought silk lining typified the nicety of the man.

Rowden let himself be persuaded to stay on as sheriff. "But only until affairs have been straightened out here," he insisted. "I understand your problem. You need someone who isn't identified with either the cowmen or the nesters, someone both sides will trust. As a matter of fact, I don't see how I can avoid the responsibility, but as soon as things are straightened out I'll turn the job over to somebody else."

As Soames had foreseen, the cowmen backed his judgment. There wasn't the same unanimity among the German settlers. Rowden's expedition against the nesters blamed for the O-bar-O massacre had aroused uneasiness among them. Neither Lehman nor Pflueger, the two influential German members of his posse, had been present at that fight.

"That wass the Schneider family you surrounded," Lehman explained. "They had a good name. It iss hard for their neighbors to believe they were guilty, Rowden. What makes you think they were?"

For answer Rowden exhibited a shotgun. Three wide notches were cut in its stock. "Everyone who's seen this gun has identified it as Otto Schneider's. His neighbors knew he notched it for the Indians he'd killed. We found it near Luke Nesbit's body. Besides, once we picked up the trail it led straight to the Schneider cabin."

"But they should have been brought in. This killing wass not good. They should have had a trial."

"That's what the sheriff thought," retorted Rowden grimly. "They shot him as he walked up to the door. No, that fight wasn't of our choosing. We didn't open fire until we saw poor old Sparks go down.

"See here, Mr. Lehman," he continued. "Luke Nesbit had his friends too, remember. If I'm going to enforce the law it will hit both sides alike. You've got to understand that. That's the only way I can bring peace to this valley. That's what you want, isn't it?"

The merchant was convinced. So were most of the other Germans, finally. Will Rowden became sheriff of Apache with no outspoken opposition.

His office bristled deputies, several of them men who'd ridden with him when he disarmed the town. Burly-shouldered Frank Toomey, forever caressing the prongs of his mustache, was his chief deputy. Pete Falkner, cold-eyed, alert, his speech salted with Spanish, and several others like him were recognized as sheriff's men. They were the hands Rowden had brought with him. He had several German deputies, too. August Lehman didn't think much of them. He spoke to the sheriff about it.

"My boys are cowmen," Rowden explained. "I think it's a good idea to have a few nesters, too. It builds confidence. That way both sides are represented."

The little German merchant shook his head sadly. "Confidence? I'm sorry—but not in thiss lot." The blond tuft on his chin bristled when he pursed his lips in disgust. "They are riffraff—Unger, Pakebusch, Blucher. It iss a good idea having some Germans in your office but not these."

Rowden smiled. "I could pick better ones myself if I had my choice. The trouble is, the ones I'd like to get are too busy. I take what's available."

Lehman remained uneasy. He couldn't tell exactly why himself, except for his mistrust of some of the deputies. He took a trip up the valley in his high-wheeled buggy to visit his friends at the Forked W. "Maybe the trouble iss over at last," he confided to Ma Williams. "Things never have been so quiet. I hope they stay that way."

"Hell's bells! Don't you go borrowing trouble, August. Course they'll stay that way. I reckon Will Rowden's just the man we needed to straighten things out."

The sheriff was no longer a stranger in the valley. He spent considerable time in the saddle, usually accompanied by his chief deputy. Everyone knew him; no one seemed to know him well. He had unusual courtesy, yet he wore his manners stiffly, never unbent. Characteristically he remained "Mister" to everyone. None called him Will Rowden, at least not to his face.

It was different with Frank Toomey. He was quickly on easy terms with half the families in the valley. There was something about his ready, booming laugh that inspired confidence. Everyone called him Frank. And the way he rolled his eyes and twirled his wide mustache at the womenfolks was so obvious that it became a jest. No one resented it. Every farmer knew there was no harm in old Frank.

Twice Rowden dropped by the Snake on a Rock. Soames made him welcome; Clee was as eager as ever with her questions. On the first visit he picked up where he'd left off before. Again he maintained the pretense of addressing Soames but the range of his conversation was carefully calculated for Clee. There was a challenge in his mind the first time. No girl could be so desirable as he had built her up in his memory. He only needed to see her again to discover that. It didn't work. He found himself straining, waiting for her next word. Just being in the same room with her soothed him.

There was no coquetry in her. Her delight in his coming was obvious. She reproached him for staying away too long. "We've missed you," she said.

He hugged that thought to him hopefully as he rode away. Yet he left in a glum mood. Nothing had progressed. Soames was a dour watchdog—Rowden hadn't had a moment alone with Clee.

He thought the next trip was going to prove as unsatisfactory. This time he rode in early, on the way over from the Forked W. He took his time once he crossed the river, kept scanning the horizon. Having learned that she rode often, he hoped to intercept her beyond her father's vigilance. Taking hope when a distant rider raised an arm in greeting, he dug in his spurs and went careening forward. He slowed to a sensible gait when close enough to recognize the rider. It was one of the Snake on a Rock hands. "The new sheriff's a silent man" was the bunkhouse verdict of him after that morose ride.

He thawed in Clee's presence though. When she listened he grew eloquent. This evening was much like the others. With the rancher present there was never a chance for the things he wanted to say. He went to bed unhappily.

Next morning it was different. Soames had ridden out at dawn to comb the western reaches of the range for some old mossy-horns which had evaded too many roundups. Clee was alone when Rowden stepped into the dining room. It was the opportunity he'd been waiting for and yet, when it was presented, he turned cautious. He was afraid that once started he'd spill out too much. After all, this was something he'd built up in his mind. She didn't share it. He couldn't risk a declaration.

She didn't seem to realize any strain. In a gay mood, her approval of him was so easy to read. It put him on his guard. No girl could be so guileless, he thought. It wasn't in him to move until he was sure of his ground. The opportunity slipped away. Breakfast ended; his horse was saddled and waiting. He turned to pick up his hat, with more impatience for himself than he'd ever felt for John Soames's vigilance. His first time alone with Clee had been wasted. What was wrong with him, anyway?

Clee followed him to the door, held out her hand to say good-by. Still silent, he raised it to his lips. He glanced up and, seeing nothing but astonishment in her face, he raised her hand again, turning it over this time to press his lips into her palm. He felt her fingers tighten at the contact.

When he straightened up he tried to read her eyes. Their look baffled him. In her throat a pulse throbbed. Still he hesitated. "I think you knew right from the first," he said finally.

She nodded. "I think I did too."

All his indecision was gone. He kissed her then and, when he felt the pressure of her lips under his, the tremor of her body as she clung to him, wondered why he'd hesitated.

"I almost went away without doing this," he said later.

"Why?"

"I guess I was afraid. What if you didn't love me?"

"But didn't you know? I cared so much I thought it surely showed."

Her frankness surprised him, made him more tender. "With you I'll always know where I stand, won't I?" He kissed her again.

In the kitchen a dishpan fell with a tremendous clatter. They sprang apart, startled. The heavy thump of the cook's boots sounded his progress toward the door. Mischief brimmed in Clee's eyes. "I think he saw us. That sounds too much like an alarm."

"I was just going." Rowden picked up his hat.

"Are you scared of a dough wrangler?" she challenged.

"Right now nothing could scare me," he assured her solemnly, and the violence of his embrace swept her off the floor. "I'll be back soon," he promised after a final kiss.

Pete Falkner was sent on an errand as soon as the new sheriff reached town. The Kennedys over in Mason County rode a lot of dun horses, Pete remembered. "Good ones, too," he assured Rowden.

"Buy me the best one on their range, Pete. I don't care what it costs."

Falkner grinned. "It will be moonlight, *amigo*. A man with a long rope should be able to take his pick."

"None of that," Rowden growled. This mission was too serious for humor. "A man would trail the horse I'm hunting across half a dozen counties."

Falkner was back in ten days. The sheriff grinned when he concluded his inspection of the dun filly. In color, she was a match for his own mount. Not so tall and built along less-rugged lines, but for his purpose she was even better-suited. Rowden was pleased. Even the price she'd cost didn't dismay him. "You know a horse when you see one, Pete."

"I wouldn't swap her for that *caballo* of yours, *jefe*." He shrugged. "For you—maybe. You are *muy grande*. But for a man my size—phut! Give me an hour's start and you'll never catch me this side of the Rio Grande."

"She'll have a small rider, Pete," Rowden promised.

He was leading the new mare when he arrived at the Snake on a Rock next day. Soames was away but Clee had seen him coming. She met him at the corral, and showed her delight when he handed her the halter rope.

"She took a lot of finding, that little lady, but I had to get her for you, Clee. The color does match your hair and you wouldn't accept mine."

"What's Jack going to say?" She looked stricken. "You shouldn't have done this, Will. You know how he is."

Rowden shook his head and smiled. "He can't be so bad, judging by his daughter. When he understands how things are between us——"

"That worries me. I wish we didn't have to tell him yet."

"Why? It's nothing to worry about, Clee. I feel like stopping everybody I meet just to tell him I love Clee Soames. That's how I feel about it."

She laughed at that but the worry still haunted her face. "Jack's queer the way he acts about me. It's always been that way. He'd let me have 'most anything I wanted except friends—men friends, that is. I dread to think what's going to happen when I tell him I've fallen in love with you."

"He can't fence you off from the world forever."

"He has done it for several years. I've thought about it a lot, Will. I'd rather tell him right off but sometimes I think it'd be better if we didn't say anything till we're ready to be married. Then he couldn't stop us, no matter what happened."

Her calm mention of marriage startled him. In her mind everything was settled. He felt a moment of panic as if he'd stepped into a trap. This was a move he had never contemplated. She's tricky, he thought. Trying to slip a halter on me before I realize what she's about. Watching her though, his suspicion faded. There was no guile to her. What she thought, she said. His nettled wariness turned to amusement. Does she think a man wants to marry every girl he kisses? he wondered. He didn't feel cynical though—he only argued that way to quiet the misgivings of his mind. Marriage? Why not? Worse things could happen. Sardonically he tried to gloss over his motives. Wasn't the Snake on a Rock the biggest ranch in the valley? And yet, looking at Clee he knew that wasn't the answer. None of his jaded notions fitted her. Knowledge of this shook his old confidence. Nothing else really mattered. He wanted her.

Several times that day he was tempted to tell her of the doubts that plagued him. This was new to him, too. Her candor invited his confidence. Secrecy was his habit but with her he longed to throw it off. Always, a look at her happiness checked him. It was on her face to see, in her voice—something to hoard. This guarding of something precious gave him a feeling of tenderness he hadn't known before.

They rode together—the new mare must be tried. Once they raced. Indulgently he gave her the advantage at the start—and was surprised to find he couldn't overtake her no matter how he tried. In the fury of the pace her hair shook loose. Flecked with sunlight, it streamed behind her in the wind. Later they found a knoll where the grass was deep, spelled their horses while they sprawled in the turf. From here the plain stretched as boundlessly as the dreams they shared, until it reached the blue of the hills which molded the horizon. He didn't want to end it, and put off leaving until she insisted. The ride back was long.

"Are you so anxious to be rid of me?" he demanded.

"You know better than that." She kissed him. "I'll be glad when you never have to leave me again."

It was past midnight when he reached town. The ride had not been lonely. It was crowded with the day's memories. He might have stopped at Lazy B headquarters—he'd ridden close enough to see the welcome of its yellow lamps, but had gone on. There was a mellowness in him he didn't care to share.

John Soames arrived home late, after Clee was asleep. He didn't learn of Rowden's visit nor of the present he'd brought until he saw the dun mare in the corral next morning. The animal's color warned him. At first glance he thought it was the sheriff's own mount. His skilled eye quickly detected the difference. In some ways he liked the mare's quality better. But he guessed where she was from and was uneasy as he hurried to the house. He found Clee at the breakfast table.

"Was the sheriff here yesterday?"

"Yes. You've seen the mare, haven't you?"

He nodded. Disquiet made him gruff. "I don't like the idea of him comin' round when I'm not here."

She saw the sullen thrust of his jaw and tried to forestall his anger with a smile. "But Jack, how could he tell whether you were here or not? I reckon he was disappointed not to find you."

"I suppose he came to fetch me that dun mare?"

"N-no."

"So it was you he came to see. That's what I said I didn't like."

She remembered something Rowden had told her. "You can't build a fence around me forever, Jack."

"Maybe not a fence, but don't forget I'm still runnin' the Snake on a Rock. Nobody comes here behind my back."

That angered her. "Nobody has," she flared. "He didn't know you weren't home. I've told you that."

He ignored this. "How about this filly? You want to buy her?"

"She was a present, Jack. Please listen to me. He went all the way to Mason County after that filly because I'd admired his horse. You can't be rude to people after they've gone to all that trouble. Don't you see?"

"And you took it?"

"Of course. It would have been like a slap in the face if I hadn't."

"H'm. Sometimes that's just what's needed. Of course I aim to take the mare back. I'll ride in this morning."

"No, Jack. You can't. I've tried to explain——"

"I'm taking her back—now," he repeated testily.

She tried to fight back the tears. Her fists were clenched, her face white. Mostly it was baffled rage and this feeling of helplessness. For the moment at least, loss of the mare was unimportant. Her father's misunderstanding and the threatened breach between him and Rowden were what mattered. She couldn't keep her mouth from trembling. Her eyes became wet.

It had been years since Soames had seen his daughter cry. He stared at her anxiously. Anger he knew how to meet. It was easy to roar down an argument. But this was something different. He cleared his throat with an uneasy rumble. "Now look, honey . . ."

The tears came faster. When Clee tried to choke them back she sobbed.

"Damn it, honey! You know I'll buy you anything you want. It's just . . . just . . ."

He couldn't combat the tears. He tried awkwardly to comfort her but she wanted none of it. She flung off his arm. He backed off in distress. "All right . . . all right . . . all right." He meant the tone to be soothing but it swelled louder and louder in competition with her sobs. "*All right!* Can't you listen? I said *all right*—you can keep the mare!" He slammed the door behind him as he retreated to the corral.

That day he rode to Apache. If Clee wanted that filly she would have it. She'd always had anything she wanted, he told himself stormily. But she wasn't going to accept a present from any man. His spleen had turned on Rowden. It was a long ride; he had much time to think. This was no boy who could be handled like Larry White. He didn't like Will Rowden but yielded him a grudging respect.

The sheriff looked up and smiled when he saw Soames in the doorway. He'd rather expected this visit, after what Clee had told him. Because of her he was determined not to quarrel.

"Come in," he called. "Always glad to see you, Mr. Soames."

"Always glad to see you too, sheriff—*here*." The cowman stressed the last word. In his hand he held a leather sack, filled with money from the sound of it, for it clinked as he shoved it across the table.

Rowden raised his brows. "What's that for?"

"I've just bought a dun mare for my daughter."

The sheriff's long white fingers thrummed his chair arm. "That was a gift, Soames. I don't want your money."

"My girl doesn't accept gifts. We pay for what we get."

"Suppose the mare isn't for sale?"

Soames pointed at the sack. "There's enough there for two top horses."

Rowden measured the anger in the rancher's flushed face. He didn't want a showdown with Soames. Finally he asked, "Do you want a bill of sale?"

"I reckon your word is good enough for me." At the door the cowman turned. "It's a long ride out to the Snake on a Rock, sheriff, and I know you're a busy man. Any time you want to see me you can catch me in town. I'm here pretty often. Just leave word at the Reid House."

Rowden sat silent, frowning at the door, after his visitor left. Then, shrugging, he loosed the thong that bound the sack, spilled the money noisily across his desk. There were two hundred dollars here—big, Maximilian dollars—the only silver that had been available in Texas during the war years. He still scowled as he carefully stacked the coins in a drawer of his desk.

Two weeks dragged by. To Clee they seemed interminable. The first few days weren't so bad—she hadn't expected to hear from Rowden at once. But when a week passed and there still was no word, she grew anxious. Many times a day she stepped out on the gallery to scan the horizon, looking for an approaching horseman. Nothing but grass met her gaze. Once when she squinted into the distance she realized her father was watching. He said nothing; neither did she. With each day that passed, her heart grew more leaden. It was hard for her to understand why Rowden didn't come. In her room she had a calendar on which she marked the days. By usual standards it hadn't been so long. Yet she had counted each hour by its minutes and the time seemed endless.

One night she announced her plan to visit Apache. "I think I'll go see Letty Reid for a few days. I haven't been there lately."

Soames was tempted to oppose the trip. There had been times he might not have noticed the marks of strain on Clee, but he had been watching and had not missed her restlessness. He thought she looked haggard, and he was worried. Often, these last weeks, he'd wished for a way to bring Rowden back without backtracking himself. He was concerned.

"Not a bad idea." He spoke carefully, anxious that his worry should not show in his voice. "I can't go myself but I'll send a wagon along. We always need supplies."

Clee started before dawn the next day. Sometimes she rode by the wagon, chatting companionably with the driver. Occasionally she relieved the monotony of the pace by spurring the mare ahead in a mad race with her own shadow. After the man made camp for their midday meal, she abandoned the slow vehicle. The easy-gaited mare would cut hours from the journey. "I'll see you tonight in Apache," she said. The grinning driver waved his whip as she rode off.

It hadn't been easy for Rowden to stay away. Each day he'd been tempted to cross the river and head south for the Snake on a Rock in defiance of Soames's warning. Always he restrained himself. It wasn't just that he wanted Soames's friendship. Often, these days, he found that he forgot the considerations which had brought him here. He was thinking of Clee and didn't want to force her to decision between her father and himself. Her position was difficult enough; he didn't aim to complicate it. This day he'd been far west in the valley, to the Scalp Creek Breaks beyond the Forked W. Pete Falkner had picked a camp site there and Rowden had wanted to see it. Frank Toomey and three other riders were with him on the homeward trip. When they glimpsed a mounted figure emerge from the river's screen of greenery and turn east to pick up the same trail, he recognized the dun mare and drew up. "That's a friend of mine," he told Toomey. "You go on. I'll see you in town."

The thing that had worried him most was whether Soames would be able to turn the girl against him. Time after time he'd rehearsed each move he'd made in the valley, scanning it anxiously for some mistake which might be turned against him. He couldn't be sure. Things a man might think of no consequence could be telling in the mind of a girl like Clee. That worried him. His mouth tightened. If she had changed, there would be a score to settle with her father at some future time.

The first glimpse of her face reassured him. She had recognized his horse, waited in the shade of a spreading cottonwood, and the happiness he remembered was in her smile when she welcomed him.

His doubts vanished. He swung down from his horse, lifted her down and folded her in his arms wordlessly. What could he say to tell her of the emptiness of these past weeks?

"The trouble with me is that I haven't any pride." Clee finally pushed him away. "Any time you happen to remember me I seem to be waiting. You snap your fingers and I lift my lips for a kiss."

"Where do you get such foolish notions?"

"Are they so foolish? Where have you been, Will? Is something wrong?"

"Nothing now." He kissed her again. "It's been so long." He told of her father's visit. "He doesn't want me at the Snake on a Rock."

The stubborn set of her chin then reminded him of John Soames. "I wondered if it was something like that," she said. "At first when you didn't come, I was just plain mad. Then I got anxious. You take such risks, Will. I was afraid something had happened. But I knew I'd surely hear if there'd been trouble. When I decided Jack had something to do with it I made up my mind to come and find out. Oh, Will, what are we going to do?"

"Nothing's going to stop us, honey. The only difference is, I can't come to the ranch. You'll have to meet me somewhere."

"Where?"

"Any place you say."

"I hate it to be like this, Will. It seems so . . . so sort of sneaky having to steal away to see you."

When he held her in his arms this way he could bury his face in her hair. He liked the fresh smell of it. "I wish I knew another way, honey. I don't. And I must see you—I've got to."

"I know." Her head burrowed closer into the hollow of his shoulder. "I've been miserable without you, too. It isn't as if it was for long, is it, Will? Soon we can be married. That will end all this, won't it?"

Married! There it was again. He shied away from the thought. He'd had time to think of it though. It no longer sounded like a snare. "How soon, honey?"

"Whenever you say. Now?"

He kissed her again, tenderly. "Yes, now—today," he wanted to say. He was surprised how the completeness of her surrender stirred him. Caution held him back. He temporized. "I don't want to come between you and your father. We need time to think about this, Clee. I'll find a way to make him understand."

They found a grassy slope by the river, where an elm spread its shade. They tethered their horses and sat on the bank. By leaning forward she could see herself in the placid water and, as she watched, his head appeared mirrored over her shoulder. "Look," she said, pointing. "They can see us."

"It doesn't matter. They're in love, too." He pulled her back into his arms. She didn't know how to dissemble. Her kisses were as eager as his.

He stroked her back gently as she nestled in his arms and she arched her body against the pressure.

Her golden hair fascinated him. He ruffled it with gentle hands and, when a coil was loosened, delighted in running the shining strands through his fingers.

"You're mussing me up," she protested at first. But when she discovered the pleasure it gave him she let him tumble it about her shoulders without further objection. All of their love-making was like that. His was a delirium, with none of his scheming in it. She had no defense. She couldn't deny him when his desire left her trembling, too. It was a fever in them both.

It was dusk when they approached Apache. They stopped at sight of the lights ahead, seized on this opportunity for a final kiss. She clung to him. "When will I see you again, Clee?"

"Tomorrow—the same place. I'll leave town early and ride fast, darling."

She delighted him. In love she didn't look back. Instead she was thinking of tomorrow.

Chapter 5 HELL TO PAY

EVERYONE hoped for peace in the valley under Will Rowden. The troublesome O-bar-O war was ended and he was given the major credit for it. As far as could be learned Luke Nesbit left no heirs. The other ranchers decided to round up the stock on his range into a trail herd. The proceeds could be held in trust should anyone show up with a claim. It was two weeks before arrangements were completed. Each valley outfit sent a few hands to the drive and Dave Blake of the Lazy B was in charge. Surprisingly they managed to find only twenty-four hundred cattle wearing the O-bar-O brand, where Nesbit's spring tally sheets showed more than eight thousand head. "Someone's stripped the range ahead of us" was the way Dave Blake explained it. "Run off enough beef to stock a fair-sized ranch."

The magnitude of such a theft puzzled them. How could more than five thousand cattle be herded out unseen?

"'T wasn't one big herd but a hundred little ones." Dave voiced the suspicion forming in every cowman's mind. "The nesters have been stocking up on beef."

The farmers, aware of this mistrust, turned sullen. Only Rowden's vigilance averted a new outbreak. What happened to the herd remained a mystery, for old Luke was gone and there was no O-bar-O outfit to push the inquiry.

Depredations didn't stop there, however. Every ranch reported losses and nester complaints were constant. Each faction blamed the other. "No wonder those clodhoppers are fat," John Soames growled. "They're feeding their families on our stock."

"The cowmen are still trying to run us out," the nesters grumbled. "We find our fences broken down, our cattle missing."

Rowden and his deputies rode up and down the valley. No one complained of their vigilance. Yet no thieves were caught, the thefts increased in number.

August Lehman voiced his concern to the sheriff. "I knew it wass too good to last." He shook his head sadly. "Alwayss it iss the same—trouble, hate. Soon will come bloodshed again."

Rowden's restless fingers drummed his desk. "If I could just get my hands on these thieves. When I ride west to the ranch country they hit the farmers. When I go down there they're busy on the range. Seems as if they always know where I am. There's a pattern to it, Mr. Lehman. They know my movements too well. If this was an organized gang I'd have caught it long ago, but I can't watch the whole valley at once. That's the trouble. They're nearly all in it. It isn't ordinary thieving—it's cowmen fighting nesters and nesters robbing cowmen. Just the same old war breaking out in a new way."

On another occasion he told the merchant, "Sometimes I've half a mind to ride off and let 'em fight it out."

"No, no, no!" Lehman waved his pudgy hands in alarm. "You can't do that. You have made a start. Patience—that iss what it takes. You're the one who ended the O-bar-O war. Remember, the valley believes in you."

The sheriff stayed on. His anxiety over the situation was obvious. He lengthened his patrols but where he rode nothing happened. As the depredations continued, the sullen temper of the valley mounted. No one was exempt from suspicion. Rowden could see it in the hostile eyes of nesters, hear it in the voices of cowmen when they rode into town.

His meetings with Clee continued, always secret. They had several regular trysting places along the river, and one not too far from Snake on a Rock headquarters, where scrubby oaks sheltered in a fold of hills screened them from prying eyes. The intervals of his absence were too long. Clee rode to them gladly. It was their furtiveness she disliked. "How long must we go on this way?" she would ask. "I don't like this sneaking around. It makes me feel ashamed." To her their love was something joyous. She didn't want it tarnished.

"I'm sorry it must be like this, honey. It isn't your fault or mine. If only your father would understand."

"Once we're married he'll have to understand, Will."

"Just let me get this trouble in the valley straightened out, Clee. Then, if your father still objects, I'll take you away from here. First I must finish my job, though."

She understood his concern over the way things were going. They talked of it frequently. She overheard cowmen who stopped at the ranch.

Often their remarks troubled her and she'd want to hear the answers from him.

"They say you have too many deputies, Will. It looks like a private army."

"They? Who?"

"I heard Dave Blake talking with Jack last night. He wasn't criticizing you," she added quickly. "It was your men he didn't trust."

"I'd be helpless without them, honey," he assured her. "I can't be everywhere at once."

"They don't like the nesters that you've made deputies—Pakebusch and Blucher and Unger."

"They . . . they . . . always they. Tell me who says these things, Clee. It helps if I know."

"Ma Williams was by. She says they're the last men in the valley she'd trust."

He kissed her and smiled. "I have to use what tools I can get, honey. I'll admit those nesters aren't much but I have to have some Germans in my office. The prosperous farmers won't leave home."

These rumors troubled her but her faith in Rowden remained unshaken. Always she came straight to him with them and his explanations made the answers seem simple.

"If it wasn't for these meetings with you, Clee, I don't know what I'd do," he assured her often. He said it first because he thought she'd like to hear it. And yet he was sincere with her too. His need for her grew on him. He was restless the days they were apart. Nothing was important enough to keep him away when she was waiting.

At least not until today. Three of his men were caught.

Pete Falkner was with him when Toomey brought word of what had happened. Charlie Springer and two other leather slappers had been trapped hustling a herd of beeves across the upper stretches of the Lazy B range. Dave Blake and four of his hands had spotted the herd, intercepted the three men as they rode out of a draw.

"If I hadn't been so far behind they'd have got me, too," Toomey added. "I topped the ridge just in time to see what happened."

When the sheriff was annoyed, his hands betrayed it. His restless fingers beat a tattoo upon the desk. "We'd foreseen something like this. Charlie had his story down pat. Why didn't he use it?"

Toomey shrugged. "Can't say. Guess they just wouldn't listen. I watched while they roped the fellows' arms behind them. Then I headed for town."

It didn't sound good. Rowden was worried. Why hadn't Charlie told them he was a deputy sheriff bringing in a herd of stolen cattle that he'd recovered? Or, if he had told them, why hadn't they listened?

"You had two guns in your belt," the sheriff reminded Toomey.

Falkner scowled. "If I had been on hand there would have been some lead throwing—*pronto.*"

Toomey flushed. "I told you they had the drop on our boys. They had me five to one."

The sheriff didn't give them time to argue. He headed for the horses. There was no time to lose. He didn't like the looks of this. There was already too much talk about his deputies. A thing like this could risk his whole setup. The trouble was that Charlie knew too much. Otherwise Rowden might have let him face the music.

"Want to gather up any more riders?" Toomey asked.

"No time. Besides, I don't aim to have that kind of trouble."

They rode hard, reached the Blake brothers' headquarters almost as soon as the Lazy B riders. Rowden took in the scene. His three deputies, securely roped, were lined up along the corral. Both Blakes were present now and a dozen of their hands. They stood waiting, expectant, ready for trouble. This was no time to hesitate. Rowden spurred straight in among them, swung off in front of Merrill Blake. "I didn't know the Lazy B was having trouble with the law." He nodded toward the prisoners. "What goes on here, Blake?"

"They said they were your men. I didn't believe 'em, Sheriff."

More than one Lazy B man had a hand on his gun.

"Yes, they're my deputies. What I need is co-operation if I'm going to stamp out this thieving, Blake. We've been in the saddle three days running down this gang. They got away but at least we recovered the stolen cattle. These boys were bringing the herd back."

"Back?" The cowman still made no move to free the prisoners. "They were headed west up the valley, Sheriff. Apache doesn't lie that-a-way."

Rowden nodded. "Of course. We'd set a place to meet. We were over west trying to head off the cow thieves."

The Blake brothers exchanged doubtful glances. "You must admit this had a bad look, Sheriff," Dave said.

Rowden knew he'd won then but still he moved cautiously until the deputies were released. The cowmen hadn't lost their suspicion but the ruse succeeded because of their uncertainty. Rowden's assurance turned the scales.

He was a day late meeting Clee. She already knew what had kept him away. "They say——" she began.

"Who says?"

"The Blakes. They still think they captured some cow thieves, Will."

He lost his temper then. "If anyone says I——"

"That's not what they say. Nobody has accused you but they suspect some of your men are pulling the wool over your eyes. Is there any danger of that? Are you sure of Charlie Springer?"

"Of course I'm sure. I don't like the sound of these stories, Clee."

Her questions were revealing. Up to now he had congratulated himself that no suspicion touched him. As long as cowmen and nesters blamed one another, he was secure. That was the tempting prospect which had brought him here. He had fanned that hatred cleverly, worked himself into a position of trust. Even his riders wore badges of authority. How else could the O-bar-O range have been stripped? That had been a rich haul. He was warned now. More caution was needed. Perhaps the nesters should be prodded into another bloody outbreak. That might be arranged, and its flareup would furnish good cover for his movements.

The conversation hastened his decision to establish the camp in the Scalp Creek Breaks. Pete Falkner had found the site and taken him to see it. At its western end the valley gradually narrowed until the hills converged. It wasn't a gentle meeting. The ridges had collided, broken their spines in the shock. Their scattered remnants spread a desolate barrier there. Crumped hills piled on one another. The shallow troughs of the Breaks were boulder-strewn and choked with brush. It was a safe place for a camp, still handy to the valley's cattle. Charlie Springer was put in charge of it and word was given out that the sheriff had rid himself of some deputies.

Rowden didn't send Falkner away. He might have need of Pete's quick gun and he was one of the few men the sheriff trusted.

Peter Falkner had been a condemned desperado in the Austin jail and Rowden an official of the state police when they met.

"They tell me you're quick with a gun," Rowden had said.

"You have been listening to someone who knew me, señor."

Rowden had then unbuckled the pistol belt he wore under his coat, handed it across. "Let's see."

Falkner wasted no time with the belt. The pistol slid into his hand. He pressed it against Rowden's side. "Quiet, *amigo!* You're going to help me get out of here."

"Sure I am—but not that way, friend. There aren't any cartridges in that six gun. But I've got something better in my pocket—a pardon signed by the governor."

The prisoner broke the pistol open, spun the empty cylinder. "What sort of trick is this?"

"No trick. I want to see how good you are on the draw. Strap on the belt and show me."

Falkner obliged. When his hand flashed for the weapon it moved with incredible speed. The trigger chattered as it came from the holster snapping. Rowden nodded. "That's good enough for me. I'm looking for a partner—someone who wants to make a lot of money quick. I think you'll do. That's why I went to the governor about you."

"You want a *compadre*, eh? *Amigo*, if you can help me cheat the necktie social they are planning, I am your man."

"There's plenty in this for both of us," Rowden promised as he led Pete Falkner to freedom. "But I want a partner I can trust."

"Rest easy. You saved me from a stretched neck. One thing about Pete Falkner—he does not forget his friends."

Pete had proved himself on more than one occasion since then. Rowden felt sure of him, and the way things were going he might be needed here.

Frank Toomey had demonstrated his usefulness over the years. He'd been Rowden's lieutenant in the state police when that dreaded organization had been formed by a carpetbag governor who needed a private army to maintain himself in office. There was no one like Frank for worming his way into the confidence of strangers. The nesters all knew and liked him, listened to what he said. He was a great help in handling them. He was resourceful, too, and had figured many useful ways to wring money from the helpless country during carpetbagger days. He had thought up the martial law tax. Nothing had done more to advance Rowden with Governor Davis and in the state police than had that master stroke. The sheriff smiled when he thought of it. He'd seen the plan's possibilities the minute Frank suggested it. They were on their way to Hillsboro with their hated troop of state police. Jim Davidson, the adjutant general, was along. The simplicity of the plan appealed to him. Here was a chance to humble these Texans and line their own pockets as well. The Hillsboro affair gave them just the opportunity they needed to try it out. They were on their way to teach the town a lesson. Some of their scalawag police had been thrown in jail by an armed mob there.

Lieutenant W. T. Pritchett had commanded the police detachment. There'd been a murder in Bosque County. The lieutenant claimed to be hunting the fugitives at Hillsboro. He demanded to search the home of Colonel J. J. Gathings. The governor's private police always enjoyed ransacking the homes of prominent ex-Confederates. Gathings protested, refused them admission without a search warrant. Lieutenant Pritchett ignored him and had his troopers sack the house. As a reaction against this, twelve or fifteen armed citizens captured the police and threw them into jail. They had later been released under nominal bond which they forfeited when they fled the community.

"We've got to show 'em they can't defy the state police and get away with it!" Jim Davidson flew into a rage.

Governor Davis agreed. "Take Rowden with you and teach 'em a lesson," he ordered.

Frank Toomey couldn't have come up with his suggestion at a better time.

Their first move on entering the town was to declare martial law. Colonel Gathings was the initial object of their wrath. He and seven other citizens were placed under arrest. The courthouse was converted into a jail surrounded by a cordon of police. "Let 'em sweat there for a day and they'll be ready to talk turkey," Rowden decided.

Gathings was brought before Davidson and Rowden the following morning. "Have a chair, Colonel," the adjutant general invited.

The doughty colonel walked stiffly across the floor, opened a window. "I'd rather stand," he said. "The air in here is bad."

Davidson flushed, but Rowden raised a hand to silence his retort. Rowden was enjoying this scene. He tilted back in his chair, a half-smile twisted his thin lips, and his ever-restless fingers fluttered upon the table. "Let him have his tantrum, General. He's paying for it. The longer he stays mad, the more money it costs him."

"What am I charged with?" Gathings demanded.

Will Rowden shrugged. "Does it matter, Colonel? This is martial law here now. You won't be appearing before any wishy-washy judge."

"You can't deny a citizen his civil liberties."

"Citizen?" Rowden's eyebrows arched in surprise. "You lost your citizenship when you fought in the Southern army. It's time you learned your kind doesn't count any more. Don't tell us what to do. You're a prisoner, aren't you? This is martial law, isn't it? Now I'll tell you, Colonel, we're willing to talk things over reasonably with you whenever you're ready to listen. Just remember, though, that it's costing you and your friends a hundred dollars a day to be obstinate. We can't keep all these police here for nothing, you know."

Gathings turned red with anger, held himself in check with obvious effort. "So you've already fined us before we've had a trial! Who set this hundred-dollar-a-day figure anyway?"

"I did. If we have to wait here very long I'll raise the ante."

"I can't pay it. I won't."

Rowden nodded pleasantly. "The longer we wait the more we get. We're in no hurry."

"This is an outrage!"

"Call it what you please, Colonel. We have to teach you old Confederates a lesson. I've found you can sometimes humble a man quickest through his pocketbook and, besides, it's a way I like. But we're not hard men. I'll tell you what we'll do. Pay us three thousand dollars today and we'll call off this martial law and let you and your friends go free."

"This—" the Colonel choked on his wrath—"this is plain bribery!"

Rowden held up his hand. "You didn't let me finish, Colonel. Several things are going to happen here quick if you aren't open to reason. The first is we're going to quarter our police on the town." He pulled a sheet of paper from his pocket. "Here's a list of all the prominent families. We'll quarter two men in each house."

"Those butchers?"

"State police, Colonel."

"Half of them are Negroes."

Rowden smiled. "It will give me pleasure to see the Rebels in this town cooking and waiting on our Negroes for a change. If that doesn't work we're going to give you a trial. Martial law can be mighty quick. It shouldn't take us more than five minutes to handle your case. You won't have time for any fancy appeals, either. Who can you appeal to? The governor?" He grunted. "The governor sent us here."

The personal intimidations didn't terrify Colonel Gathings. What worried him was the threat to quarter the police on the town. There would be trouble, he knew, and he couldn't foresee its end. "Let me talk to my lawyer."

Rowden shook his head, took out his watch and laid it open on the table before him. "We don't recognize lawyers—not in our kind of martial law. We'll give you exactly fifteen minutes to make up your mind."

The colonel walked the floor. "If you'd let me see my lawyer . . ."

"Fourteen minutes," called Rowden.

Several times Gathings tried to protest. Always Rowden inexorably called out the remaining time. He would give no other answer. There were two minutes left when the prisoner finally yielded.

In better days the colonel could have supplied the sum from his own purse. Now it was different. "I'll have to get in touch with my friends," he said. "I don't know where I could lay my hands on such a sum on fifteen minutes' notice."

Gathings wasn't released. His friends were brought to him and Rowden made a careful list of the names. "We may want to raise money here again," he explained to Davidson.

The war-impoverished town was scoured for funds. The menace of the hated police spurred the effort. Every family made its contribution. When the money was brought in the fund was still two hundred and thirty-five dollars short of its goal. "That's all the cash there is here," said Gathings.

"I guess this will satisfy us." Rowden counted the money carefully—twenty-seven hundred and sixty-five dollars. It had been a profitable day's work. Next morning the prisoners were released and the state police quit the town.

Small wonder the incident had become historic in Texas. The governor was enthusiastic over it. He saw its possibilities. "That's the best scheme ever invented, Rowden," he declared. Applying the same pressure, he proclaimed martial law in Limestone and Freestone counties and assessed a penalty of fifty thousand dollars which was paid by a three-percent tax. Rowden advanced rapidly in the state police.

It was the governor who first sent him to Apache County. "We've never bothered sending the police to the frontier," he said. "But maybe we've been overlooking something. There's a German colony there, Union sympathizers all through the war, and they've asked for help. The trouble is over fencing. The way I get it, the O-bar-O ranch is driving off the homesteaders. It might pay us to investigate. Better take some police with you, Will. That's a wild country."

Rowden decided against an escort. He didn't want to advertise his mission. Instead, he took big, gunwise Frank Toomey. He was sure of Frank's loyalty—he'd paid well for it. Once there, his henchman's easy way of making friends and ferreting out information would be helpful.

He saw things on this trip that made him uneasy. Back in the cities Texans were sullen, restive, but held in restraint by the menace of the state police. As he journeyed west men were more outspoken in their resentment of carpetbag rule. A dose of martial law would be good for these people, Rowden thought, but how could it be enforced in these wild stretches? Where could he enlist enough police and how effective would they be on a rugged frontier? He was a foresighted man. He'd always known this easy money wouldn't last forever. That's why he banked in St. Louis. When it came time to get out he'd have something to show for his days in Texas. He had no intention of leaving prematurely, however. Pickings still were easy. But listening to the talk he heard at each night's stop, he sensed that the time to leave was nearer than he'd realized. He cautioned Toomey about it. "We will have to keep our ears open, Frank. Some day, not too far off, it's going to be right unhealthy to be a carpetbagger in Texas. When that time comes you and I are going to be hard to find around Austin."

He saw no opportunity for the state police in Apache. The money was on the wrong side, defended by two many six guns. He asked a good many cautious questions and Toomey was able to learn a lot too. Old Luke Nesbit of the O-bar-O was self-willed, stubborn, too long used to handling things his own way to pay anyone else to settle his difficulties. Even if he could be handled, that wouldn't work. No decision could be made against the German nesters. They were Yankee sympathizers, had votes but lacked money to buy privileges or hire police to fight their battles. No, he could see no profit in bringing troops here.

He prolonged his visit though. The nesters were the underdogs but they outnumbered the cowmen. It was those votes that made him think. With proper leadership they could run the valley as they pleased. Most of the ranchmen had been in the Rebel army, had no voice at the polls. All that was lacking was a leader, a man like himself with a clever knack for handling such situations. He and Frank Toomey rode up the valley. The grass was high and the herds were sleek. Crops stood tall in the nester fields near town. There was opportunity here if he could but find the key to it.

"How many Germans are there here, Frank?"

"Must be between four an' five hundred—town an' all."

"Against a few scattered ranches. Yes, they must outnumber the cow-men nearly ten to one."

"I was numberin' women folks an' brats. If you're countin' votes, a hundred's close to right."

Rowden nodded. "That's still plenty. They need organizing, that's all."

Toomey made friends easily among the nesters. "It's just the ones on the O-bar-O that are havin' trouble now," he said. "Their fences are torn down, cattle stampeded across their fields. Some of them have lost a year's crop in one night that way."

Rowden wanted to see for himself, meet and talk with one of these unfortunates. Toomey took him to see Kurt Pakebusch. Kurt was a bony nester with a bent stance. His teeth were rusted away to a scraggy ridge. It gave him a slubbery look when he opened his mouth. He showed them his cornfield, trampled flat. "Und me mit seven mouths to feed. I quit farmin'. Now I chop vood mit Heinrich Unger."

Rowden didn't dismount. He stared across the wasted field. "Why don't you fight back?"

"Vhat can vun man do? I'd chust get mineself killed." Defeat stared from his bleak eyes.

"What you need is a sheriff here—someone who'd know how to chop these cowmen down to their proper size. It could be done easily enough."

Pakebusch shook his head. "Talk—talk! Always by us it's lots of talk but nobody does not'in'."

"Suppose you had a chance to elect a sheriff who'd do something? Would you vote for him? There are more nesters than cowmen. How'd you like a chance to give old Luke Nesbit a dose of his own medicine?"

"Nesbit!" The nester spat a stream of amber juice into the dust. "Nes-bit iss a no-good son-of-a-bitch. Ever'body is scared of him. Vhere you goin' to find dis so-big man?"

"I might even try it myself. I've handled tough customers before."

Pakebusch's eyes widened. He nodded. "Mister, get us rid of ol' Luke Nesbit und I vill get you ever' nester vote in de valley."

"You weren't serious about that, were you?" Toomey asked Rowden later.

"Maybe. This is a rich valley, Frank. There's money to be made here if a man plays his cards right. Best of all, it's a long way from Austin. It's a good place to be when things blow up there."

Back in the capital he advised the governor to stay out of Apache. "There's no profit on the frontier. The big money's in the towns and cities. That's where we can use the state police best."

He proceeded with his own plans quietly. He had men out over the state. They reported signs of the same restlessness he had observed on the frontier. The war had been over eight years. That summer, 1873, he was convinced that the days of carpetbag rule in Texas were numbered. He did not intend to stay with a sinking ship. His last visit to the governor was to procure a pardon for Pete Falkner. The next dawn he slipped quietly from the capital, headed for Apache.

The carefully laid out plan worked smoothly at the outset. Rowden's pretense of looking for a ranch had been accepted at face value by the cattlemen he met, and explained why Toomey and Falkner rode with him. When he added that he'd left Mississippi because of carpetbag misrule, he won ready understanding. Toomey mixed with the nesters. Kurt Pakebusch and others like him who'd suffered in the struggle with the O-bar-O were ripe for handling, and Rowden had moved with sure cunning. Removal of Luke Nesbit was necessary. There had been little risk in that ambush, for the skilled guns of Falkner and Toomey had backed up the nesters who waited for the O-bar-O to ride into the trap. Rowden emerged as the hero of the resulting crisis. Of course it was best to furnish culprits for that atrocity. That would please both factions. Choice fell on the Schneider family, plodding farmers whom Toomey had tried to enlist for the enterprise. He had been cautious, had dropped the subject when he discovered they'd have no part in it. Just the same they knew enough to be dangerous. It had been an easy matter to plant convincing evidence against them later. There were no Schneiders left to talk. That had offered an opportunity to dispose of old man Sparks, too. A box had thoughtfully been provided for the sheriff's body before it was brought back to Apache and no one thought to open it or it might have been discovered that he had a slug from a six gun in his back. None of the Schneiders owned a pistol.

Immediately after Will Rowden became sheriff the office began paying dividends. Pete Falkner had gathered together some leather slappers—Charlie Springer and other hard-eyed men he'd known in his precarious past. The O-bar-O range was well stocked and now there was no outfit there to interfere. Five thousand cattle were herded across the hills to market before the ranch outfit arrived for its roundup. There was no limit to the opportunities. In some ways this was better than the state police had been. Of course, he had to take care of his men but he didn't have to split with any higher-ups.

Rowden liked things to move according to plan. It fed his vanity when men and events fitted nicely into the niches his mind had grooved for them. He was exasperated now because too many of his schemes went awry. There was Steve Wright, for instance, a good man for this business—a "Pecos cowboy," Pete called him—tough, and ready with his guns. Steve had disappeared on a nester raid in the lower valley. They found him later, his head half blown off by a scatter-gun. There was little profit in these raids against the small farms. They were only a necessary part of the business to keep the nesters stirred up. It didn't make sense, losing a good man that way. By rights, those farmers should be timid men. Another of Pete's boys vanished on the Forked W range. When they finally found him the buzzards had been there first. He wasn't a pretty sight, swinging from a tree. These constant irritations never ended. The valley didn't react the way he intended. Even Clee bothered him sometimes with her constant talk of marriage. And yet he was beginning to wonder about that. His feeling for her was genuine. The thought of a wife no longer startled him. Maybe he would do it. But not yet. He needed the information she brought. Through her, he read the minds of the ranchers in the upper valley.

Then Charlie Springer had let himself be trapped. He would have to keep that outfit out of sight. It was more than fifty miles to the Scalp Creek Breaks. It would be awkward but there was no help for it.

After all, things were going smoothly in the main, he thought. These irritations were minor. It was just their unexpectedness that bothered him. It shook his confidence when his plans were balked.

He glanced up. Through the open door he could see his chief deputy riding in. His eyes narrowed as he noted the sweat dripping from the horse. Something was wrong. Frank wasn't due in until sundown. He waited expectantly while Toomey dismounted. Frank moved easily for a big man, always with the creak of leather where his ammunition belts crossed.

"Well?" Rowden waited for the news, knew it was bad from Toomey's look.

"There's been a killin', Sheriff."

Rowden glanced again at the horse. It was in bad shape. Frank hadn't wasted any time. He straightened his arms at his side so his nervous fingers wouldn't betray him with their tapping. "Who was it?"

"It was Tom Williams. There'll be hell to pay this time."

Rowden flattened his two hands on the table before him, stared at them while he fought for control. He didn't want Frank to guess how upset he was. "Of course," he said finally, "it had to be the best-liked man in the valley. Nothing else would do. The owner of the Forked W. This time our story's got to be good. What happened?"

"He rode in on some of the boys at a brand camp, caught 'em with their irons hot. We must have had every brand in the valley in that herd. There wasn't any story for that one, Sheriff. He'd seen the whole layout."

"Where was this?"

"Up in the foothills, on the north edge of the Forked W range. The boys felt safe up yonder, but Williams must have been on the prowl. He had his gun ready when he rode in. If it hadn't been for me and Pete——"

"Better start from the beginning," Rowden said wearily.

"Charlie Springer was workin' the brand camp. He had our Dutchmen with him, Pakebusch and Unger holding the herd, Blucher cutting out, and Charlie workin' the runnin' iron himself. When it comes to blotchin' up a brand, he's an artist. First thing they knowed there was Tom Williams ridin' right into the camp and his gun was out.

"That's the way things stood when me and Pete rode in. I knew right off it was Williams or us. 'Williams,' I says. 'I've been runnin' these rustlers three days but I never expected to meet up with you at the trail's end.'

"He just laughed. 'I reckon we been ridin' the same trail then,' he says. 'I got four prisoners here for you.'

"I told him I'd take 'em in. I had my rod out an' the boys kept their hands a-waggin' in the air so Williams holstered his gun. 'I reckon I'll have to take you in too, Tom,' I says. 'There's been plenty of brands switched here and we'll have to get to the bottom of it.'

" 'You'll have a hell of a time makin' anybody in these parts believe I'm a thief,' he says.

"I knew he was right, of course. It was his six gun I was after. These old-timers are too handy with a gun to suit me. I had him covered though and he didn't kick up none when Pete moved in and took his weapon.

He still wasn't worried, figured we was on the level. He didn't wise up till he noticed Charlie and the other boys had dropped their arms. Then he crowded his horse right into me. 'What's goin' on here, Toomey?' he asks.

"Pete took the play then. He gave a laugh. 'We don't waste much time on cow thieves, mister,' he says. 'I think it's time for a necktie social and I aim to start with you.'

"Williams knew right where he stood then but he didn't have any gun. He made one last play. 'If I'm your prisoner it's up to you to take me in, Toomey,' he says. He was no fool. 'Give me back my gun so I can defend myself and I'll ride in with you. You have my word for it.'

"When I shook my head he dug in his spurs and started to ride. I brought down his horse with the first shot and the boys finished him off quick."

Rowden still frowned at his hands. "I don't like it."

Toomey looked aggrieved. "Shucks, I thought it was just your kind of case, Sheriff. Smart thinkin'. It had to be him or us. The way it stands, a posse killed a cow thief. I've even got the stolen brands to prove it an'—" he shrugged—"Williams ain't talkin'."

"With anyone else that story might work. Against Tom Williams it will go down hard." Rowden deserted his chair, paced the room restlessly. "Where are the cattle? We'll need evidence."

"I thought of that. The boys are bringin' a few of 'em in. I knew you'd want to know about it so I rode ahead."

Rowden reached his decision. He wanted no part in the Williams killing; the blame must be shifted. Once he saw a way to do it his orders came fast. "Get another horse and go back for those steers yourself. Tell the other boys to scatter. I don't want them seen out there. They mustn't be connected with this."

Toomey turned to obey, stopped in the doorway, tugged uneasily at his mustache. "Hold on. This puts the whole thing on me. If it's bad as that I don't like it."

"You didn't have anything to do with it either." Rowden explained what he had in mind. "Here's your story. You were trailing stolen cattle. When you rode into that camp there was no one there but Tom Williams. Folks won't believe he was a thief so don't you swear he was. All you know is you found plenty of blotched brands and you brought the cattle in to prove it. There was a running iron hot in the fire. You might even say Williams told you he was trailing the same thieves and had just found the camp. Anyway, it was your duty to bring him in and that's what you were doing when a mob of cowmen stopped you, took the prisoner away from you and lynched him.

"Get it? It was cowmen who killed Tom Williams—not us. It's got to be that way. If his friends get mad, let 'em get mad at somebody else."

There was a worried frown on Rowden's face as he watched his lieutenant ride away. This was another time he wouldn't show up for his meeting with Clee. He didn't dare leave now. What would she think?

He rehearsed the story he'd given Toomey, too. He didn't like it too well but it was the best he could do in the circumstances. For once the future was clouded. He had no place in his carefully laid plans for this emergency. He was worried.

Chapter 6   STRANGE HOME-COMING

"HELL's bells!" The sheriff thought Ma Williams' expletives went strangely with her faded blue eyes and the fine tracery of kindly lines that puckered her weather-beaten face. There was no gentleness there now, however. Her anger burned in her eyes and was in the sudden shrillness of her voice. "Hell's bells, Sheriff. 'T wasn't cowmen killed Tom an' 't wasn't nesters, either. He was always their friend. August Lehman will bear me out on that."

When the German merchant bobbed his head the blond tuft on his chin wagged goatishly. "Alwayss he wass a good friend of the little people," he said. "Both sides trusted Tom Williams. That's why thiss doesn't make sense."

Rowden made a show of his patience, tilted back his chair and pursed his lips judiciously before he spoke. After all, he'd expected the story to be questioned. He must let them see how fair he was. "No, I can't see where the Williams killing has any connection with the old nester feud. You know how he died."

"Lynched!" Ma's voice exploded in the room. "Good God, man! You'll never convince anybody that Tom Williams was a cow thief."

Will Rowden's slim fingers turned quiet. "I'm not the one who's accusing him. Even Frank Toomey doubted it after he found him with a hot iron in the fire and half a dozen stolen brands in his herd. It was that posse." His voice softened. "I know how hard it is for you to understand, Mrs. Williams. After all, you were his wife. But they believed it. There's nothing very strange in what happened when you understand that. Let's not drag the war between cowmen and nesters into this. I've done my best to put an end to that."

"I reckon you ain't heard the talk that's going round up the valley." Ma tilted her rocker forward, leaned out to stare at the sheriff through troubled eyes. "Cowmen did it, Toomey says. Where from? Where you goin' to find cowmen in Apache County that didn't know an' trust

Tom. I don't believe it. The rannies of my outfit don't believe it. Neither do the Blakes an' their boys at the Lazy B, nor the folks of the Snake on a Rock outfit. It wouldn't even make sense if it had been a stranger, 'stead of a straight-shooter like Tom, that ever'body knew. Not the way they argue. 'Sure,' they say, 'cow thieves have been caught an' lynched before. An' after it was all over ever'body knew who did it an' why. Nobody had any call to feel ashamed. This was different. Who was in that mob? Nobody knows, least of all the cowmen themselves.'

"If this was all square an' aboveboard like you say, what happened to the men who killed him? Hell's bells, what are they hiding for if there's nothing wrong? All we've got is the story told by Frank Toomey an' it don't sound too good."

"Toomey is a deputy sheriff. He was only doing his duty."

"Maybe it was his duty to turn an unarmed prisoner over to a posse of five men he can't even name." Ma's contempt was written on her face. "A posse! Phooey! Posses don't hide out in the brush in this country."

"Frank Toomey is a good officer. I believe him. Not only that—he brought in the stolen cattle. That's mighty good evidence." The sheriff's shrewd eyes took in the room slowly. He'd come at Lehman's invitation, had welcomed it in fact. There was no avoiding this meeting. The sooner he faced Ma Williams the better. She had come to hear his story herself and, surprisingly, she had ridden in alone. He'd been prepared for the whole Forked W crew, grim-faced and bent on trouble, and had admitted as much to her.

"'T ain't our way," she replied, simply. "We don't draw our guns till we know who we're fightin', mister. Hell's bells, where's the sense in killing somebody who don't know any more 'bout this than we do? But don't get any false notions about us, just 'cause we move slow. Once we find what's at the bottom of this, there ain't a ranny in the outfit won't be on hand throwin' lead, includin' me."

"I wish I knew how to help you," he said.

Letitia Reid spoke up. "Ma has already put her finger on it. What happened to the posse that killed Tom Williams? Why did they disappear? Surely Frank Toomey knows everyone in this county, at least by sight. Why doesn't he talk?"

The sheriff's fingers resumed their restless tapping. "Those men were masked. They had bandannas over their faces."

"Bah!" Ma snorted. "You call that a posse? The more I hear, the more it sounds like cold-blooded murder."

"It takes more than a handkerchief to hide a man," Letitia added. "What about their horses? What brands did they wear?"

"It's easy to think of these things when it's too late." Rowden's voice now betrayed his impatience. "I can't see where Toomey should have acted differently. He was outnumbered five to one."

Why couldn't Letty Reid keep out of this, he wondered angrily. There was no reason she should be present, just because Ma Williams was stopping at the Reid House. The sheriff didn't like her. She was a comely wench, he conceded, and smart. That was the trouble. You never knew where she might poke her nose next. She had a forthright way of popping up in places where only men belonged. Like now. Give her half a chance and she'd run the town. What bothered him most was his inability to place her properly. Why couldn't she be in one camp or the other, like everybody else? Then he'd know what line to take with her. The way it was, the town was nester and she got along with her neighbors. But she had too much truck with the cow people. She knew on which side her bread was buttered, he reckoned. There wasn't any hotel money in nester pockets. When they came to town, they camped in their own carts at the wagon yard.

He turned again to Ma. "I'm sorry about this, Mrs. Williams, but remember, I have to face the facts as I find them. I've given you this straight, just as it came to me. What I don't like is this talk about nesters. What would farmers be doing in that end of the valley? Remember, I brought peace here. I aim to keep it that way."

He turned to Lehman. "I'm counting on your help in this. We've had enough of killing."

He noted the anxious look on August's face, felt sure that he had closed the conversation on just the right note as he quit the room.

Ma sat stiff in her chair, her eyes on the closed door. The violence of her anger had spent itself and she looked suddenly worn. "It was murder, August. I know it. Where can a body turn if the law won't listen?"

Lehman stood beside her, patted her shoulder awkwardly. Perplexity worried his eyes. "Now, now, Ma. Will Rowden iss a good man. He just didn't know Tom like we did. All he can think of iss the O-bar-O war. He iss trying to keep down trouble. Now me, I don't understand what happened. Alwayss, in Apache, it iss some new quarrel. All I know iss, whatever they say, Tom Williams wass a good man and he wass on the right side."

"There ain't enough folks like you, August." Ma touched the hand on her shoulder. "That's the real hair in the butter. I can't remember when you weren't tryin' to help both sides alike. I mind the winter of the sleet. Before we knew ourselves how bad we'd been hurt, there you came with an offer to stake us. An' we still had debts from the war years on your books."

"Oh, pshaw, Ma. I'm a smart man. I know who to back." August plucked at the blond wisp on his chin. "I wish we wass back there now. Sleet we could handle, bad as it wass. When the storm iss in men's hearts it won't carry on the books."

Grady had wanted to ride by the Forked W first to see Ma and had decided against it. Up the valley there were old friends at every ranch. In town it was different and he'd rather remain unknown until he picked up the trail he was hunting.

He had reread Ma's letter a dozen times. Tom was dead. The circumstances of it were beyond belief. Tom Williams, who had been a second father to him; Tom, whom he knew like the palm of his own hand; Tom, who never owned a dishonest thought, arrested for cattle theft and murdered by a mob. "You knew Tom and you know it was impossible," Ma had written. "No man who ever knew him would believe such charges. I guess I'll never learn what really happened or what was behind it, for there's no law here now. Nothing but murder and distrust. It's worse than the Comanche trouble, during the war years." She had told him what little she knew. A deputy named Frank Toomey, from Apache, made the arrest. She hadn't known the names of the men in the mob. Toomey claimed they were masked, but there had been five of them. "We know that much is true because the boys went with me afterward to fetch Tom home and Curly tracked the killers as far as he could. He lost the trail when he hit the traveled road near Apache. There were six horses, counting Toomey's."

Grady was inured to violence, yet he found it hard to picture Tom dead—Tom, always so sturdy and able, so generous with his strength and his knowledge.

Grady knew what he aimed to do. Every man in that mob must be tracked down. No law here now, Ma said. Well, he'd make his own. When he thought of Tom, his throat turned dry and he felt heavy inside. It reminded him of the way he felt the day of the Indian raid, when he'd found his mother and sisters scalped. Only then he'd been just a half-baked young'un. Now it was different. His first lessons with a six gun had been practiced with Tom's own pistol. When he remembered his early days at the ranch, the training he'd sought for fighting Comanches, it seemed to him that all the lessons had been in preparation for this day. Even the last two years in the Rangers had been a part of his schooling.

The landmarks were familiar now. The sun had faded the early morning blue from the hills. Heat shimmered over the baking ridges that stretched tortuously westward, like the twisted spines of lazy serpents. Apache lay beyond the rocky rim ahead, sprawled along the river bank, a mere huddle of shacks when last he'd seen it. Then it had been a town with the hair on, supply hub for the ranches scattered up the valley. He'd heard of the changes there. "It's hemmed in with fences and farms now and the nesters keep on coming," Ma Williams had written once. "You hear more German than English in the town." He recalled there had been some Germans there in the old days, too, but his visits had been rare and he'd changed considerably in the two years he'd been away. There were none who would remember him. For the job ahead that was just as well. There had been six men at the killing of Tom Williams. He knew only one of them by name—Frank Toomey, and Toomey lived in Apache. Here's where the trail must start.

He stopped where a live oak offered shade from the noon sun, untied the whang strings from his slicker and spread it on the ground. He'd thought this out. There were certain identifying marks of his calling he wished to hide; his .50-caliber Sharp's brass belly, his extra cartridge belt and one of his six shooters. He hesitated between the two pistols. The one on the left he wore butt foremost for a saddle draw and it was this one he placed in the pack finally. He glanced at the remaining holster, worn low for drawing speed and with the flap cut away, and was tempted to sever the thongs that held it flat against his leg, fighting fashion, but decided against that. When he adjusted the pack his short canvas jacket hiked up in the back, revealed a Bowie knife in a worn scabbard strapped there. He'd thought of hiding this too, but decided against it. Finally he drew his remaining six shooter, broke it and slipped a sixth cartridge into the empty cylinder under the hammer. Like most Texans, he normally wore his weapons "five beans to the pod," but he was a little uncertain of the trail ahead and wanted to be ready.

A horseman had crossed the brow of the slope to the west and was moving down toward the trail. Grady squinted at him, measured the horse first, a sturdy animal, high in the withers, but with a snuffy roll to his eye. The brand was strange to him. Then his eye took in the rider, from the square tips of his custom boots to the flat crown of his wide hat. There was one of the new Winchester repeaters in his gun scabbard and his pistol holster was tied at the thigh like Grady's own, he noted. This was a slender man, with quick darting eyes, black as midnight, and an easy grace which he didn't leave in the saddle as he swung to the ground.

"*Buenas tardes,* señor." His eyes wandered to the pack on the ground. "Riding a new trail?"

Grady wasn't ready to commit himself. The stranger was likable but he mistrusted the signs he read. The dark eyes were overwatchful. That late-model carbine was costly; the man who bought it set great store by his weapons. Most flagrant clue of all was the unusual way he wore his pistol. A leather slapper, Grady thought. This rider will throw lead fast. Aloud he said, "What does it matter, old trails or new? Mostly they're pretty much alike. I've ridden plenty."

"Me too."

"Yeah, and some in the border country, I reckon."

The stranger touched his pistol butt. His hand moved slowly. Grady tensed, his arm gave a twitch and his fingers fanned open in readiness.

"You saw how I wear my gun, *cacha* first for a border draw."

"Partly that. You're easy with the lingo, too."

The black eyes twinkled. "I like an *hombre* that's ready, *amigo.* I saw your hand. But I move faster than that when I mean business."

Grady nodded. "So do I."

The stranger spilled tobacco into a cigarette paper and passed across the sack. He noticed that Grady took it with his left hand, his right still hung near his holster, and his eyes lit up again. "You and I could ride together, *amigo.* We would get along. There is a town named Apache just over those hills. If you are as tired of range grub as I am, come on along."

"What's it like?"

"A nester town, full of sodbusters and most of them German at that. Cowmen are not too popular there."

"Doesn't sound likely."

"Not so *malo* as it sounds though." The stranger held out his hand. "I'm Pete Falkner. I have friends there."

"Nesters?"

"Not my *estilo*, but my friends get along with them all right. It is a safe place to stop for an *hombre* who's been riding the ridges, if that's what's troubling you."

Grady noted the phrase. Riders who avoided the beaten trail in Texas were outlaws. There was no mistaking how this stranger had measured him.

"You seem pretty sure of me," he said.

"A man who rides with his holster tied down does not do much talking with his mouth." The stranger grinned and slapped his own thigh. "I wear my guns low too, but the sheriff here asks no questions. I don't know any place where a Pecos cowboy could be as sure of finding friends."

Pecos cowboy! There it was again. For the second time Grady realized he'd been identified with the wild bunch and was glad he'd put that telltale brass belly out of sight. It was a good start. Already he'd picked up useful information. So Apache was safe for outlaws! He felt sure Pete Falkner knew.

"My name's Grady Scott." He held out his hand. "Who would I ask for in Apache if I should need a friend?"

"When you ride with me you already have a friend, *compadre*." They exchanged grips. "Will Rowden's the sheriff but you are not likely to see him; he is not *simpático* with strangers. Frank Toomey is your man if I am not around. He's deputy sheriff and a good man to know."

"You're not a deputy, are you?" Grady asked it fast.

Falkner shook his head and laughed. "I do not like the law any better than you do but Toomey is different. He takes care of his friends."

As they mounted, Grady watched Pete cheek his horse. He grasped the halter firmly, pulled the animal's head far around so that he couldn't wheel away in pitching, but would be drawn into a tight circle. It was a common trick when riding a strange bronc. It made him wonder if some cowhand to the west weren't missing one of his string.

They rode in silence at first. Grady had decided on his role. If Falkner accepted him as an outlaw, what better way to start his search? He was still under scrutiny, he knew. Several times, from the tail of his eye, he saw his new friend looking him over.

"If you are not in too big a hurry," Pete said finally, "Apache would be a good place to light a spell."

"I've come a far piece. Nobody's trailed me this long."

"There is nester trouble here. Some of the ranches are paying fighting wages—if you like working for wages."

"Not my line, exactly." Grady turned to face his companion squarely. "Is that what you aim to do? Hire out your gun?"

Falkner made up his mind. He was sure of his man by now. "No, I am running an outfit up in the Scalp Creek Breaks, near the head of the river."

"What brand?"

"Why, a good many different brands, if you are trying to pin me down, *compadre*. We are not particular. We are a sticky rope outfit. I have sized you up for *muy hombre*. I do not think that will scare you off."

"No, I don't scare easy."

"How would you like to throw in with us? We need good hands. Every rider gets a cut and it's plenty big. That beats *un salario*."

"How does this deputy—Toomey—fit in?"

"He is a *compañero*—a partner." Falkner grinned. "I told you I had friends in Apache, *amigo*."

Grady turned to face the trail ahead. He didn't want Pete to read his eyes just then. "This sounds interestin'" was his comment. "Reckon I'll string along."

Fences and plowed fields began to appear. In a corn patch a farmer unbent from his task, leaned on his hoe to watch them pass but gave no sign of recognition. When they topped the rise the trail widened into twin ruts. Here they overtook an oxcart. The driver turned hostile eyes on Grady, didn't return his "Howdy." His wife plodded in his footsteps, half raised her arm in a timid gesture, dropped it when her man scowled back at her.

"So these are nesters. I can't say I admire their manners," Grady muttered.

"I told you. Cowmen are not popular around here," Falkner reminded him.

Apache had grown beyond recognition. Most of the town straddled a wide, dusty street, hedged by a litter of nondescript dwellings, some log, others adobe, a few of hewn lumber. Four establishments dominated the town: the wagon yard with its barn and high corral, half surrounded by dusty vehicles in uneven ranks; a hotel; Lehman's General Store which sprawled over half a block and gleamed with whitewash; and farther beyond, half way to the river crossing, Scanlon's Saloon where a dozen horses dozed at the hitch rail. Grady turned in at the wagon yard after promising to meet his companion later at Scanlon's.

"I want a stall in the barn and some corn," he explained as he unsaddled.

The proprietor spoke with a thick German accent and had the same hostile manner Grady had encountered on the road. "Vass iss wrong mit der corral?" he demanded. "Und corn iss for vork stock und comes high."

"I'll pay for corn." Grady was losing patience.

The hotel, the town's only two-story building, was built of sawed lumber, with a porch across its front and, most surprising of all, surrounded by a whitewashed plank fence. The Reid House, its sign proclaimed, "HUGH REID, PROP." Grady had never been inside before. He remembered the building, but the fence and whitewash were new. He dropped his bedroll and slicker bundle in a chair and rang the bell on the counter.

"You're late if you want to eat. Dinner's at twelve."

He turned. His first startled impression of the girl in the doorway was her complexion. Her skin looked too pale to a man fresh from a weather-beaten frontier. He liked the crisp look of her starched blue apron. It matched her eyes, he noticed.

When he jerked off his hat a lock of unruly hair spilled across his forehead. He dabbed at it. "I'm right sorry about that, ma'am. I've been lookin' forward to some store victuals." He sniffed. "These smell mighty good." He still stared. She was standing against the light and the wave of her brown hair caught the sun's sheen. It looked soft, he thought.

She blew into the lamp chimney she was holding, then crammed it with crumpled paper and gave the paper a vigorous twist.

This was a new trick to him. She saw his curiosity.

"I like lamps to shine," she explained. "Hallie never does it right, so I polish the chimneys myself."

"But paper! Where I come from our lights would get right smoky if we had to wait for paper to clean 'em."

Her busy eyes measured first the man, glanced at the bundles on the chair, then hesitated over the bulky package made by the rolled slicker. She liked the looks of him, tall, lean, hard. The gray eyes so startling against the sun-scorched face were smiling now. His equipment was good, she noted. That was the trouble—too good. Her sharp eyes hadn't missed the way he wore his weapons nor the lithe swiftness of his movement when he whirled to face her. Like so many of the others who come through here now, she thought. Another wild one.

He grew uncomfortable under her scrutiny, lost his easiness and twisted his hatbrim through his fingers. That decided her. She liked a man who still had a boy's shyness around women.

"I reckon we can fix you up a snack. Hallie!" she called. "Hallie!"

The gurgle of water in the next room stopped. "I's scrubbin' in hyar, Miss Letty."

"Scrubbing!" Letitia sniffed. "You don't know the meaning of the word. Now get that floor dry and put the coffeepot on. We've got a hungry man to feed." She smiled and lowered her voice when she turned back to Grady. "Hallelujah's idea of cleaning is to splatter water over everything."

"I guess I'd better see the boss and get me a room first," Grady said.

"I'm Letitia Reid. I run the hotel."

Grady showed his surprise. "But the sign said——"

"That was my father. He's dead." The explanation was terse. "How long will you be staying?"

"I don't know—several days, maybe longer. It all depends."

Letty pulled out a book for him to sign, watched as he wrote "Grady Scott," hesitated over an address and finally added "Menardville, Texas." She explained where the pump and wash bench were, out back, then led him upstairs. The splintery planks of the corridor had a scrubbed look; the room she showed him matched it. With a deft movement she switched the chimney in her hand for the one on the dresser lamp. She was flustered slightly when she realized he was watching her. "I told you. I'm finicky about bright lamps. I reckon every woman's got a streak of old maid in her and that's mine."

"Shucks, I'm the same way about a horse, ma'am. Some folks think I waste a sight of time that way, I reckon."

She liked that. There was easy understanding in her smile but her eyes were alert from habit. She watched him drop his bedroll in a corner. He handled the rolled slicker more gingerly, laying it across the bed.

"You won't be here long," Letty commented. "If you're looking for a job you'll land one before night."

"I can't see myself building fences or tailing a plow for some nester. That's not my style."

"No. I have eyes in my head." Her stare turned critical. "You might be better off if it were. I'm thinking of the ranches. They're paying fighting wages at the Snake on a Rock." She looked him full in the face as she added, "Plenty of Pecos cowboys are riding through here. I don't know where they're headed."

Grady was nettled but he only shrugged. Her eyes are as sharp as her tongue, he told himself. It's the leg thong on my holster. I should have cut it off before I rode in.

His opinion of her mellowed when he sat down to the "snack." The fried chicken was cold but the biscuits were fresh and the gravy hot. He hadn't tasted such food since he'd left the Forked W.

Later he made his way to Scanlon's Saloon in search of Pete Falkner. It was time he met Frank Toomey.

Letty watched him go and there was a puzzled look in her eyes. His behavior baffled her. At first she had decided he'd come to Apache to hire out his gun. She'd seen too many of the men who rode the ridges not to recognize the signs, and yet somehow his actions didn't follow the set pattern. Such men were more cautious, chose their seats with care where, back to the wall, they could keep each door under scrutiny. "Cat-eyed" was the Texas term for such manners. The newcomer wasn't like that. He dropped into the first chair handy and it wasn't against a wall. When that had surprised her she'd tried coming in the door at his back. He hadn't even looked up. If he's really a wild one he won't last long. He has a lot to learn, she told herself darkly.

But her interest was piqued. After he left she went to his room, felt of the slicker, finally untied and spread it open. Her lips were pursed as she examined the arsenal. The cartridge belts were worn. This holster, like the one he wore, was cut away. It was the Sharp's carbine which attracted her attention most, however, its brass belly worn bright from the scabbard. It didn't fit in with the rest of his equipment unless—and then she smiled. That must be the answer, she decided. Later she took time from her work to cross to the wagon yard. The proprietor, Henry Uhl, was a friend. He remembered Grady Scott when she inquired. "Which horse was he riding?" She peered into the corral.

"Nicht dere." The stableman led her to a stall. "Corn he must have like he vass plowing. Nein?"

Letty looked at the big blood bay, a powerful animal and sleek with care. So he fed his horse corn! There was a Ranger camp near Menardville. It all fitted. She was smiling when she returned.

She would have been less sure of her conclusions had she watched

Grady when he left the hotel. His manner changed abruptly, grew more alert; his gray eyes darted warily right and left. He had stepped into the outlaw role he was determined to play.

He had no illusions about Pete Falkner. Pete was as venomous as a sidewinder, would strike as fast at the first hint of suspicion. He wouldn't be easy to fool, not for long. Right now he was a friend because he needed riders as handy with a six gun as with a rope and he'd misread the signs about Grady Scott, had him placed as a fugitive and a killer. His step quickened. Falkner could lead him to Frank Toomey. The surest way to find the trouble was to be in with the troublemakers.

He was guarded in his movements, playing his part carefully, as he pushed through the saloon door and walked the length of the bar to the far wall where he could back up to the corner. Then he turned, surveyed the room swiftly. It was half filled with nesters, stolid men in coarse boots, who watched his entrance in silence.

He had weighed the risk of being identified. But who would know him here? The town had changed, was filled with newcomers. Only Scanlon's place and Lehman's Store looked familiar. Ma's orders had kept him out of the bar. He was a stranger there. It was different with the merchant. He'd visited the ranch occasionally, might remember him. Grady thought the chance was slim. That seemed long ago. He'd filled out a lot, was no longer a thin-shanked boy. He counted on that. His greatest danger was from an encounter with some ranny who had known him well but his darting glance didn't reveal a cowman in the place. Gradually the buzz of conversation was revived, but in guttural German. He couldn't understand what was said. Two nesters standing at the bar spoke rapidly, then turned to face him.

"Where you from?" one asked.

It was the sort of query a fugitive would resent. "I don't like questions," Grady retorted.

That's asking for it, he thought. My play is coming up and I've got to make sure it's one Pete Falkner will hear about.

The room had grown quiet again. The man who asked the question glanced around as if to be sure of his support, then slid along the bar toward Grady. "Me, I don't like cowmen who come snoopin' around, 'specially when they won't answer questions. Sometimes we miss stock after they're gone."

Grady stiffened. His arm still rested carelessly on the bar but there was no weight on it now and his poised hand was only a few inches above his belt. The fingers flexed once, then grew still. Across the room someone rose from a table, walked toward a corner where three shotguns were propped. Another pushed back his chair. Grady recognized the danger signs. Unless he kept on top of this situation, he was in for trouble.

"Wait!" he called. "It won't be healthy for anyone to reach for those scatter-guns."

Facing the room, Grady lost sight of the bartender temporarily, but not for long. Something was jabbed against his side. From the corner of his eye he could see what had happened. A shotgun was shoved across the bar in the hands of the determined Scanlon.

"Get your hands up. We're not going to have any shooting in here."

"I hope not." Grady was sparring for time. His right arm, still stretched along the bar, was directly under the gun barrel. He raised his left hand slowly, until it was eye level. No one else had moved, he noticed with grim satisfaction. All reliance was placed on Scanlon's weapon.

"When he turns to face me," the bartender ordered, "Unger, you step up behind him and relieve him of his six shooter. All right, stranger, turn."

Grady turned. His left hand was at his hatbrim. With one swift motion he swept off the hat and slapped the bartender across the face with it. At the same time his right arm, swinging fast, knocked up the gun muzzle.

The weapon roared harmlessly into the ceiling.

Before the astonished audience realized what had happened, Grady's six gun was in his hand and he was backed into the corner, facing them.

"Here, here! What goes on?" A big voice boomed from the door.

There was a mongrel hubbub of explanations in two tongues.

"He's a cowhand lookin' for trouble," someone explained.

"Take his gun away from him, Frank."

Grady surveyed the man in the doorway, big, wide-shouldered, his face florid and his smile half hidden by the drooping mustache at which he tugged. Except for the eyes the face might have been handsome. They were a trifle too close-set and their cold stare denied the heartiness of his manner. At his side Pete Falkner was dwarfed by the man's bulk. Falkner muttered something Grady couldn't hear but he saw the hard eyes shift to him.

The hearty voice boomed again. "Nonsense, boys. This here's a friend of mine and a friend of Will Rowden's too. Now sit down, have a drink on me and forget this foolishness." Falkner edged his way through the crowd, the huge man shouldering a path after him. Suddenly the room was noisy again.

Falkner was grinning in admiration. "I never saw the sombrero trick worked smoother, *amigo*," he said. "What did I tell you, Frank? Here's a man that is *muy hombre*." He introduced them. "This is Frank Toomey, Grady. He is a deputy sheriff here. I told you I had the right friends in Apache."

"Lucky I came when I did." Toomey flashed his wide smile again. "These nesters don't like strangers, specially when they wear spurs. 'T wouldn't take much to set off another war between homesteaders and cowmen in this country."

"*Cómo no!* Seemed to me he was doing a right good job of taking care of himself." Falkner smiled again.

"If anyone thinks he can take my six shooter——"

The deputy clapped Grady on the shoulder. "Forget it. I like a man to be handy with his irons. We need more of 'em. Anyway, you ain't going to be bothered again, now they know you're a friend of mine." He ordered a round of drinks, tilted back his head, parted his mustache with one hand and tossed the liquor down without touching the glass to his lips. He lowered his voice to a bass rumble. "Pete tells me you're goin' to stick around awhile. He thinks you'd be a good man to ride with on a dark night and he ought to know. He's rode plenty."

"I've done all sorts of riding myself," Grady assured him.

"Yeah," said Toomey. "Yeah, I reckon you have." Those shrewd eyes stared hard at Grady, then shifted away.

"I'm interested." Grady let himself smile now. "But I like to see my hole card before I place any bets."

The deputy ordered another drink. Again he opened his mouth wide, threw the liquid down. Then he stared into the mirror back of the bar and twisted at his mustache until its drooping tails satisfied him. He took his time about answering, chose his words with slow care.

"The sheriff and me don't get up Scalp Creek way often. We don't bother our friends. We just want to be sure we've got friends up there, in case we ever need 'em. The right kind of friends."

"I've told you Grady is all right. *Por Dios*, I know the signs," Pete explained. "I would not take him up there with me if I was worried about him, would I?"

Toomey turned around, propped his elbows against the bar and favored Grady with one of his smiles. "Yeah—now you've had a peek at the hole card, my friend. How do you feel about it? Night ridin' can be right profitable, specially if you've got the right folks on your side."

"I'm not worried. Pete and I can get along. We understand each other."

A newcomer peered in the door, saw Toomey and pushed his way forward. His spurs jingled, he had every mark of the cowman, but his arrival created no stir among the nesters. Grady decided he was known here. Dust streaked the sweat on his face. "I've ridden hard," he began, then paused to glance questioningly at Grady.

"Go on," Falkner ordered. "This is a *compadre* of mine. Grady, this is Charlie Springer. I expect you two will ride together, plenty."

"There's hell to pay," said Springer. "A bunch of cowmen are headin' for town, all friends of Tom Williams. It looks like trouble."

"Yeah?" Toomey tugged at his mustache and scowled. "We've been expecting it, ain't we? What outfits are in this?"

"The Forked W, the Snake on a Rock and the Lazy B. Soames is with them and so are both the Blakes."

Grady knew these outfits well but he gave no sign. These were men who knew Tom Williams never stole a cow in his life.

"Yeah—" the deputy was thinking aloud—"we'll spread the word among the nesters. They'll be ready for 'em."

"This is a pretty strong outfit ridin' in," Charlie Springer reminded him. "They didn't send boys on this errand."

"You don't know these nesters, Charlie. Most of 'em don't even own a six gun but have you ever seen a man with a load of buckshot from a scatter-gun? Messy. Yeah, buckshot means buryin' every time. They'll be riding into a trap. The boss figgered they might try this an' made his plans accordin'ly. We'll have the nesters stirred up an' waitin' here at Scanlon's. If these rannies are huntin' trouble they'll find plenty of it here. Shotguns behind each window. I hope they come. We'll cut 'em to pieces before they get a chance to draw." He scowled thoughtfully. "Better get back to Scalp Creek, Charlie. With the ranches stripped of men this is the time for the boys to loosen up their ropes."

Grady glanced at Falkner. If that was his outfit up on Scalp Creek, why was Toomey sending the orders? Yet his decisions were accepted without question. I've a lot to learn about Frank Toomey, he decided.

The deputy went on with his plans. "I reckon the sheriff had better hear 'bout this. I'll find him first. We'd best not waste time. While I'm gone, you pass the word among the nesters, Pete. You know a lot of 'em."

"Which side are we on?" Grady demanded. "I don't waste much love on nesters myself."

"We are not on either side," Pete explained. "While they're fighting it out they are too busy to bother us, *amigo*. If they squabble long enough, we'll be rich."

"That's about it," Toomey agreed. He turned to Grady and hesitated. "You'd best hole up here till we get back," he decided. "You can't be much help right now, but we might need some guns handy, in case things go wrong."

Grady watched them go. He was worried. He must get word to his friends but he couldn't ride to meet them without exciting suspicion and he had no intention of abandoning the role which already promised so much. He had no definite plan when he left Scanlon's except that the hotel and the wagon yard were at the far end of town and the cowmen would come that way. He saw neither Falkner nor Toomey. They had vanished on their errands.

Letty Reid heard him coming and met him at the foot of the stairs. She had a smile for him this time. "Do you know my friend Major Reynolds?" she began.

Grady stopped. Maj Reynolds! Why, it had only been three days since he'd parted with Maj in camp near Menardville! If she knew Maj—maybe he could trust her with a message? He decided against it and his answer was cautious. "I don't know many army people."

"Oh, Major Reynolds got his title in the Confederate Army but he's in the Rangers now—the Frontier Batallion. He stayed here quite a while last year. We came to be good friends."

"I'm sorry, ma'am, I don't seem to remember your friend." Grady's face was expressionless.

"That's odd, you both being Rangers and all."

He grunted. "So you think I'm a Texas Ranger?"

"Look," she said, "part of my job is sizing up the guests. If I didn't, I wouldn't stay in business long. There's a pile of old bedrolls in the attic, left behind by the boys who neglected to settle up before they rode off. That's how I cut my wisdom teeth. Maybe you're supposed to work under cover here," she added seriously. "If so, don't worry. I can keep my mouth shut. But you're a Ranger. You're loaded down with fighting hardware and the way you wear it I know you know how to use it, but you're not just a Pecos cowboy riding the ridges. I know that too, from your manners. You're not cat-eyed. Nobody's trailing you. And then there's your Sharp's brass belly. Every Ranger's issued one. You had yours hidden in your slicker."

"Not an uncommon gun, ma'am. Plenty of men carry Sharp's fifties."

"Yes, but they don't hide them, and men who really specialize in weapons carry the new Winchesters now. I checked on you at the wagon yard, too. You don't see many horses like that blood bay of yours. He was being fed corn. That's a Ranger habit, too."

"I declare, you've got a right good imagination, Miss Reid. Why should they send a Ranger here? You haven't any Indian trouble."

"Why wouldn't they? There are worse things than Indians. It's almost open warfare here—nesters against ranchers, and outlaws stealing the valley blind. Only last week Tom Williams was murdered by a mob and there was a deputy sheriff there. Nobody's been arrested for that. We need some kind of law here. That's why I was so glad to learn who you really were. I figured you'd come here to investigate."

He shrugged. "You're all mixed up about me. I wasn't sent here by the Rangers." He hurried up the steps, anxious to escape. That girl's too smart for her britches, he told himself. If she gets to airin' her views in front of Toomey or Falkner I'm in for trouble. In his room he buckled on his second six gun, adjusted the leg strap, loosened both pistols in their holsters, then settled down to wait. From his window he could watch the dusty street, ride herd unseen on all who entered the town from that direction.

Ma Williams came from the other way, was at the gate before he saw her. There was no mistaking that familiar figure. His throat constricted when he noted how bent she'd grown. Her step had slowed.

He was halfway down the stairs when she entered the door. "Ma," he called softly.

For a moment she simply stood there, peering at him silently, her head tilted a little, and the familiar trick called back memories of endless kindnesses. She had stood like that the day Tom fetched him home, a lad of thirteen, orphaned by the Comanches. Thinking she didn't recognize him, he closed the gap with wide strides. But when he neared her he saw that her lips were trembling and there was a mist blurring her kindly eyes. She dabbed at them with the back of her hand, embarrassed that Grady should see her so.

The hands on her shoulders were gentle. He kissed her.

It wasn't her way to be demonstrative, but she clung to him, briefly, with hungry arms. Then she pushed him back, to see him better.

"Hell's bells," he muttered huskily. "Hell's bells!"

"Hell's bells yourself." Her voice was a shade unsteady. "I knew you'd come, Grady."

He pulled her toward the stairs. "Come up here where we can talk. We mustn't be seen together."

Ma couldn't understand the necessity for that at first, but she followed to his room, listened while he explained the role he was playing. "It's the only way I know to find out who killed Tom," he concluded.

"An' then what?"

His eyes smoldered. "You know how I felt about Tom. They'll pay for what they did to him. I'll track every one of them down."

She closed her eyes. "Once you find out who they are, we could turn them over to the law."

"What law, Ma? Seems to me the law's mixed up in this. On the wrong side."

"I know. It worries me, Grady. Maybe I did wrong in sending for you. This is what I had in mind, but there's been so much killing. There's no end to it. An' none of it will bring me back Tom."

"There's no other way," he declared grimly. "Just like you said, it will go on and on, worse and worse, unless we put a stop to it. Sure, I want to find these men for Tom's sake. That comes first. But that's not all. Someone tried mighty hard to make him out a cow thief. I want to know the why of that, too."

"I keep coming back to that, myself." Ma's voice turned brittle. "Sometimes I feel sort of old an' puzzled an' helpless an' then I remember they killed him for a cow thief. That's when I turn all hard inside, an' bitter, so I can't think very straight. The boys at the ranch feel the same way. So far I've been able to hold 'em back but sooner or later they're going to bust loose. Then there'll be hell to pay."

"They have busted loose, Ma. They're on their way here now and a dozen of Tom's old friends are with them. They've got to be warned. They're riding into a trap at Scanlon's." Grady told her what he had heard, the steps Toomey had taken. "If I'm seen on this side of the fence my usefulness in the Toomey camp will be blown sky-high, but they've got to be warned."

"I'll stop 'em," Ma promised.

It was nearing sunset. She didn't know where the cowmen were and couldn't risk missing them if she rode out the trail. "They won't get past me here," she declared. "They'll never get to Scanlon's. Hell's bells, I can still handle my own people."

Grady was sure she could. He was no longer needed here. It was suppertime when he quit the hotel and the streets were nearly deserted. He crossed to the wagon yard, waited there where he could watch without being seen.

Ma Williams didn't go in to supper. Instead she chose a hickory rocker on the porch where she could watch the road as it snaked over the last low hill and dipped toward the town. The June sun was still an hour high, and Grady, from the wagon yard, could follow the movement of her chair as she teetered back and forth. He couldn't watch the trail from where he stood but he knew the cowmen were coming when Ma left her post, moved deliberately to the middle of the street and waited. She was a tall woman and spare. In the saddle she wore a man's floppy hat pulled low over her eyes and around home a sunbonnet usually framed her kindly face. He remembered her best that way but she was bareheaded now and he was surprised to notice how gray she'd turned.

The ranchmen were sixteen strong and there was a girl with them. That astonished Grady. When he first glimpsed her, still a hundred yards away and against the sun, he thought his eyes were playing him tricks, that this was a slender boy. They wouldn't fetch a girl on a fighting errand. Then his frown deepened as the wind rippled out her skirt. She rode astride, deep in her saddle like a cowman, and she was mounted on a deep-chested dun mare that looked almost gold in the dying sun. Her twill skirt, so full that it even hid her boot tips, was a light tan, seemed to blend her with the animal. She was in argument with John Soames who rode beside her and her expression was petulant; nonetheless her features were striking, the eyes bright with wrath, full lips curled in protest. She was tanned a sunny brown. With her blonde coloring the tint of her skin looked vivid.

Grady remembered John Soames although he'd never known him well. Five of the cow hands with him rode horses wearing the Snake on a Rock brand. Most of these he knew. The Blake brothers were there too. Merrill and Dave were old friends of his. With them they'd brought three hands from the Lazy B. Four men from the Forked W brought up the rear, two of them newcomers since Grady's time but he smiled as he recognized the others. Peg Denham, riding easily despite one empty stirrup, his wooden stump angled awkwardly from the saddle; Curly Stark, who'd shown him how to take his first scalp. As they passed, Curly shoved back his hat to wipe the shiny pate that had given him his nickname. Even from here Grady could see the patchwork of wrinkles that seamed his leathery face. The fringe of hair around his ears had frosted white and he was bent in the saddle, but Grady knew how to estimate the endurance of that wiry frame. Whatever happened, here were two trustworthy friends.

Ma Williams met them in front of the hotel. Grady, too distant to hear, tried to follow the conversation with his eyes. A few of the men had dismounted, others moved as if to push past her, then reined up. Ma didn't yield ground. The girl who rode with them caused another complication. Soames had her bridle reins, tried to persuade her to dismount. When she refused he appealed to Ma. Finally, that failing, he seized the bits, started to lead the dun mare toward the hotel hitch rail. The girl jerked at the reins, tried to pull free but Soames hung on. Grady tried to figure this out. Soames doesn't want her along, that's certain, he thought. And he's right. This is no place for a girl if there's going to be any lead scattered. Ma's smart not to help 'em. If they can't cut that girl out of the herd, maybe they'll cool off.

Soames succeeded in tying up the dun mare and remounted his horse. Several of the others followed his action. It looked as if Ma had failed. Grady loosened both pistols in their holsters, ready to quit the shelter of the barn for the scene. He was scowling. He didn't want to abandon his role. But if Ma failed he had no choice left; he couldn't let old friends ride into a trap. He stood in the broad barn doorway, waited. No one noticed him, their attention was centered on Ma who had seized Soames's bridle reins. She would, Grady thought. Ma's not the kind that gives up. He stopped.

Letty Reid followed Ma's effort from the doorway. She lacked Grady's certain knowledge of the trap that had been set for the ranchmen but she knew the temper of the town. For a time she thought Ma would succeed. When Soames remounted his horse she knew better. If they'd just take time to listen to her, Letty thought. Time! That's what she needs. Suddenly she darted behind the counter, picked up a battered dishpan stored there as a supper gong and seized the old iron ladle that lay beside it. Banging lustily, she hurried to the porch. The clatter spooked some of the horses. One started pitching. She gripped the ladle harder, kept up her pounding.

"Supper!" she called. "Supper's on. Come on in, boys."

The men had been in the saddle most of the day. The pan music sounded good to them. "Town victuals!" Walter Hart smacked his lips. He was the youngest rider at the Forked W and was called the "Kid." "I bet I could fight better on a full stomach."

A burst of laughter followed this comment. Ma seized upon it. "Most sensible thing that's been said yet, Kid. Letty Reid's cookin' ain't to be sneezed at. Come on in an' eat. Then if you're still set on huntin' trouble, one woman can't stop you."

Two or three men dismounted promptly. Others hesitated. Then there was a general movement toward the hitch rail. Ma led the way and met a worried Letty at the steps.

"What'll I feed 'em, Ma? Nothing's ready. I just figured it might help to remind 'em they were hungry. Sixteen hungry men!"

Ma patted her on the back. "You saved the day, honey. We'll rustle up somethin'." She thought a moment. "How 'bout coffee an' hush puppies for a starter? That'll be quick an' it'll give 'em somethin' to chomp on, while we're throwin' a meal together."

"Ought to be catfish with hush puppies," Hallelujah complained, when they set her at the task. This was a plantation delicacy she'd brought to the frontier with her: corn meal batter made with eggs and milk, and with finely chopped onions mixed in for flavor. This was dropped into deep fat by the spoonful, fried until the balls were brown and crunchy.

"Now I know what happened to the holes out of doughnuts," Ma said, the first time she sampled them. "Where'd they get such an outlandish name, Hallie?"

"Allus had heaps of houn's round a plantation, ma'am, an' you could count on the pups to set up a racket when fish war a-fryin'. We'd jes' toss 'em one of these to stop thar yippin' an' yell, 'Hush, puppy.' Reckon that's how come it."

Patrons of the Reid House had spread the fame of hush puppies across the valley. Hallie kept the rannies happy with platters of the crisp balls while supper was cooking.

When Grady witnessed the result of Letty's strategy he retreated to the wagon-yard barn. There the proprietor eyed him suspiciously. "Me, I t'ought you'd joined dem" was his comment.

Grady shook his head. "I just wanted to find out what was going on. I'm working with Frank Toomey."

The German's manner changed. He reached into the first empty stall, pulled out a shotgun, nodded grimly as he patted it. "Me too. If it gifs a fight so many of dem von't ride home. *Nicht wahr?*"

Grady stared soberly at the weapon. Caught in an open street with buckshot belching from windows and doors, the cowmen wouldn't have a chance. They'd be cut to pieces before they even saw their enemy.

It was nearly dark when Grady again slipped from the barn. Ma had gained an hour's respite, thanks to Letty Reid, but what would follow he could not foresee. If only he could talk to Curly Stark, explain the situation, he felt certain he could turn them back. Men listened to Curly, would follow him. The problem was to reach his friend. Certainly Toomey would be warned that the cowmen had arrived and where they were. By now the Reid House must be watched.

Grady crossed the street openly, then melted into the deepening shadows. He worked his way stealthily behind a row of dwellings and approached the hotel from the rear. Curly had given him first lessons in this craft; the Indian campaigns had smoothed out his skill. He moved in utter silence, crept from shadow to shadow. The lamps were lighted now. He kept safely back from their glow, yet could see everything within clearly. Ma Williams was helping in the kitchen. The men crowded the dining room. The stairs went up from the wide front hall which served as lobby and office. The cowmen had taken the precaution to leave a guard with the horses out front but he was a stranger to Grady. As Grady watched he saw Dave Blake push back his chair and head for the door. Grady followed on noiseless feet as Dave exchanged places with the horse guard. He waited until the other man was gone before he called cautiously. Dave's six gun was out when he whirled to face the shadows.

"It's me—Grady Scott, Dave. I've got to see you."

"Grady!" Blake started forward, then grew more cautious. "I don't know. Doesn't sound like Grady Scott to be skulking in the shadows."

"Wait." Grady rolled a cigarette before he moved. He crouched on his heels so that the horses at the rail were between him and the street before he scratched the match that illuminated his face briefly.

"What's all the secrecy about?" Dave inquired after they had gripped hands.

Grady told him why he was here and how he had worked his way into Toomey's confidence. "It's the only way I know to find out who was there when Tom was killed, and if he learns I'm in touch with you he'll smell a rat. But I had to come. Toomey has the whole town stirred up. They're expecting you to walk into their trap." He explained what he had seen and heard, described the scatter-guns that were waiting behind the darkened windows at Scanlon's.

"We're more than a match for any gang of clodhoppers," Dave protested.

"In a fair fight—sure. But this wouldn't even be a fight. You've got to listen to me."

Dave finally agreed to get Curly out of the dining room. He was to go in first and, at Grady's suggestion, blow out the lamp which burned in the front room. "Then I'll follow you in and slip upstairs. You send Curly up. It will be safer to meet there than out here."

As soon as the lamp went out Grady followed, slipped softly up the steps. Curly came almost immediately. Grady pulled him into his own room and shut the door.

"Why don't we light a lamp, you old horned toad? Who you hidin' from, son? If yo're in trouble you know you can count on me."

That was like Curly. He already had half the story from the darkened room. Again, as with Dave Blake, Grady gave his warning, only with greater detail now. Curly heard him out without interruption.

"So you want me to side in with Ma an' head the boys fer home, thus avoidin' trouble an' givin' you time to track down Tom's killers?"

"That's it exactly."

"H'm, I ain't too shore I can turn it, Grady. The boys are mighty riled."

"You've got to manage it, Curly."

"Son, this hyar's a sore that's been a-festerin' fer quite a spell. A heap's happened since you sashayed off to jine the Rangers. 'T ain't just a fence war hyar now. We kep' clear of that smoke 'cause we figgered ol' Luke went out of his way a mite a-huntin' trouble, but we got our backs humped up over the way he was dry-gulched. If Rowden hadn't stepped in, we'd 'a' had us a showdown then an' thar. He seemed to know what he was about, made hisself a name a-pacifyin' the valley an' trackin' down Luke's killers. We had us a breathin' spell. But not fer long.

"Somebody's been stealin' this valley blind. Gen'rally, we blamed the nesters 'ceptin' we couldn't find no trace of the cattle. Course it's easy to eat a critter an' bury the hide, leavin' no trace, but not at the rate stock's been vanishin'. Shucks, we've lost enough beef to fat up this whole end of Texas an' these Dutchmen still look hongry. Folks got to askin', if this new sheriff's such a heller, how come he can't catch cow thieves? The law ain't been much help. Oh, Rowden's all right hisself, I reckon, but we been lookin' sort of hard at some of his deputies. That's the hell of it. You don't know who to trust. No law, and ever' day the nesters get more ructious. We had all the makin's fer a fust-class war afore Tom was murdered."

He growled contemptuously. "Tryin' to tell us Tom Williams war a cow thief. I'd sooner suspeck God. Ever' ol'-timer in the country war mad clean through when he heerd that. Who said it? Toomey. I aim to settle with him, personal, fer that. 'Wait,' Ma says. 'Let's get the straight o' this. Give Rowden a chancet to do somethin'.'

"Well, we've waited—long as we aim to. Now we're hyar an' you ask me to turn the boys back. 'T won't be easy. It goes agin the grain with me, too."

"There's still no sense riding into scatter-guns in the dark," Grady argued. Anger curdled his words. Thought of Tom's murder was like finding Molly's wracked body. He itched for vengeance. "I'm on their trail," he pointed out. "I aim to track down every man that was there. Give me a chance, Curly. Tossin' your rope before buildin' your loop don't catch the calf. What if we had a showdown tonight? Suppose Toomey died before I had time to get the truth out of him? We'd never know whether we'd got all the gang that was in on the killing or not. I want 'em all."

The final argument won.

"I'll see what I can do," Curly agreed, "but I'll have my hands full. The boys have got their horns sharpened. I'd best get down thar an' start talkin'. Afore I go, thar's one more thing you ought to know, Grady. The mob that kilt Tom war from right hyar in Apache. I was thar when we found him an' I tracked 'em hyar an' know. Thar was six of 'em, countin' Toomey. That's the only word o' truth he told. That's somethin' to go on."

Reluctantly Curly headed down the stairs. He didn't relish the task ahead.

Someone had relighted the lamp below. The hall was filled with men and Ma had resumed her argument. Grady's escape in that direction was cut off. This didn't bother him greatly. He could drop from a window without any trouble.

The discussion below had become a jumble of sound. From the stairs Curly's voice rose above it. "Whar you goin', John?"

"I'll be down in a minute." Grady didn't recognize the voice, realized that Curly intended this as a warning.

It was time to get out of here. The window of his room faced the front and didn't suit his purpose. He crossed the hall, opened the first door he found. Someone had left a light burning here. Its beam flooded the hall. He slid through fast, closed it softly behind him and turned to face the room. Staring at him, storm in her eyes, was a girl. The yellow hair identified her. She was the one who'd ridden the dun mare.

Outside, heavy footsteps sounded in the hall, checked his impulse to escape that way. He raised a finger to his lips.

Clee's first thought was that Rowden had learned she was here and had sent her a message. He hadn't shown up at their meeting place. That was what had brought her here. All week she had waited without word, her anxiety growing. When news came of Tom Williams' death and Toomey's story of it had angered every ranch, her uneasiness grew. This sharpened the conflict between her loyalties. Will Rowden she loved. She yearned for the valley to know and respect him as she did. Yet, according to the angry talk she heard at home, Rowden listened to Toomey, believed his story of the murder. That was unthinkable. She had known Tom Williams all her life. Nothing could shake her confidence in him. She must see Will, make him understand. He would listen to her. That had been her purpose in riding for Apache. Her unexpected meeting with her father just a few miles short of town had made her need to see Rowden even more desperate. She refused to turn back.

Now she studied Grady carefully, not missing a detail. He was marked by the way his holsters were tied down—not a man to trifle with. She liked his litheness, the way he was balanced on the balls of his feet. The stretch of his shirt across the shoulders suggested his strength. It was his eyes she noticed most of all. She thought them strange at first before she realized that it was his deep burn that made their gray seem so light. "What do you want?" she demanded finally. "How did you get here?"

"I was wondering the same thing about you, ma'am. Since when do cowmen fetch their womenfolks along when they're bent on powder burnin'? Does that make sense?"

He noticed that her brown eyes were long and wide-spaced. Her lips were parted and he noticed the fullness of them. Close up she was even prettier, he thought.

"They didn't want me here," she admitted. "I was riding in alone when I met them. My father tried to send me back." She tossed her head and a lock of yellow hair tumbled across her forehead. "I wouldn't go. Are they going to smoke out the nesters?"

"I don't know. I hope not."

She didn't like that. It sounded disloyal to her people and, from the look of him, he belonged on their side. "Nothing can stop them, if they've made up their minds," she retorted.

"That's not always a one-sided game, ma'am."

"You think these clodhoppers would have a chance against real fighting men?"

"They might surprise you."

She laughed contemptuously. "Not unless they've hired men like you to do their fighting for them. Is that why you're here?"

He shook his head.

"Then maybe you'd like a job on the right side. We pay fighting wages at the Snake on a Rock. You could do worse. It's the biggest outfit in this country and we know how to take care of what's ours, whether it's men, stock or land."

Grady nodded. "I know the Snake on a Rock. Your name must be Soames."

"Clebourne Soames," she agreed. "'Most everybody calls me Clee. John Soames is my father."

"Yes, I know him."

"Then you'll ride for us?"

"No, I didn't say that. I'm here on other business."

He remembered her now. At least, he remembered the Soames girl of years ago, a spindle-shanked towhead when he'd seen her last. He'd glimpsed her only on rare occasions and they'd both changed considerably. She'd shown no hint of this beauty then.

Her gaze shifted to his weapons. "You don't look as if you'd be afraid of a man-sized job," she taunted. "You wear those six guns as if you knew how to use 'em."

"I don't pack 'em for ballast, ma'am, if that's what you mean."

She remembered his unceremonious entrance. "What are you doing here? Who are you hiding from? I don't like the looks of it."

"My business here won't hurt you or your friends. You can believe that. Now I think I'd better go." He stepped past her, toward the window.

She watched him curiously. "What's wrong with the stairway?"

"I don't want to be seen. I aim to drop out one of these back windows. That's how I came to be here. I didn't expect to run into you."

Her suspicion grew. "If I screamed you'd be trapped," she warned.

He crossed the room, turned back to grin at her. "I don't think you'd do that."

She thought she would. She even backed toward the door, took a deep breath in readiness. He watched her with quizzical smile.

"You think I'm afraid to do it?" she demanded.

"No, not afraid. If you were scared you'd scream sure 'nough. I just think you're the sort of girl who'd give me a chance."

"Oh, go ahead and jump!" she finally exclaimed.

He blew out the lamp before he clambered over the sill. Clee heard the soft thud of his boots when he hit the ground. There was no sound after that. She listened, was tempted to watch from the window but caution restrained her. That might give him away. A plan was forming in her mind. She wanted to leave the hotel unseen, too, had wondered how it might be accomplished. This suggested the way. She checked the locked door, pocketed the key, before she peered down into the dark. It seemed a long way to the ground and she hesitated until she remembered how easily Grady had accomplished it. She leaned out again, calculated the distance. By easing herself out, clinging to the sill, she'd shorten the drop. It wasn't so bad as it looked.

Grady crouched by the building until he got his bearings. Not far away shadows hung thick about a group of live oaks. He snaked his way toward this shelter. Once there he straightened up, looked back, assured himself that his visit to the hotel had gone unobserved.

"Have a nice visit with your friends, señor? *Por Dios*, I suppose you tipped them off what to expect." The voice came from the gloom behind him but Grady recognized it. He fought back an impulse to go for his gun. He had measured Pete Falkner. A false step now would bring a bullet. He wondered how long he'd been watched and how, in the dark, he'd been so readily identified. "You've got me wrong, Pete. If those were friends of mine why would I be dropping out of windows?"

"If they were not friends what were you doing there at all? I saw you and *la rubia* were not strangers."

"Yeah, me and the blonde." Grady took his hint from that. "Woman trouble sure can mess things up, Pete. But I didn't go back there to see her. I've got a room in the hotel. I went back after my other six gun. The way things look I may need it tonight."

Falkner's voice was still hard with suspicion. "Toomey told me I was too quick on the trigger when I took you in, but you had all the *señales* of a salty hand, especially when I saw your hat-fanning trick. We need riders and I thought you were our kind."

Grady was encouraged. Pete wouldn't stop to ask questions if he was sure. He had witnessed only the scene in Clee Soames's lighted room. "Shucks, let's not have a falling out over a girl, Pete. I reckon it was that yellow hair that had me roped. If you were watching, you know I was dodging the cowmen. That tells the whole story, doesn't it? I belong in your camp. You need hands like me and I want in on your deal."

Falkner studied this in silence. "You were dodging," he admitted finally. "So this time I believe you. In my business I cannot afford to measure men wrong, *amigo*," he added. "Come on, it is time we met Toomey.

"Only remember, I'm no *novicio* with a six gun and I do not aim to catch hemp fever. String along with me and you will do all right, but do not give me cause to mistrust you again. I'm not the kind to listen to excuses twice."

Chapter 8 MINE!

TOOMEY was at the sheriff's office, getting final instructions.

"Remember," Rowden cautioned. "Whatever happens I want this to be a fight between cowmen and nesters."

The deputy shook his head. "Without us, these Dutchmen would already be headed for home. They ain't anxious to fight, Sheriff."

"We'll lend them a gun slinger or two—and some courage." Rowden smiled. "But keep our boys out of sight as much as you can. Once the shooting starts, the clodhoppers will have no choice. They'll fight when they're cornered. And while the valley's tearing itself to pieces, we'll clean up and get out."

They were interrupted by a rap at the door. Toomey, only a step away, yanked it open impatiently. Then his jaw sagged and he blinked at the visitor. Rowden thrust him aside, hurried forward.

"Clee! Was this wise?" He pulled her inside and closed the door carefully. "You've come at a bad time. There's trouble here. The cowmen are in town."

"I know. My father is with them. I had to see you, Will. All week I waited but you didn't——"

He frowned a warning and glanced at the lingering deputy.

She paid no heed. The waiting and uncertainty had piled up her worry. She had recognized Toomey. His presence here crystallized her fears. He was at the root of this trouble. It was his fantastic story of Tom Williams' death that had aroused the ranchmen. Over and over she had assured herself that Will had nothing to do with the trouble. His only fault was his confidence in his lieutenant. He'd accepted the story too blindly. She intended to warn him. "This is Frank Toomey, isn't it?"

The deputy, flattered by the recognition, grinned and gave his mustache a flourish.

"He'd better hear what I have to say since it concerns him."

"Wait until we're alone." Rowden was irritated. Clee's mood was new to him. He took Frank by the arm, steered him toward the door. These two hadn't met before. This was his way. Each relationship had its separate, guarded pigeonhole. He dropped his voice, was purposely vague in his last instructions, conscious of Clee's presence. "We've covered everything, Frank. You know what to do. There's bound to be trouble and it's best I stay out of sight. Better spread word I'm out of town. If you need me I'll be right here. Now get going."

When he turned around Clee's expression baffled him. She stood taut, her stare was bewildered. The thrust of her legs gave her the odd look of being braced against the floor. He wondered what had disturbed her so. Surely nothing he'd said—he'd guarded his tongue.

"At last we're alone." He tried to keep the annoyance out of his tone. This wasn't like Clee's usual glad welcome. He raised her chin, kissed her. There was no warmth in her lips. As well kiss a stone, he thought. "I've missed you, Clee. It's been too long——"

"I waited," she said. "When you didn't come I went back day after day, hoping you'd at least send word. Then I heard about Tom Williams and was more anxious than ever to see you. I could have helped you, Will. You needed me for you've been listening to the wrong people. I'd have told you the truth. The truth, Will. You've got to understand it. There's something terribly wrong here."

These anxieties had been with her all week. Now her mind was in turmoil. She was simply spilling out words against the time this bewilderment would end. Time—that was what she needed—time to understand what she'd just heard. A few guarded words had destroyed her image of Will Rowden. No one but Rowden himself could have accomplished this. She'd been proof against the doubts she'd heard of him, her father's dislike, the growing uneasiness and suspicion throughout the valley. They didn't know Will Rowden as she did. Now her bewilderment was greater because her trust had been so great. She had come here in confidence. Once he knew the truth—and he would listen to her—his action would be certain and swift. He'd shown his competence in dangerous situations before. She had been troubled by her divided loyalties, but in her love for him there had been no room for question. Fearlessness, integrity, every fine quality she thought he possessed, were a part of her devotion. She was a fierce partisan.

A lie, a cheap excuse, the admission that he was dodging danger, had destroyed the whole illusion. One flaw and the whole structure crumbled. This wasn't the man she loved, this stranger who stared at her now, the coward who expected trouble and was hiding from it. She groped for another meaning, some better explanation for the sorry words she'd heard, and could find none. "It's best I stay out of sight," he'd said. "Better spread word I'm out of town." He didn't leave room for her confidence there. As she stared at him now with new and bitter wisdom, memory of their other meetings shamed her. Their rapture was dead and they had turned shabby—as stale as the smell of old tobacco that hung in this bleak room.

"You're overwrought," he said. "I wanted to meet you, Clee, but I couldn't get away. There's trouble here, I tell you."

The words came vaguely through the fog that still clouded her mind. She focused her attention on them with conscious effort. He took her in his arms and she stood there, passively, her head against his shoulder. She didn't want to look at him, not right now.

"You mean Tom Williams?"

"Yes, damn him! All we needed was an incident like that to ruin everything."

She pulled away to face him then. "I've known him all my life. He wasn't a cow thief, Will. You can't expect his neighbors to believe that. You're listening to the wrong people. What makes you trust Frank Toomey?"

"You, too?" Rowden's face hardened. "Stay out of this, honey. When we catch a rustler with a hot iron in his hand we know where we stand. The cowmen have just been wanting an excuse to make trouble, that's all. Well, if they come looking for it they'll find it."

"I belong with the cowmen," she reminded him.

"No, you don't. You belong to me." He smiled, reached for her, but she retreated a step. Her eyes always fascinated him. Usually it was no trick to read their gladness. He frowned into them now and could find nothing but bewilderment.

"What's wrong with you, Clee? You act as if you're afraid of something."

"I'm not the one who's afraid." She listened to her own voice with surprise. Its harshness was strange. She made an effort to smooth it out. "I'm not the one who's hiding here, from trouble."

"Now it's out." He grimaced. "Mighty quick to think the worst of me, aren't you? You've been listening to your father. He's poisoned your mind against me."

"I wouldn't have believed it from anyone but you. It was what you said yourself."

"Now look, Clee—" he had the manner of being patient with a child—"sometimes it's wise to guide things from behind the scenes. Any fool can pull a trigger. The smart man lets things develop until his opponents show their hands. Then he steps in."

"You're the sheriff here. Trouble is your job."

The interruption irritated him. "Will you listen? You've gone off half-cocked on this because you don't understand. I'm playing a waiting game."

She wanted desperately to believe him. Anything was better than this lost emptiness. She tried. But his words came too glibly and she couldn't find sincerity in them.

"Besides," he added, "this way I have a chance to be alone with you, my dear. That's what I wanted most of all." He liked that final touch, thought it would turn the trick.

It was too smooth. She was listening with new perception, weighing the sound of his voice as much as the words themselves, aching for her old trust but still unwilling to be fooled.

She stood quiet. There was no belief in her.

Already his patience was frayed. More than once in recent days he'd fought the feeling that control of the valley was slipping through his fingers. Fools meddled with nicely balanced plans and they went awry.

Take this man Williams, for example. He'd blundered into a branding camp, seen too much. As a result, a scheme two years in the building was threatened. A lesser man might have given up, but already he had adjusted his plans to fit the emergency. That was the difference between him and these others, he thought. He knew how to use them so that even their vengeance would work for him. The difficulty was, there were so many of these emergencies. It shook his confidence.

He hadn't believed this could happen, though. As he watched Clee, a dozen other scenes tantalized him. Times when her lips had been willing, her arms hungry. That was what she needed now. Words didn't help but she'd never failed to respond to his love-making. She wasn't proof against kisses. He seized her by the shoulders and when she pulled back it angered him. His grip was rough. She turned her face to avoid him. That was a final exasperation. There was fury in his lips now. They bruised her throat. He pulled her dress aside and kissed her shoulder. His arms hurt her. He crushed her to him until she was breathless. "No matter what happens, nothing's going to come between us, Clee. You understand that, don't you? Nothing. You're mine—you always will be."

When he slid her dress lower, he felt her stiffen. He drew back, puzzled by her lack of response. Everything was going wrong tonight, even with Clee. He stared at her silently in an effort to fathom her mood. This was a problem to be handled with the same resourcefulness he applied to other difficulties. Her calm puzzled him. He could cope with a stormy scene but this was different. Nothing seemed to stir her. As he watched she straightened her dress. Covering herself from me, he thought. She's never done that before. Frustration made him savage. This quarrel was so needless, so unexpected. He wouldn't tolerate it any longer, not even from her.

"This is a lot of nonsense, Clee. What are we quarreling about? I told you I wanted this time alone with you."

Her mouth twisted as if she found a sorry flavor to his explanation. "Please don't make an excuse of me, Will."

He brushed a hand over his face to hide the sudden flare of his anger. "Don't you believe anything I say?"

"No." Her throat was constricted and the words came hard. She had to force them out slowly, one at a time. "No, I don't. I can't. That's what's so terrible. If I can't believe you, Will, what have I got left?"

Choking back a quick retort, he grasped her by the wrist. The less said the better now. There was a simpler way to end this. He had never appraised the honesty of her zeal in love. He only knew kisses could set her to trembling, an unexpected caress could make her gasp. When he reached for her she pulled back again and the gesture inflamed him so he lost all caution. His hands were relentless. She buried her head in his shoulder to avoid his lips and he kissed her hair until her braids were loosened.

She stood stiff and unyielding. "Wake up, Clee—wake up! What's wrong with you? If you think I'm going to let this silly quarrel come between us, you're wrong."

"I think I'd better go."

Her voice was matter of fact.

It was this apparent indifference that angered him most. "Do you think I'll let you go? You can't walk out on me this way." He peered at her, tried to penetrate her calm. "You're mine, Clee—mine! Do you hear?"

She didn't know how to answer him. She wanted to get away without saying anything more until she'd had time to think.

"I'm going." She whispered it this time.

She started for the door.

"I said you couldn't." Rowden seized her, forced her back and this time she struggled to free herself. The feel of her body, soft under his hands, tortured him. "You're mine," he kept repeating. "Mine—mine! You can't leave me."

She wrenched loose, backed away. He followed, his arms stretched wide to bar her escape. Gradually he edged her toward a corner. "Mine!" he still chanted, half under his breath. She tried to dodge when he grabbed for her, but he caught her by the front of the dress. For a moment he held her there. Then with a swift motion he tore it open, laughed at her effort to clutch it together and cover her breasts.

"What are you hiding from me for? Haven't you changed your tune mighty suddenly?"

"This isn't love." Anger burned her face. "Don't you know the difference?"

He could read her now—too well. Her contempt turned him savage. He tore at her dress, wanted to hurt her as her words had stung him.

"Don't, Will! Let me go. You wouldn't want me if I didn't love you."

"I want you any way I can get you."

When he seized her, thrust aside her arms and covered her with kisses, she sobbed. This was humiliation, anger, heartbreak. She had no time to cry. She fought. When her blows went unheeded, she twisted her fingers in his hair, jerked back his head. That was when he struck her. His fist caught her in the face, her head cracked against the wall. It numbed her but she didn't lose consciousness, was aware when he twisted her back across the desk.

"No, Will! Please God, no! Not this way."

Her cries alarmed him. He hammered at her again. He still was snarling, "Mine ... mine ... mine!" when she slipped into unconsciousness.

Chapter 9 CORNERED

CURLY had trouble turning back the cowmen. He put his cards on the table with John Soames and the Blake brothers first. Ma was present. "Grady aims to find out who was thar when Tom was kilt. He figgers Toomey's the man to tell him. That's why he's jined that outfit. What he needs is time."

"We've had too much palaver and too little action," Soames growled. "That's been our trouble. Now we're here, let's finish up the job."

"An' spring this trap that's set for us?" Ma asked.

"We can play that game, too, now we know about it. I'm surprised, Ma. I thought the Forked W would be the last outfit to back out on this deal."

"Who's backin' out?" she demanded. "We're just fixin' to move in, but we want to know where we're goin' an' who we're after before we put on our war paint. Hell's bells! That's just plain sense."

Soames remembered Grady Scott only vaguely. "He's purty young. What makes you think he can get the job done?"

"He'll outdraw, outshoot an' outride any ranny you ever sot eyes on," Curly maintained. "An' he's got the savvy to back it up. What he says he'll do, he'll do."

The Blakes knew Grady well. "If we scoured Texas, we couldn't find a better man for the job," Dave agreed.

The Snake on a Rock boss still objected. "They'll think they scared us off. I don't like the looks of it."

"'T wouldn't do a speck of harm," Ma argued. "Give 'em some rope an' maybe they'll overreach themselves. That might smooth out the trail for Grady.

"An' don't forget Clee's in town, John. When the lead-throwin' starts, a lot of bystanders are apt to get hurt. There'll be a likelier time for it."

He yielded grudgingly. "What are we goin' to tell the boys? They won't like this."

He knew the rannies. They would fight for their outfits but they expected to have a voice in such decisions, too.

"We can't tell 'em Grady's here or what he's up to," Ma admitted. "Somebody might get careless in his talk. This trap they've set has got to be our excuse."

The men argued over the decision, tried to point out that they could outmatch the nesters at either gunplay or trickery. "We was fightin' Injuns whilst they was larnin' to plow," Jim Evans snorted. "One cow hand's worth a dozen clodhoppers any time. Give me leave an' I'll handle this by myself." Jim was a seasoned hand but new to this range, and he'd had a few drinks to spur his temper. Chafing at the restraint that kept him away from Scanlon's, he had found a way to procure a bottle of whisky by bribing Hallelujah.

The others shared his reluctance but they listened to their leaders, voted with them. Jim turned angry at what he termed Curly's buck fever. "Me, I thought a lot of Tom Williams," he drawled. "There's things about his killin' need explainin'. I've come here to larn 'em and I don't aim to light a shuck out of here 'til I do."

"When time for the showdown comes," Curly retorted, "I'll be settin' in, lookin' at the hole card, but this ain't the time, Jim. Let's not wade into a game where the cards are already stacked agin us."

"'Pears to me some folks are gettin' as gun-shy as a feemale institute," Evans growled.

Walter Hart sided with Evans whom he greatly admired. The two were cronies. "Are we going to stick our tails between our legs and run home at the first sign of trouble?" he demanded.

"You've been outvoted," Curly reminded them. "We're goin' home."

"You're ridin' without me then," Jim retorted. "If the Forked W is goin' to lay down now I don't want any part of it. Just give me my time."

Curly nodded. "Sorry to see you go but if that's how you feel——"

"It's how I feel."

The Kid demanded his time too.

Soames decided that the Snake on a Rock outfit should remain in town overnight. "We're not runnin' away," he said. "Anybody wants to find us, they know where we are."

He made the decision partly as a sop to his stubborn pride, partly on Clee's account. He'd been to her room, found it dark and the door locked. She didn't answer when he knocked and he decided she was asleep already. She'd had a long ride that day.

Nevertheless, he sternly warned his hands to stay away from Scanlon's and avoid trouble. "If you want a game of cards, play right here," he admonished. "We won't start anything we can't finish and this ain't the time for that now."

The Lazy B outfit rode out that night and with them went Ma Williams, Curly and Peg. "Me, I'd feel easier if the Snake on a Rock had come too," Curly confessed.

"Don't worry about John Soames," Ma advised him. "He's bullheaded but he's got judgment. He'll stay out of trouble, he's too smart to tackle the town alone."

For a time the Snake on a Rock crew played cards in the dining room where Letty had cleared a table for them. Jim Evans and the Kid joined them there and Jim was generous with his bottle, passing it around freely. Then, since they were riding at dawn, Soames's outfit turned in early. The town was quiet, the crisis evidently ended, when Evans decided to go to Scanlon's for more whisky.

"You think we'd better?"

"The town's so quiet, only thing that bothers me is maybe the place is closed." Evans grinned and patted his holster. "Don't worry."

The Kid flushed. "Who's worried? Come on, let's go."

Scanlon's was crowded and Grady noticed the number of shotguns tilted against the wall and among the tables. There was no mistaking the temper of this crowd. They had come expecting trouble and were ready for it. A few were boisterous. The majority, however, were cold sober, and the room fell quiet as he followed Pete to a table in the rear where Toomey sat waiting. The scrape of Pete's chair sounded loud against the hush. He pulled it around against the wall, facing the door. "What's the word from the sheriff, Frank?" he asked.

Toomey caressed his mustache. There was a smirk on his face. "He's busy. Yeah, right busy by now, I reckon. Rowden's always so full of business, you wouldn't guess how handy he is with women. When I left the office he was entertainin' the likeliest-lookin' wench you ever set eyes on."

Pete scowled and shot a glance at Grady. "Seems like everybody is having calico trouble tonight. I do not like it. When I love, I love, and when I fight, I fight. They do not mix so well, *amigos*."

"We don't need the sheriff here," Toomey assured him. "It's best that he stays out of sight. This is between cowmen and nesters, he says, and he doesn't want our crowd mixed up in it. The only reason we're here is to ride herd on the nesters, keep 'em stirred up, crowd 'em into a showdown if they hang back. Mind now, these are orders."

Falkner smiled and nodded. "Smart," he commented.

For an hour they waited and nothing happened. As the time dragged out Grady's confidence grew. The cowmen had listened to Curly. There would be no fight. He studied the crowd about him. There were men of all types here, but for the most part they looked like any other lot of sober, industrious farmers. He hadn't expected men of this stamp. The prevalent tongue was German although here and there he heard English spoken well. He questioned Toomey about them. "Most of these are good people. They're not the sort I expected to find baiting a trap."

"They've had their fences torn down, their stock run off, their crops trampled," the deputy explained. "It's like any other war. Rowden says folks fight best when they think they're defendin' their homes." He tossed off his drink and regarded Grady shrewdly over the rim of his glass. "Remember that if you ever want to start a war, Grady. You can always stir up the riffraff but if you want real trouble, rile up the solid, substantial folks. Then you've got something."

Grady stared around him again. The crowd's patient quiet reflected its determination. He realized, with surprise, that he was afraid. It wasn't a physical fear for himself. It went deeper than that. He knew worry for the ranch people, his people, scattered up the valley. What chance had they against a man who could mass an army of stolid, law-abiding farmers against them? He wondered who had arranged this? Was it Toomey? Or was it the sheriff whom he had not yet met?

A chair was overturned. Rowden straightened it, stared around carefully for any other signs of the struggle. His eyes stopped on Clee. She lay there so still and white that it made him uneasy. He crossed the room, laid his hand over her heart and felt its faint hammer. His fury had spent itself. He was surprised that she could stir him to such a frenzy. He always had prided himself on his sure control. It was her defiance that was to blame, he decided. She goaded me into it. Curiosity over his own emotions absorbed him. He wasn't thinking of her.

He didn't notice when she opened her eyes. Looking down, he saw she was watching him. She hadn't moved. It annoyed him to find he couldn't tell what she was thinking.

Now she's going to cry, he thought, and was surprised when she didn't.

"You must learn not to tell me what you will or won't do," he broke out finally. "I'm the one who decides that."

"Now I'm going home" was all she said.

He watched her cross the room. She's learned her lesson, he thought. He didn't try to stop her. He was relieved that there would be no scene.

Outside Clee leaned against the door, her teeth bit into her lip to stop its trembling and hold back the sobs. He wouldn't see her tears—she was determined on that. She quivered with shame, disillusionment, bitterness, but he wouldn't see her hurt. Her hatred helped her, strengthened her pride. She braced herself against the building, checked the first spasm of her grief. Then she started running. She fled blindly at first, conscious only of a need to leave the shameful scene behind. There was a moan low in her throat. She strangled it behind set teeth.

The taste of blood in her mouth made her queasy and she fought back the wave of sickness. Her legs felt heavy. She tried to lift them faster. Finally she faltered and, no longer able to hold back the nausea, clung to a tree and retched. The violence of the attack left her trembling with weakness and dizzy for a time. Gradually her vision cleared and she discovered where she was. The tree she clutched for support was the outer sentinel of the dark clump of live oaks behind the hotel. Its bark was harsh against her bruised face. She was conscious of its hurting, but still didn't move. The effort was too great at first.

Shadows were a black pool under the oaks—friendly, she thought, and inviting, an impenetrable curtain behind which she could hide. It cost her an effort to move; the weakness dragged at her. She had to will each separate step as she crept into the gloom. There her memories caught up with her. She shuddered with the violence of sobs too long held back. She flung herself face down on the ground. She could cry now and in the first fierce convulsion of her agony she hammered her fists against the soft earth.

It was much later when she slipped in the kitchen door. The card game in the dining room had broken up. She crept to her room unseen.

Rowden was uneasy. His first relief at being rid of Clee was ended. Now he regretted that he'd let her go. She was overwrought—no telling what she might do or say. It was this uncertainty which bothered him. He didn't like sitting here alone, waiting. Finally he quit the office, crossed to Scanlon's in search of Toomey. He glanced toward the Reid House. The town was quiet. Scanlon's windows were shuttered tight. Except for the yellow blob reflected from the transom over the door, no light showed anywhere. He hesitated. He had planned to stay out of sight tonight and it nettled him to realize how he had changed his plan. Again he peered up the deserted street. It was no matter. The danger had passed—the cowmen weren't coming.

"Here is the sheriff," Pete said.

Toomey looked surprised. Grady watched Rowden approach. He stopped for a word at several tables. His smile was quick. The tension of the room seemed to ease with his coming. The hum of conversation grew louder. They trust him—Toomey is just his messenger boy, Grady thought. He was more sure of it after they met. The sheriff was a handsome man. His elegance set him apart from these others; it emphasized the pallor of his skin, too. He had a disarming mildness; there was nothing written on his face, until you saw his eyes. They were flinty and black, and reminded Grady of the glistening obsidian arrow points that the Kiowas often used. They didn't warm when Rowden smiled.

"So you're a friend of Pete's," he said. "You'll find you're ace-high here if Pete says you're all right." His voice was soft. Grady found himself disliking the unctuous tone of it. It didn't match the chill of those bleak eyes. His hand was white and slender but there was steel in his grip.

Heinrich Unger bustled in just as the sheriff was taking his seat. He came straight to the table with word that some of the cattlemen were leaving. He'd been posted to watch and had seen them ride out. Grady didn't care much for Unger. He was an unkempt man. A week's black growth of bristles smudged his face. His shirt was soiled and his pants were caked with grease. Unlike most nesters, he wore a cowman's wide-brimmed hat. It was floppy and of poor quality. He was the first nester Grady had seen wearing a six gun. He had spurs on his boots—but they were heavy farmer boots. "Not cowhand, not nester" was Grady's silent verdict. "But the worst of each."

Unger was on easy terms with both Toomey and the sheriff. "Too bad dey scared off so easy," he grunted. "Dey vould have got vot Tom Villiams got, mit nobody to tell vot happened, choost like before."

"Nobody knows the straight of the Williams' killin' but me—and I ain't talkin'," Toomey boasted. Unger slapped him approvingly on the shoulder.

Grady held his gaze on the table to mask his interest but the sheriff switched the conversation before more could be said.

"I guess there's not going to be any show tonight, boys. We might as well have a drink." He said it loudly. The word was picked up at other tables, passed quickly around. Threat of a fight ended; the crowd began to disperse. It was the more substantial element which left first. Grady watched the men crowd toward the door. Where before they sat in silence or spoke in brief monosyllables, now they laughed easily and were in noisy good humor. Soon more than half of them were gone.

As the tension eased vigilance relaxed, and that was how Jim Evans and the Kid wandered into the bar unchallenged. They had already ordered drinks when they were noticed. The babble of conversation died again. Grady turned to learn the cause of the silence. Every eye in the room was on the two cowmen. He didn't know either of them except that he'd seen them riding horses with the Forked W brand. Their presence angered him.

They were fools to come here, he thought. There'll be trouble but they were warned.

He wondered how he should act when the shooting started. They were from his old outfit. By every instinct he was on their side, but if he helped them now his chance of discovering anything from Toomey was gone. He recalled Unger's reference to Tom's killing. I'll stick to my course, he decided to himself. It's their own funeral. He was angered by the decision but saw no alternative.

"Here comes Butterball," Toomey growled. "Some time he's going to poke his nose in my business once too often."

Grady glanced up. August Lehman stood in the door. His brow was puckered but the china blue of his eyes gentled his stare as he surveyed the room.

For a moment Grady was uneasy. The merchant had visited the Forked W some, in the old days. It was a risk there was no dodging. Even if Lehman still remembered the gangling boy of those days, 't wasn't likely he'd recognize him. He'd changed considerable since then.

"Too bad he had to show up." The sheriff's fingers grew restless. "He's hard to handle and too many folks listen to him."

Lehman headed straight for the sheriff's table. Grady faced him squarely. If he was going to be remembered, now was the time to face it. The merchant's mild stare flicked around the table, slid past Grady without recognition.

"I'm glad to see you here, Sheriff. I guess you're worried too." He nodded toward the cowmen at the bar. "Trouble iss easy to start and hard to stop in Apache."

"Oh, I reckon the danger's past." Rowden's face thawed in a smile. "Things look right peaceable now. You go on home and get some rest, Mr. Lehman. I'll stay until Scanlon closes up. There's nothing to worry about."

Lehman didn't move. "Alwayss it iss calm just before the storm. Maybe you could tell those two boys to leave. That would stop trouble."

"Now you know I can't do that. They haven't done anything."

Toomey pushed back his chair noisily and made no effort to hide his irritation. "Yeah, I reckon he wants you to arrest 'em on suspicion of bein' cowboys, Sheriff." He peered around expectantly but his sally went unnoticed in the tension. Every eye was on Lehman.

"That iss not such a bad idea. In jail they'd be safe." The merchant turned to the sheriff. "Your job iss keeping peace, *hein?* That iss one way to do it."

"I can't lock up innocent men," Rowden answered flatly. "Don't try to be funny again, Toomey. It backfires."

"But if it saves their lives?" Lehman wouldn't give up.

"The answer is no." The sheriff was emphatic. "See here, Mr. Lehman, I appreciate your efforts but I'm still running my office. I'll do it my way. Those boys are safe here as long as they don't try to start anything. I'm here to keep an eye on things."

Grady had seen some hope for the two Forked W riders in Lehman's persistence. Now he knew better. Rowden wants trouble, he thought. He'd like to get Lehman out of the way before it happens, but he isn't going to let him stop it.

The merchant turned to the nearest table, began speaking to its occupants in rapid German.

Unger sidled up near enough to hear what was said, then translated the conversation for the sheriff. "He's trying to make dem go home. He says only two cowhands von't cause no trouble."

"Most of the men who'd listen to Lehman are already gone." The sheriff turned away. "He'll not get far with this bunch."

Grady watched Unger with dislike. There's someone else itching for a fight, he thought. Then his eyes narrowed, his weight shifted and involuntarily his hand dropped toward his holster. He had noticed before that Unger wore a six shooter, but as he turned away Grady had his first clear glimpse of the holster and belt. The flap had been cut away, not too expertly, for the leather had been shorn down too far. He remembered that because it had been his doing. He remembered how he'd first learned to draw with the belt Tom Williams had lent him. He moved slightly to get a better look, recalling another identification mark. The belt had been too long for slender, thirteen-year-old hips and he had cut out a length at the back, laced it together. Later, when Tom wanted to wear it himself, he'd had to splice it there with thongs. Grady's suspicion became a certainty when he saw that splice. Now he knew another man who was present when Tom was killed.

Rowden knew the decision was his. Lehman's presence worried him and he hesitated. The stage was set for trouble. The two men at the bar didn't have a chance. What was there to gain by waiting? Too much had happened. This was the time for it.

"Remember—" his voice was quiet—"it must be the cowmen against nesters. Let Unger start it."

The nester glanced around the table uneasily.

Nodding toward Pete Falkner, Toomey said to Unger, "Look who's here. You'll be covered every minute. There's nothin' for you to worry about."

Unger found reassurance in that. He emptied his glass, rose slowly and walked up to the bar. Even then he was careful to leave a wide space between him and the cowhands. As he called for another drink he looked down the rail toward them, and there was a small swagger in his manner. The odds here were overwhelming; he was careless of consequences.

Here it comes, thought Grady. He had risen. Now he stepped back a pace until he could feel the wall against his shoulder blades.

August Lehman saw Unger's move, too. He squeezed past two tables to reach the cleared space in front of the bar. "The folks at the Forked W have been friends of mine for a long time. I want you boyss to have a drink with me."

His voice was purposely loud. It stilled the room's clatter.

Evans and the Kid stared in surprise. They hadn't expected to find a friend here. When he saw who it was, Evans made room at the rail. "Why, shore, Mr. Lehman. I'd be right proud to drink with you."

August Lehman was small; he barely reached to Evans' shoulder as he wedged himself between the two cowmen, his back to the room. Grady watched in silent admiration. He's short on size but long on guts, he thought. The little cuss has guessed Unger's move and is darin' him to shoot now.

Toomey was swearing under his breath. "Damn his Dutch soul to hell! He thinks we won't shoot, long as he's standin' there."

Unger stared uncertainly back, looking for instructions.

"Me and Grady can pick them off without nicking the little billygoat in the middle, can't we, *compadre?* Let us handle it," Falkner urged.

"No, this has got to be a nester fight," the sheriff decided. "I'll get Lehman out of the way. Wait!"

He walked toward the door with elaborate unconcern, as if he hadn't noticed the scene at the bar. There he turned, called the merchant. August looked around.

"I've been thinking about that scheme of yours," Rowden said. "On second thought, maybe you've got something."

"What scheme?" The merchant didn't budge from his position.

"For stopping trouble here. You mentioned locking someone up."

"It would work, Sheriff. Maybe it iss the only thing that would." Lehman spoke earnestly.

"I guess you're right, but it's a little irregular. What would the charges be? I'll do what you suggest, but I reckon I'll need your advice. We'll have to work fast."

Rowden had shrewdly guessed the one thing that would move Lehman. He left his position, hurried forward.

Unger saw his chance. "The Forked W," he said. "Seems to me I've heard of it. Tom Williams' outfit, vassn't it?"

"Yes." Evans' answer came loud and clear. "I reckon I'll drink to Tom Williams—the straightest cowman who ever straddled a horse."

The first shot came fast, like an echo to the words. The Kid staggered, braced himself against the bar, drew his weapon as he turned. Evans was quicker. His gun blazed as he wheeled.

Grady had been firm in his purpose to stay out of this. It was the sight of that holster Unger was wearing that upset him, he thought later. That and Jim Evans' toast to Tom Williams. Right now he didn't take time to think. His six gun was tight in his fingers the instant the first shot was fired. Even then he realized there was no chance against these odds. His instinct was to help the men escape. Two big lamps hung from the ceiling. Grady fired twice and the room was suddenly black. Against the din of shots he could hear the splash of trickling kerosene from one of the broken lamps.

Chapter 10 A PRISONER

GRADY held his fire. He could see nothing. After the bright splash of each shot the black seemed more impenetrable. When he backed against the wall the bar was to his right. Somewhere off to the left a table overturned where some nester floundered. The sound drew a quick shot. A ragged volley answered. Glass splintering behind the bar added to the confusion.

Grady edged cautiously to the left, feeling his way along the wall. Between the two factions, he could be caught in their crossfire. There was a rear door here somewhere, he remembered. If only he could locate it. He found it with his outstretched hand, moved cautiously until the knob was located. It was unguarded, forgotten.

He had hoped for this. Escape by the front was out of the question. That door was too far away and surely would be watched. This was the only way.

He turned back to his right, found the bar, slid furtively along it. The firing was sporadic now, each flutter of shots followed by an interval of watchful suspense. Every sound drew bullets. His danger was as much from one side as the other. The cowmen wouldn't expect to find a friend here. He felt his way along, exploring each step with extended foot before moving. Something blocked his path, a sodden bundle against which his boot caught, and the floor was slick around it. In this way he found the Kid. The inert body was half propped against the bar, where it had slid. He bent beside it. His hand came away wet and sticky.

The other Forked W ranny must be close. If he went farther Grady knew he risked a bullet from the man he was trying to help. He remained on one knee, crouched for safety. "Forked W," he whispered. "Forked W. This way. There's a back door." The words were drowned in the roar of a gun from across the room. He tried again. The answer was so long in coming he was beginning to wonder if both men were dead.

"Who are you?"

The response came faintly but from surprisingly close at hand. The cowman was hugging the floor too. Smart, thought Grady. That's how he's lasted so long.

"A friend—used to ride for the Forked W." Grady risked stretching out his hand then, touched the other's sleeve. "Come on. I'll get you out of this."

Evans hesitated. He'd been tempted to fire at the sound of the first whisper. His finger ached against the trigger. He knew the Kid was down. He was alone. His grim determination now was not to sell out cheap. He'd take as many nesters down with him as he could.

His grip on the pistol relaxed gradually. What did he have to lose? If there was a way out, he'd live to come back again—and he'd come back, because of the Kid. It was a new thought. It took time to get used to it. Yes, they'd have cause to remember the Kid, he grimly promised himself.

He reached out, across the Kid's body, until his groping fingers found his unknown friend. "You lead, I'll follow," he whispered.

They moved silently, kept low. Twice probing bullets splintered the bar behind them but they couldn't fire back. Gun flashes would betray their movement. Grady didn't raise up until he reached the door; he held his breath as he inched it open. A sound now would ruin everything. Clouds hid the stars; the outside night was sooty but still less black than the room. Its faint glow outlined the opening. Sweet air freshened the stale fumes of burnt powder. He thrust his companion through the door, then turned back and flattened himself against the wall.

"The back door!" someone shouted. Grady hadn't counted on the volley that searched the opening. The lead whined uncomfortably close. Then there was a rush for it and he heard them coming. He thrust out a leg to trip the leader and there was a pile-up in the exit.

The confusion gave Jim Evans more time. He'd found a horse now, and he emptied his gun at the building as he galloped away. This discouraged pursuit.

Scanlon lighted a lamp, stared ruefully at the wreckage in its glow. The long bar mirror which had been his pride was splintered in half a dozen places, and its glass splattered half the room. The Kid lay where he had fallen and under his head the sawdust had turned red. Across the room one of the nesters was sprawled over a tumbled chair, one limp hand stretched toward a fallen shotgun. The crowd was in an ugly mood over the discovery that one of their friends had been killed. Grady noticed that August Lehman was the only one who stooped over the Kid's body.

"I can't understand it," growled Toomey. "It beats me how that other ranny got away. I don't like it."

"Ve should have vatched dat door," Unger muttered.

"Maybe Señor Scott can tell us the answer," Pete Falkner said. "He was there."

The harshness of the voice warned Grady. He whirled to face his accuser and saw that Pete already had gripped his six gun and had the edge on him in a draw.

"I warned you against any *engaños,* Grady," he said. "I told you I would have my eyes open for tricks."

The sheriff turned his bleached face toward them. "What's this, Pete? I thought you vouched for this man." His voice was mild but the words spilled out fast.

Falkner didn't turn his head. His watchful eyes never left Grady's right hand, and his fingers were tight on his weapon. He bent slightly forward, his whole body tense with expectancy. Grady read the signs and knew he was looking at death if he made the slightest move.

"He is a killer, Sheriff. I was not fooled about that but he is on the wrong side. I guessed it when I saw him at the Reid House tonight, but he told me he'd gone back for his other pistol. That time I believed him."

Rowden glanced across the room, where Lehman still knelt beside the Kid's body, and lowered his voice. "What made you change your mind?"

"He shot out the lights when the *combate* started. I saw him. We would have ended those two in three seconds if it had not been for that."

Grady didn't deny it. Who here would take his word against Pete Falkner's? "Sure." He grinned. "I always take the lights first. It avoids unpleasant questions later about who killed who. I thought it was a good idea." From the corner of his eye he measured the crowd. Those near enough to hear were hostile, but he thought some of them approved this reasoning.

"*Ja,* dat vass a goot idea," said Unger. "Und goot shooting, too."

"The same two *tiros* could have put windows in both cowhands," Falkner retorted. "We would not be worried now about the man who got away."

There was a growl from the nesters who had bunched close to hear. They liked Falkner's answer best.

"You were standing right there when you doused the *lámparas,*" Pete continued. "And you were still right there when another lamp was lighted. Anyone getting out that door had to pass you. That is not all. Someone standing there tripped me when I started out after Evans or I still would have got him."

"A lot of guesses." Grady sensed the growing hostility of the nesters but he kept on trying. "If I'd been on the other side why didn't I get out when I could?"

"I have been trying to figure that out. Maybe you thought you would learn more by staying here." Falkner's unwavering eyes picked up something else. "Look at his left hand, *jefe*. Blood on it! But he is not wounded. It is the Kid's blood and he is laying right where he fell. This *hombre* was over there by the bar while the lights were out. He is on the other side, all right."

The crowd's angry murmur revealed how convincing this last proof was.

Sheriff Rowden was taken by surprise but he was careful not to show it. He'd hoped that Falkner was wrong. Then his chilled stare saw the red on Grady's fingers and he knew better.

His first anger was for the gunman. It was his job to know the wild bunch that rode with him and he had vouched for Grady Scott. The sheriff had no patience with mistakes. They were often fatal.

He didn't let his fury warp his calculations, though. First, the damage must be corrected. Scott must be silenced before he had a chance to talk. There was no telling how much he'd had time to learn here. The presence of August Lehman complicated things. The merchant had a strong following and he was shrewd. "Too smart for an honest man," Rowden had once told Toomey. "It's too bad. With him on my side, we'd run the whole valley without a speck of trouble."

"A little lead would cure that," the deputy had suggested.

"And stir up another hornet's nest like this Williams affair? Not unless we have to, Frank. You steer shy of Lehman. Let me handle him."

Now Lehman was here and badly in need of handling. The sheriff wanted no more violence in his presence. He'd stir up enough trouble over the Kid's death, as it was.

With one half of his mind he worried over Lehman; with the other he listened to Pete Falkner. It was Pete's story that suggested the solution. He smiled to himself as he checked it mentally for flaws. It would do. Even August Lehman should be convinced.

When he stepped forward he was careful to keep out of Falkner's line of fire. It suited him to have Grady Scott covered. He was meticulous about such details—he prided himself on his care in planning them. That's where I'm different from Frank Toomey, who's just as much of a pack rat as I am, he often reminded himself. Or Pete Falkner, who's far more deadly with a six gun.

"You made just one mistake, Pete," he said. "Grady Scott didn't shoot out the lamps. I did that."

"But I saw——"

"You saw him draw and shoot just when the lights went out," Rowden continued suavely. "As sheriff here it was my duty to stop the trouble if I could. You've got Grady Scott all wrong. He's the one who shot the Kid."

The sheriff's explanation stunned the room to silence. Falkner's eyes widened in surprise. Grady tried to read Rowden's bleak face—but failed. He couldn't guess the purpose of this lie.

"Disarm the prisoner, Frank, while Pete keeps him covered," the sheriff ordered.

Toomey stepped behind Grady and slipped his six guns from their holsters before unbuckling his cartridge belts. When they fell to the floor the sheathed Bowie knife suspended at the rear was revealed too.

Rowden pointed it out to Lehman, who now had joined the group. "You see? Armed to the teeth. Obviously a dangerous man. From his looks, I'd say he's a leather slapper, hired out to one of the big ranches. It's his sort that's at the bottom of most of our trouble."

Pete Falkner stared at the sheriff in amazement but a sharp look silenced him. The protest came from Lehman.

"But if he iss a cowman, why should he shoot the Kid? They were on the same side."

The sheriff had an answer ready. "It does look queer, until you figure things out. The cowmen rode in here on the prod. They expected a fight with the homesteaders. Fortunately I was here to prevent that and our people kept their heads. But that didn't suit these short-trigger men." His dark stare came to rest on Grady. "Gun smoke is their trade. That's why they draw extra wages. They were bent on a killing and it had to be a cowman, so they could put the blame on the nesters. They wanted a war and this was going to be their excuse. It's pretty obvious, Mr. Lehman, once you understand what's behind it."

Grady was chilled by the smooth way Rowden warped the facts to suit his purpose. He knew how close he'd been to death. A single unguarded movement would have brought Pete's gun out, blazing. Yet as he watched the sheriff's shrewd maneuvering he realized this man was a far more deadly opponent. It had been hard for him to understand why Tom Williams had been accused of stealing cattle, after he was dead and silent. Now he thought he understood. It fitted this same malicious pattern.

Lehman puckered his lips. The tuft on his chin bristled straight out. He was half convinced. His mild blue eyes strayed from Grady to his weapons, now heaped on the floor beside him. "And this man? What happens to him?"

"He's under arrest for murder."

Feet shuffled. The crowd stirred restlessly.

"A nice legal way to get rid of me," Grady commented. "I'm an outsider. There's been a killing and they need a scapegoat. It looks as if I'm it."

Toomey snorted. "A likely story. Sheriff Rowden saw you and there were forty more witnesses to the killin'." He glanced around him for support. "You can't get away with that."

"I suppose you'll swear you saw me shoot the Kid too?"

"Of course I will. I saw just what the sheriff saw." Toomey broke open one of the six shooters he'd taken from Grady, spilled the bullets into his palm. "See? Two empty cartridges." He emptied the other weapon too. It had not been fired.

"I've told you—I fired twice at the lights."

The sheriff turned to Lehman again and shrugged. "Of course I'm the one who did that. The boys all know that. A weak story, Mr. Lehman."

"There hass been enough killing." The little merchant faced the crowd with determination. "This man must have a fair trial. If he iss guilty, the law will punish him." He looked from one face to another, fixing each in his mind. "No more posses, like the one that killed Tom Williams. The good people here won't stand for that. I've seen who iss here and I'll know who to blame if anything like that happens."

"My idea exactly," Rowden readily agreed.

"He iss your prisoner, Sheriff. You are responsible for hiss safety," Lehman warned again.

Whatever happened, the sheriff would be careful of appearances where Lehman was concerned, Grady thought. At the same time, he didn't see how a trial could help him. Rowden knew where he stood.

I reckon half the men here will swear they saw me do it, he thought bitterly. That lets them out and provides a nice legal way to get rid of me. Even August Lehman won't object."

The crowd was sullen. Those in front turned uneasy faces away from Lehman's stare but behind them, lost in the pack, others were more bold. The muttering grew.

"Aw, what the hell we waitin' fer?"

"He's a short-trigger man, hired to cut our fences, ain't he?"

"Mit a gun in his hand, he vouldn't vait for us."

Lehman took his stand beside the prisoner. "He iss going to get a fair trial," he repeated stubbornly. "Don't be foolss. A mob iss just asking for more trouble. The only way to end this iss to make the law strong."

"If it's a trial you vant, giff it to him now," Unger suggested. "De vitnesses are all here."

"August Lehman, he talks big," someone jeered in a high-pitched, nasal whine. "Maybe it's der ranch money jingling in his pockets yet. He gets fat off dem und off us too."

Grady traced the voice. It belonged to a bony-faced nester with a slack, vacant mouth. When he talked, he bared only a few blackened fangs along a decayed ridge. "Me, I'm mit Unger. Lehman don't scare me choost 'cause he's rich."

"Shut up, Kurt," the merchant retorted. "There iss no gold of yours in my pocket. Nothing but trouble comes by you."

"Lehman is right." Rowden made his decision brusquely. "Don't forget I'm sheriff here. I aim to see the law properly enforced."

He had weighed the situation carefully. He wanted to get rid of Grady Scott—the man knew too much. But this was no time to challenge August Lehman's wide influence. Things still were going wrong.

The jail was a single bare room, planked off from the sheriff's office. Lehman had tagged along, his short legs pumping to keep up, until the key turned in the lock. Even then he wasn't sure the danger was ended. Grady could hear him through the thin wall. "Now he iss safe until the trial?"

"I reckon. Unless something else happens to rile that crowd. They wouldn't have much trouble breakin' in here, if they were minded to."

"And if you're minded to you can stop anything like that." The retort was sharp. "Maybe it iss better I stay here tonight."

Rowden took his time in answering. He was nettled, but he couldn't afford to show it. Smiling, he laid a friendly hand on the merchant's shoulder and said, "Now, Mr. Lehman—you know you can trust me. Haven't I promised you there wouldn't be any mob?"

"You sounded doubtful."

"Well, I'm not. I aim to do my duty. I'll see they don't break in here. You have my word for it."

Lehman left then, satisfied. When the door closed on him, the sheriff swore under his breath and began to pace the floor.

Toomey was more placid. He lounged comfortably against the wall and let his chief do the worrying. "What's botherin' you?" he asked finally. "You've made a neat case against Grady Scott. Even ol' Lehman will be satisfied."

The sheriff stopped his restless walk. "If there's a trial, Scott will talk. How do we know how much he's learned? He spent the evening with us and we were careless what we said. Damn Pete Falkner for that! I thought he knew his man.

"No—" he strode the floor again—"we can't afford to let him talk."

"You worry too much about Lehman. He's just like the others. A little money don't mean so much."

"It's not his money. These clodhoppers listen to him, I tell you. And he's smart. If we didn't keep things stirred up he'd find a way to settle this trouble. Then where'd we be? No, I can't risk letting Scott go to trial. I don't want him spilling what he knows in front of Lehman."

He halted, nodded toward the cell. "Come outside with me, Frank." They walked through the door together. "I'm thinking our prisoner already knows too much," Rowden said, once they were under the stars. "He can hear anything that's said in there." Again he damned Pete Falkner for bad judgment.

"Yeah." Toomey glanced back and grinned. "Yeah, but the way the boys are riled it wouldn't take much to organize a necktie party. That would quiet him, in a hurry."

The sheriff shook his head. "You heard Lehman. He was afraid of that. That won't do——" He broke off abruptly. "Wait here, Frank. And remember, nothing happens to the prisoner while I'm gone. I've just thought of something. Maybe there won't be any trial tomorrow after all."

Alone in the jail, Grady wondered why the sheriff was so anxious to keep the trouble between cowmen and nesters alive. He didn't understand that. He had heard enough, however, to realize his own position thoroughly. He wished the sheriff hadn't stopped talking so soon. Then he'd know what to expect. Of one thing he felt sure: he'd get no chance to talk if Will Rowden had his way.

The sheriff was gone about an hour. When he returned, Grady heard a key rattle in the lock. "Come on out, Scott, I want to talk to you," he began. "Things look bad. I thought the nesters had gone home but they simply went back to Scanlon's. They're in a bad mood and it wouldn't surprise me if they came back here for you."

Grady glanced at the heavy log walls. "This is a sturdy building. Two determined men shouldn't have much trouble standing off a mob here."

Rowden shrugged. "Who do you think elected me to office? Not the cowmen. They're outnumbered three to one now. Do you think I'd be foolish enough to shoot into a crowd of my friends?"

"How about August Lehman? You promised him I'd get a fair trial."

"Oh, sure." Rowden grinned at Toomey. "But I can't help it if a mob breaks in. And what could he do?"

"I see." Grady's lips tightened. There was no reason to dissemble now. The cards were down. "That must have been what Toomey thought when he let a mob murder Tom Williams."

Toomey swore and his lashing fist drew blood. Grady staggered back, caught two more smashing blows to the face that rocked him against the wall. Then he struck back. The first swing missed but the second caught the deputy flush on the chin, drove him off. That was when Toomey jerked out his gun. Rowden's weapon was drawn, too. He threatened Grady with it, forced him back, at the same time shouting at Toomey, "No, Frank—no! I want no shooting here."

Toomey didn't fire. Instead he used his gun as a club. The first blow dazed Grady, slit his scalp so the blood gushed down his face. He tried to brace himself against the wall. Toomey hammered at him until he slid unconscious to the floor. Then Rowden pulled Frank off.

"You want to kill him?"

"He knows too much. Why'd you stop me?"

"I told you, Lehman wouldn't stand for it. My way's best and our skirts will be clear."

"Yeah. But suppose something goes wrong?"

Rowden shoved his deputy toward the door. "Nothing can go wrong. I've got it all planned. He'll be dead by morning. Now fetch me a pail of water."

The sheriff examined the unconscious prisoner while his aide brought water. "He's hurt plenty" was the verdict. "Maybe you took the starch out of him. If you did he won't run and that's what I want."

"I put the fear of God in him," growled Toomey. "He'll run when the time comes."

"Some of the boys are waiting at Scanlon's. Go get 'em. They know what to do. I want Scott to hear a mob."

"I suggested that myself and you told me you didn't want it," Toomey protested.

Rowden showed his exasperation. "Quit trying to second-guess me, Frank, and do as you're told," he ordered. "You wanted the real thing. This is just a scene I'm staging to convince Scott he hasn't got a chance." He glanced down to make sure the prisoner was still unconscious, then added softly, "It's not the mob he needs to fear but he won't know that. Now get going."

When Grady awoke he was lying in a puddle of water and the sheriff stood over him with an empty bucket. His head throbbed and his vision was foggy. It took a moment to clear. Even then he didn't move. He peered cautiously around the room. "Where's Toomey?" he asked.

"I chased him out of here. How do you feel?"

"Like a mule had just kicked the top of my head off. When's he coming back?"

The sheriff took a chair across the room and waited. "I hope he doesn't come back. If he does he'll probably have friends with him. That would be bad. I'd rather not be responsible for you tonight. Lehman's going to blame me if they hang you, but I'll even risk that before I'll shoot into my own friends. I don't see why I should risk my life for a Pecos cowboy who comes in here on the prod, causing me trouble."

Grady felt better. His head still throbbed but he could think more clearly now. "You keep reminding me of that," he said. "What's up your sleeve?"

"I figured you were smart." The sheriff leaned forward, elbows on knees. He lowered his voice cautiously. "If you escaped it'd save me a lot of trouble. Pete Falkner wouldn't like it; neither would Toomey nor a bunch of these nesters who'd like to give you a necktie party before you had time to talk. Lehman would have his feathers ruffled, too, but that's better than having trouble with my friends over you, and nobody could pin anything on me."

"Is this an offer?"

The sheriff held up his hand. "Listen!"

From outside came the mutter of angry voices. "He knows too much," said one.

"But der sheriff von't stand for it," came the reply.

"Und Lehman's promised him a fair trial."

"Ach, Lehman vags his tongue too much. I'm tired of listening." This was said in the same high whine that Grady remembered. It belonged to the man called Kurt. "Vat does it cost Lehman to talk?" the whine continued. "He ain't mixed up in dis. He vasn't mit us ven Villiams vas killed."

For once the sheriff dropped his impassive mask. He forgot Grady, and his lip twisted angrily.

He heard that too, Grady thought. This man Kurt has convicted himself. Now the sheriff can't afford to let me go—he blamed himself for his predicament—I was on the right track. Now I know three of the men who killed Tom, but the knowledge isn't likely to do me much good. I should have stayed out of that gunfight. They didn't suspect me until then.

But what could I do? he wondered. They were fools, sure, but they were Forked W riders, here because of Tom. And it was two against forty.

For a time the crowd lingered outside, discussed the situation loudly. Except for Kurt's high whine, Grady couldn't distinguish the voices. At one time the wrangling grew so heated he thought they were going to attack the jail at once. The sheriff seemed to think so too, for he grew uneasy. Silently he crossed the room to double-bar the door.

"I thought you were going to let them take me," Grady challenged.

Rowden shrugged. "I don't want to be here when it happens. I'm too smart for that."

For half an hour the mob argued outside the jail. There was no doubt about their purpose, but someone—Grady thought it was Toomey, from the voice—counseled patience, urged them to come back later after the sheriff was gone. It would be simpler that way. "Don't worry, Scott will still be there when we come back. He can't get away." That seemed to convince them. They finally moved off.

There was a false note in all this, Grady thought. If they want me, why don't they come on, instead of doing so much talking about it? Something's wrong here if I could just figure it out.

He wished his head would quit throbbing. It was hard for him to think clearly.

"Well, how about it?" Rowden demanded after the night had grown quiet again. "Want a chance to get out of here?"

"I've been figuring on it, of course. It strikes me you're not going to be very popular around here either way. What happens when your friends find out you let me escape?"

Grinning, the sheriff picked up the poker from under the stove, crossed to the cell door and used it to batter the lock. The latch, on the outside of the door, was ponderous but not particularly well-made. At the fifth blow it yielded. Rowden stepped back, surveyed the scene through shrewd eyes. "See? You have friends, cowmen probably. I'm too smart to be mixed up in this."

"What's your game, Rowden?" Grady asked. "First you pin this killing on me. Now you're helping me escape. I don't get it."

"I reckoned you understood." The sheriff looked him over slowly. "You know too much. If it wasn't for Lehman I'd let the boys hang you, but that damn Dutchman bothers me. It's simpler this way."

"I might come back."

Rowden shook his head. "You're too smart for that. The cowmen will be gunning for you when they hear you killed the Kid and every nester in the valley is your enemy now, too, not to mention a few others— quick men like Pete Falkner. No, I give you credit for having sense enough to keep going, once you're on your way."

"I'll need a horse. Mine's in the barn at the wagon yard."

"You'll have something to ride. You could take mine. I could leave him for you, some place."

Grady shook his head. "My own horse will travel faster and farther than anything I've seen around here and when I leave I'll be in a hurry."

The sheriff refused the suggestion. "Not practical. Suppose someone saw me at the wagon barn. But I'll get you a good animal. I don't want you caught either. After tonight I wouldn't want you brought back here to talk."

They perfected their arrangements briefly. Rowden would procure the best horse he could find and leave it tethered to the hitch rail at the side of Lehman's Store. They discussed this point. Grady wanted the horse left closer. Rowden argued that if seen near the jail the horse would excite suspicion. The merchant had a hitch rail on two sides of his building. "That's the safest place," the sheriff insisted. "You won't have any trouble finding it and if I use the side rail you can keep off the main street."

They reviewed the plan before parting. The broken cell lock cleared the sheriff. He explained that the outer door to his office always was left unlocked. Grady was to wait thirty minutes before walking out. That would give Rowden time to find a horse and leave it at the appointed place. Until then, he warned, it was safer for Grady to remain right where he was. "That will give me time to scout around, too," he added. "If I see anything wrong I'll come back to warn you."

"How about a gun?" Grady demanded. "Suppose I run into trouble?"

The sheriff shook his head. "No weapons. I'm giving you a chance but I won't go that far. You might even try to use one on me."

Chapter 11 ESCAPE

Jim Evans didn't know the man who helped him escape from the gunfight at Scanlon's. He expected the fellow to come along and was surprised to find himself alone outside. He loosed two horses at the rail. Even after he mounted he waited an uneasy moment, hoping his unseen friend would come. Then he heard the confusion at the door behind him when the nesters discovered he was gone. Time was up. He fired back blindly to delay pursuit as he put the spurs to his horse.

The shots had awakened the town. At the Reid House the Snake on a Rock outfit had poured out, six guns ready. Soames himself was in the street when Evans rode up and said, "They got the Kid with their first shot." He explained what had happened. "How I got out I don't rightly know, except it was dark and I ran into a friend who led me to the back door just about the time I thought I was goin' to be bedded down for keeps."

Letitia Reid joined the audience which circled him. "Don't you know who that was?" she asked.

"All I know, he said he used to ride for the Forked W. I waited for him outside long as I could but he never showed up."

Letty thought she knew the answer. She hadn't seen Grady since their interview earlier in the day, when he'd denied being here on Ranger business. She remained unconvinced. Everything fitted too well: the marks of a fighting man, yet lacking the cat-eyed caution of a fugitive; Ranger habits, yet he took pains to hide the typical equipment which might identify him. It surprised her how well she could call back the look of Grady Scott: lean, bronzed, hard, like a trigger spring filed thin and with the same fine balance. So he once rode for the Forked W. She wished she'd known that before Ma left. It was too late to question her. Where was he now? Not here, certainly. She could account for the other cowmen. Who else could it have been? Her conviction grew as she thought of it. She didn't understand his purpose here, nor his need for secrecy but she knew she trusted Grady Scott. Whatever his reason for remaining unknown, she wouldn't give him away. She kept her thoughts to herself.

John Soames's estimate of Grady expanded. He already had justified Curly's confidence in him. Soames was sure he knew what had happened but he couldn't say anything without risking Grady's secret. He was worried. There was danger that the nesters might push the fight further, come here after Evans. He couldn't permit that but he had only five men here, six counting Evans. Clee was in town too. He wanted her out of this, and he knew her too well even to suggest that she leave alone. It went against his stubborn grain to retreat but to stay longer was to invite a fight. This wasn't the time for it. He left orders to saddle the horses and went inside to waken his daughter.

Evans hadn't dismounted. It was Letty who discovered how stiffly he sat his saddle.

"You're hurt!" she exclaimed. "One of you boys help him inside and I'll see what I can do."

The wound was less serious than she had feared. A single shotgun slug had caught him in the shoulder. It had bled freely. When she cut away his shirt the bleeding started afresh. While Hallelujah held the lamp, Letty probed for the slug with a kitchen knife.

"You were lucky," she said when she finally dug it out. "If it had been a bullet you'd have a broken shoulder."

"Luckier than you know." Evans stared at the pellet in her hand. "That's buckshot. If I'd caught a full load of it I'd have a hole there that it'd take a hat to plug."

Letty made a pad from a clean dish towel, soaked it in liniment, then strapped his shoulder tight to hold the bandage in place. "That should last you till you reach the Lazy B," she decided.

Soames's alarm showed in the quick clatter of his boots on the stairs. Clee was gone! He showed Letty the note she'd left.

"What's there to worry about? She says here you wanted her to go home so she's decided to go."

"In the middle of the night? Alone?"

"Oh, she'll be safe enough. It's been a long time since we've had any Indian trouble. The Rangers ended that. Who else would bother a girl? After all, that's what you tried to persuade her to do last night."

"You don't know Clee." Her father remained uneasy. "'T ain't like her to give in this way."

Often he'd chuckled over her willfulness. "She's stubborn as her daddy," he would say, with secret pride. Her absence perplexed him. "'T ain't like her," he kept repeating. It hurried his departure. Half an hour after the fight at Scanlon's the Snake on a Rock outfit rode out, with Jim Evans in their midst.

"I hate leaving you here, Letty." Soames hesitated at the last.

"Nonsense. I'm glad to be rid of you. If you had a fight here my hotel would be worse wrecked than Scanlon's Saloon. Besides, I get along all right with the nesters."

It was past midnight. Most of the town had gone to bed before the fight, but now lights were burning in every window. She could hear men hurrying toward Scanlon's and as soon as Soames rode away she followed them. These were the sober, thoughtful citizens, men who followed August Lehman's lead rather than the sheriff's. She met a group of them in front of the general store, questioned them anxiously for word of Grady. What she heard worried her. The sheriff's story had found quick acceptance. The Kid from the Forked W had been killed by a professional gunman, a Pecos cowboy named Grady Scott. These men were thoroughly aroused—there were too many gunmen around, troublemakers—and they were grateful for the sheriff's prompt action. If he hadn't caught Scott and solved the shooting promptly, it might have led to further trouble. Undoubtedly something like that had been planned. It was all part of a scheme to provoke bloodshed between homesteaders and ranchers. She heard talk even of lynching.

"If August Lehman hadn't interfered, that fellow would be strung up by now, and a good job, too."

"I'm agin mobs but this time I'd have yanked the rope myself as a lesson to these lead throwers."

"Lehman's right though. Wait till morning and give Scott a trial. He'll be hanged soon enough."

Letty listened uneasily. First, she decided, she must see Grady Scott, make him understand the temper of the nesters. If he was a Ranger it was time for him to say so. He must be persuaded to talk before it was too late. Once August Lehman understood the situation, his influence would make itself felt. The sober citizens would rally behind him.

Getting into the jail might present difficulties but she thought she knew the answer for this. She returned to her own kitchen and packed a basket of lunch. He's my boarder, she assured herself. He pays me for victuals and he'll get them. I'd like to see anybody stop me.

Before leaving, she went upstairs, found her father's six shooter in a bureau drawer. She hesitated over this step, but finally wrapped the gun in a napkin and tucked it under the food.

As soon as the sheriff left, Grady searched his office for a weapon. He found his own cartridge belts and Bowie knife and strapped them on. The holsters were empty. He ransacked the place again before giving up the search. Rowden had told him to wait half an hour. He reckoned that half this time must have passed. As long as he'd been busy he hadn't minded the wait. Now it grew tedious. He tried the outer door cautiously and found it unlocked as promised. He was tempted to leave at once but realized the folly of roaming the town, even in the dark, until a horse was waiting. The floor was twenty-eight planks wide. He counted them as he walked and tried to devise a way to reckon the passing minutes. Twice around the room slowly, he figured, should take a minute. After three circles he gave this up. His head still bothered him—it throbbed when he tried walking, though the bleeding had stopped.

Someone knocked at the door. He rose, silent; his hand reached for the Bowie knife as he retreated softly to the cell.

The knock was repeated. He wished fervently that he'd thought to blow out the lamp. In the dark he'd have a better chance. But it was too late now—its glow must have been seen.

The latch clicked and the door opened cautiously. From his refuge in the cell, he was watching through a crack between the planks when Letty entered.

She closed the door behind her and leaned against it. His first relief at seeing her turned to annoyance. She might prove a complication in his escape and he decided to remain hidden, hoping she might go away. Her eyes widened, she looked frightened, and she braced herself against the wall. He realized she was staring at the broken lock on the cell door. Then he called her name.

She was even more concerned when he stepped out. Blood had matted his hair and caked one side of his face. "What have they done to you?"

"I'm all right," he assured her. "You shouldn't have come here."

She pointed at the broken lock. "When I saw that I thought they'd taken you away."

"Who?"

"The mob. They've been talking of it."

He nodded grimly. "You haven't told me why you're here."

"I had to see you. I came as quickly as I could when I heard what had happened. You must tell them who you are and why you're here. Once they learn you're a Ranger, it will be different."

"If I told them that I wouldn't last two minutes." His voice turned harsh. "The men who killed Tom wouldn't lose any time shooting me. Besides, I'm not a Ranger."

"Then it wasn't Tom Williams' death that brought you here?" Her eyes showed her bewilderment.

He decided he'd have to tell her at least a part of the truth. What was there to lose, since he'd already betrayed himself to the sheriff's crowd? "Tom was my friend. I'm here to find who killed him. You're right about that. Yes, and I was a Ranger, too, until I heard about Tom. I quit the Frontier Battalion to come here. You were almost right all the time. So right you had me worried."

She was smiling now. "And you rode for the Forked W once, too, didn't you?"

"How'd you find out all this?" Her knowledge bewildered him.

"When Jim Evans told what happened I knew it was you who got him out of Scanlon's."

"No wonder I'm in trouble. I thought I was playing it smart and you were a jump ahead of me all the time. By the looks of things you weren't the only one either."

"No one else knows who you are. I'm sure of that," she assured him hastily. "But you've got to get out of here, and quick. I'll help you. Look, I've brought you my father's six shooter." She pulled it from the basket and, while unwrapping it, told him of the threats she'd heard and his danger here.

It was the gun which convinced him. Until then he hadn't known how to place her. He told her briefly of the sheriff's offer and his plan of escape. "I'm due to start moving in another ten minutes."

She listened with growing worry. "I don't like it. Will Rowden was at Scanlon's when the Kid was murdered, wasn't he? Did he make a move to stop it? It strikes me he's suddenly mighty worried over bloodshed."

Grady felt gingerly of his battered head. "He held a gun on me while Toomey did this," he reminded her. "That didn't seem to bother him.

No, he's not worried about a little bloodshed. I haven't been able to figure him out, but that's not it."

"From what you say, the only thing that's holding him back is fear of August Lehman," Letty exclaimed. "Do you think he'll let you get away to tell this story? That doesn't make sense. No, he's letting you out of here so you can die someplace else where they can't pin the crime on him." She grasped him by both arms, peered up at him anxiously, and he saw the trouble in her eyes. "What happens to prisoners when they're caught escaping? What happens to you tonight if you step into a trap? It looks mighty convenient for Will Rowden. He'd have nothing more to worry about, no troublesome explanations to make to Mr. Lehman. The prisoner was killed trying to escape, that's all. And you—you won't be able to talk—ever. Use your head, Grady! That's bound to be the explanation."

He nodded slowly. For the first time the questions which had bothered him fitted into a sensible pattern. "So what do I do?" he asked slowly. "Sit here like a rat in a trap and wait for their next move?"

"No!" She shook his arm fiercely. "You wait here just long enough for me to slip out and see what's going on. If it's a trap they'll probably bait it with the horse. I'll find a way out if you'll just wait here for me."

"I can't let you do that. You stay out of this. What if somebody mistook you for me?"

She laughed. "Small chance. There's fully a foot and fifty or sixty pounds difference and I wear petticoats—remember? Be sensible. No one's going to harm a girl. And I'll be careful."

He argued but she wrung a promise from him to wait ten minutes. "If you're not back by then I'll know something's happened. Then I'm coming after you," he promised grimly.

They blew out the lamp so the door would be in darkness as she slipped out. He could follow her movements all the way to the street as he watched. That worried him. The night was losing its early blackness and stars were showing through the clouds. He examined the pistol she'd brought him, emptied its cartridges into his palm and snapped the trigger several times to get the feel of its action. Then he reloaded it carefully, soothed it into his holster. He didn't wait inside—he was too uneasy for that. Instead, he lurked beside the jail and discovered the pump there. There was a little water in the bucket under the spout. He sopped this up in his handkerchief and placed it over his torn scalp. By pressing his hat over this he had a makeshift bandage. He was tempted to draw more water but didn't dare risk the sound of the pump. He felt better, the damp was cool to his throbbing head, and the weight of the gun in his holster felt good too.

In spite of his vigilance Letty almost reached the jail again before he saw her. She had crept back another way, and cautiously. That warned him even before she spoke.

"It's a trap all right," she whispered. "There are several men watching this place."

"Did they see you?"

"I ran into Heinrich Unger before I'd gone a block. He's hiding at the back of Scanlon's Saloon, but when he saw who I was he just tipped his hat and let me pass."

"Anyone else?"

"Frank Toomey is on the other side but I saw him first. He's guarding the way up the back street. I went around the rear of Lehman's Store until I found the horse left there for you. Now I understand their trap. The horse is tied right across from Frank Toomey's house. Two or three men waiting there in the dark could blow anyone to bits before he reached the animal. I know it. I'm sure they're there, too, although naturally I didn't walk past that way."

"It's you I'm worried about now," he told her. "How am I going to get you out of this?"

"We're going out together, the way I came back. I've thought it all out," Letty replied. "I know where these guards are and can lead you around them."

"Oh, no, we're not. I'll draw lead if they see me. These nesters use scatter-guns—anyone near me would get hurt."

"They won't see us. Not the way I'm going."

He still didn't like the idea and refused until, suddenly quite helpless, she exclaimed: "But you can't leave me here! How will I ever get out without you?"

"Look—I'll get you clear of this place before we separate," he promised. In the dark he couldn't see her triumphant smile.

She led the way at first. Her silence surprised him. She had slipped off her shoes and moved as softly as a wraith. They crept a hundred yards. The guards Letty had seen were far to their rear when, feeling safe now, they rose to their feet and started to circle the few scattered buildings that reached this far from the town. They were challenged unexpectedly by a man lurking in the shadow of a shed.

"Stop! Who is it? Vot you doing here?"

Grady recognized the high-pitched voice. He'd heard it earlier that night. His fingers gripped his six shooter but Letty clutched his wrist.

"I'm Letitia Reid, Mr. Pakebusch. Don't you recognize me?"

"Vot you doing here und at dis time of night, Fräulein Reid?"

"Why, I've been over to Mrs. Kramer's," she answered readily. "She's taken sick, you know, and one of the boys came for me."

When the guard moved forward she warned Grady with another squeeze of his wrist before stepping forward to meet him.

"Who's dot mit you?"

"I told you—one of the Kramer boys." To the waiting Grady her laugh sounded carefree. "What on earth are you doing around here at this hour, Mr. Pakebusch? My goodness, if anything goes wrong tonight I'll know who to blame."

"Notting vill go wrong," the guard assured her, but his manner lost some of its confidence at her questioning. "Go on home, Fräulein. It's better you be in bed."

"Tell me the name of that man," Grady demanded, once they were safely past. "You called him Pakebusch. Was it Kurt Pakebusch?"

"Yes. How did you know?"

"Not an easy voice to forget and I'd heard it before."

They were within sight of the hotel when they left Pakebusch. Letty volunteered to get Grady's horse from the barn at the wagon yard. "No one will suspect me even if I'm seen," she urged.

"They will if it's my horse. Leave that to me."

"I have a horse of my own stabled back of the hotel. We can get there without much trouble."

He gripped her by the arm. "You've already been seen a couple of times tonight. If your horse is missing tomorrow, they'll know it was you who helped me."

"Just guesses. What can they prove?"

"Guesses are enough for this outfit. I've learned that. No, I don't want you mixed up in this—not any more than you are. Besides, I want to straddle my own horse when I ride out of here. I know what he can do and they may be on my tail."

"I've gone too far to back out now." She was stubborn. "How will you manage it?"

"Look, Letty—" it was the first time he'd used her name and she liked the sound of it—"scouting has been my job for a long time. This won't be hard, but I'll move faster and quieter alone.

"There's one more thing you can do for me, though. I hate to ask it but there's no one else I can trust. If something should happen to me before I reach the Forked W, I want you to give Curly Stark three names. Don't tell anyone else. It's dangerous for you even to know them. Understand?"

"Yes."

"They are Frank Toomey, Heinrich Unger and the man we just passed, Kurt Pakebusch."

"And that means they were all in on the killing of Tom Williams. Is that it?"

He hesitated. "Sometimes you're too smart for your own good," he growled. "I might have known you'd guess the answer. Yes, that's right, but remember it's dangerous to know too much in Apache. Don't tell this to anyone but Curly."

He waited until he thought she'd entered the hotel. She watched from the porch shadows as he slipped across the street. That puzzled her. He wasn't headed for the wagon yard.

There was one more thing Grady wanted to know. When Letty told him the sheriff had staked out the horse directly in front of Toomey's dwelling he was as sure as she that this was an ambush. He wanted, if possible, to learn the names of the men who awaited him there in the dark. Tom Williams' murderers had more reason than anyone else for silencing him. He had already discovered two of them that night and both were close friends of Toomey's.

He felt reasonably safe from the guards who had circled the jail. It lay on the other side of the main street. He felt he knew Rowden's plan perfectly now. Those men had been posted to bar his escape in any other direction. Once safely past them he had nothing to fear but the trap itself. He hugged the shadows, moved silently until, from a corner, he could peer across at Lehman's Store and see the horse tied there. He marked the house across the street, a narrow adobe building, and stared a long time at its black windows, but could see nothing. Then he turned back. About fifty yards to the rear was a live oak thicket. He circled this, keeping it between him and the dark windows. Even before he reached the cover he heard the stamping of horses there. He smiled grimly to himself. He was right: he had guessed that men baiting a trap would leave a line of escape open for emergencies. These weren't nesters either. Farmers generally traveled afoot but men used to the plains were lost without a horse. He renewed his caution. He didn't expect a guard here but he was taking no chances.

Three animals were tethered there. It was too dark to identify them except that one was a large dun. At Grady's approach it snorted and lunged against its tie rope. Grady blended with the shadows, stood motionless, waiting for the animal's fear to quiet. That dun perplexed him. It sent his thoughts racing to the girl he'd seen riding just such an animal a few hours before. Duns weren't too uncommon but an animal of these handsome proportions was rare. He recalled how Clee Soames had looked riding into Apache beside her father. He'd heard from Letty of the Snake on a Rock outfit's departure. She couldn't be here; he decided the horse must have been stolen.

There was nothing by which to distinguish the other two animals. He couldn't even see their brands here. He approached one horse cautiously, felt of the saddle. There might be a rifle here he could use. The scabbard was empty but he made another discovery—the stirrups were covered with tapaderos, wedge-shaped leather guards. "A brush saddle," Grady exulted. "This rider's a long way off his range. I'll recognize it again wherever I see it." He had never seen tapaderos worn in this section; that was equipment for riders in the brush country far to the south.

The other saddles had no such marks of easy distinction. With his Bowie knife he marked one of them. Back of the cantle where it wasn't too noticeable, he sliced a strip of leather about two inches long and, as proof against error, notched the scar at one corner. I'll be able to tell this one again, too, he told himself. He didn't bother about the third one— that dun horse was too easily remembered.

He didn't consider riding one of these animals; he was too bent on identifying the men who had planned this ambush. It wasn't just tonight's score he had to settle with them although that played its part. The men who had the most to hide were those intent on silencing him.

He turned toward the wagon yard. He was greatly attached to his own horse but there was more than that to his determination to get him. Rangers chose their horses for speed and durability. Nesters often scoffed at the Ranger habit of insisting on corn for their mounts—they didn't understand it was a matter of stamina. He'd proved on many an Indian campaign how they could outstrip broncs which had nothing but grass in their bellies. He approached the wagon yard with the same stealth he'd stalked the ambush, remembering the guards around the jail. If I was doing it I'd have a man posted here, he thought. It was a stake-and-rail corral. He climbed it at the back. When he dropped softly to the ground half a dozen horses spooked, clattered to the far end of the enclosure. Standing motionless in the shadow until they turned quiet, he strained his eyes toward the dark blur of the barn but could see no one there. Then he began his slow approach, circling in the cover of the fence on hands and knees. When he reached the barn he stood up. The six gun was loose in his holster. He tried it before he peered around the door. There was a man on watch. Grady smelled his tobacco before looking in and seeing the cigarette's glow. His confidence grew. That fellow wouldn't last long in Indian country, he thought. There was a runway through the barn from corral to street, and the guard at the far end watched toward the town.

Grady was one of the shadows as he slid in silently. He wanted his horse saddled before he risked surprising the guard. If anything went wrong he must be ready. The stall was located without difficulty. Here the risk was greatest. A nicker of recognition could upset everything.

"Ranger," he whispered. "Ranger." His hand slid over the sleek coat. As the horse turned, Grady grasped him by the nostrils, held him so to prevent a sound, all the while whispering the horse's name. The saddle was easy to locate on the top slat of the stall, the bridle draped over its horn. With quick fingers he adjusted the equipment. Then with Ranger ready Grady left him there and went to stalk the guard.

It was a horse in a near-by stall which gave him away. The animal neighed as he slipped past. The guard in the doorway took alarm; his gun was out as he turned. Grady, still a dozen feet away, hoped to avoid a shot that would arouse the town. He lunged forward. His opponent, taken off guard, was leaping back as he fired. The light was bad. The bullet whipped off Grady's hat and thudded into the rafters above. The time for caution had ended. Grady's six gun was flashing as it left the holster. He saw his antagonist spin and knew he had a hit. But the man didn't fall. Instead, he started running.

Grady poised his weapon. Not like that, he decided; I don't even know him. He holstered his gun, stooped and picked up a revolver from the ground. The grip was wet. I'll know him next time—he'll be wearing a bandage on his hand.

Grady mounted Ranger quickly. Already he could hear horses in the distance as he galloped out from the town.

Chapter 12   A NIGHT ON THE TRAIL

CLEE's jaw hurt. She felt of it gingerly. She hadn't been aware of this before. In her flight from Rowden she had moved blindly, too dazed by inner torment to be aware of physical pain. Oddly, it was the memory of their happy meetings that cut deepest—the times she had come gladly into his arms. The final sordid hour of lost illusions left no scar, only a physical revulsion so strong it had ended in nausea. The first keen edge of her anguish had been left behind under the oaks with her sickness and her tears. Her strength was spent. She moved wearily through a fog of dull misery. The throb of this new pain was something real; she could focus her attention on it.

She found a block of matches in the dark and broke one off. Her movements still vague, she fumbled over the striking of it. She sputtered from the acrid bite of sulphur fumes and her cough blew out the match. She lighted another and this time did not bungle. She held the match at arm's length until its yellow cloud lost its pungency. Then she lighted the lamp and studied her swollen face in the mirror. Her cheek was beginning to turn blue and her mouth was puffed from Rowden's blows. She still could taste blood where her lips had been bruised against her teeth.

These physical marks of her experience dismayed her. Her father would want an explanation. He would kill Rowden if he knew what had happened. For a fleeting instant she believed that was what she wanted. The notion fitted her anger. But the thought of sharing her humiliation with others was repugnant. She shook her head. No one must know. This was something she must hug to herself, secretly.

She stared again at her battered features, her uneasiness growing. How could she hide them? Even if she slipped unnoticed from the town there was the long ride home with her father and the Snake on a Rock riders. She couldn't face that. She couldn't stay here either. Her appearance gave point to the hurt-animal instinct to steal away and hide.

Once at the ranch she would be safe from prying eyes. She could evade her father at home, perhaps pretend illness for a few days until the bruises were gone. If only she could slip away now. The more she thought of it the more her determination grew. She forgot her weariness. It wouldn't be too difficult. Last night when her father expected trouble he had tried to persuade her to turn back. She seized on that as a pretext and framed the words of her excuse as she slipped downstairs for a pen and paper.

"You were right," she wrote her father. "If there's trouble here I'll just be in the way. I'm going home."

She left the letter in her room where they'd be sure to find it. Otherwise her absence would cause concern.

The dun mare was another problem. The hand at the wagon yard saw her coming and recognized her, although she was careful to keep to the shadows, away from his bobbing lantern. His surprise was obvious. "Diss iss no time to start out," he protested.

"Why not?" She'd thought out her answer. "It'll be cooler this way. I'll have most of the ride behind me before sunup."

His hostility toward ranch people extended to this girl. He thought of her as arrogant and grumbled to himself as he stalked to the corral to seek out her horse. She was tempted to send him back for another animal when he led in her mare. Her pride in it was gone—it was too much a reminder of Will Rowden. But she could think of no excuse for making the exchange and the man was surly. Most of all she wanted to slip away quietly. But I'll never ride her again—not after tonight, she thought as she swung into the saddle and headed into the night.

Once the town was left behind, her urgency left her. She rode easily, slouched in the saddle, relaxed by the horse's familiar gait. By dawn the town would be miles behind. There was little likelihood that she would meet anyone after that. The trail was familiar, and she found its solitude friendly.

Once she heard a flurry of shots behind her, muffled by distance. She wasn't disturbed by the sounds—they were too far away. She didn't change her gait. There were long miles ahead.

Not long after that she heard men on the trail and pulled out while they passed. They were a strong party and rode carelessly. She could hear their talk and, recognizing her father's voice among them, was thankful for the darkness that hid her. "We'll hold a powwow when we reach the Lazy B," she heard him say. That relieved her, too. She'd first thought he'd found her note and had come searching for her. If he stopped at the Blakes, she'd still reach home unseen.

She was six or eight miles farther along when she heard another horse behind her, the rhythmic, three-cornered sound that a canter makes, the flutter of hoofs still only a whisper. The springy turf of the valley smothered noise. The rider couldn't be far behind. She straightened in her saddle, checked an impulse to spur ahead. If she could hear him, he certainly would hear her if she started to gallop. It would be far wiser to let him ride past.

The mare had heard the sound, too. She pricked up her ears and pranced a few steps as they turned off the trail. Clee held her to a walk for quiet, then dismounted when she judged the distance was safe. The unseen horseman was almost abreast of her now. He hadn't guessed her presence for there'd been no change in his steady gait. She strained her eyes into the blackness but could see nothing.

The mare's whinny of recognition, sounding doubly loud against the night's stillness, caught her by surprise. She jumped and wrenched at the reins in vexation, but the damage had been done. Off on the trail the sound of hoof beats had died.

She half expected a friendly hail but none came. That relieved her at first. She didn't want to see anyone. But when the silence persisted she grew uneasy. She held her breath in the effort to listen, but could hear nothing but the faint pounding of her own pulse. She decided to remount, thankful that she'd ridden the dun mare after all. Few horses could match her for fleetness or endurance. In an emergency she could escape into the night. She moved cautiously but the saddle creaked under her weight. To her it sounded loud.

"Don't move!" The warning voice came from behind her. "I couldn't miss at this distance."

She was too surprised to utter a sound.

"What is this—a trap? Who are you waiting for?"

She found her tongue at last. "You're the one who's making the threat. I just moved off the trail to let you pass."

"Good God, it's a woman! Excuse me, ma'am. I must have given you a right smart scare."

She remembered his voice. Her first surprise over, she was no longer afraid. "You're the man who came through my bedroom to drop out the window."

"I didn't know who you were and I wasn't expecting to bump into a girl on this trail," he explained. "Leastways not in the dead of night. I remember your horse now, but it threw me off at first. When I circled around to investigate that whinny, that dun color showed up right sharp against the night and I thought I'd been herded into a trap. One of the men trailing me rides a horse like that."

She knew he meant Will Rowden and his caution was obvious. Another time, knowledge that he was a fugitive might have disturbed her. Not tonight—she was in flight too. "I know that horse," she said. "The sheriff rides it."

"Thanks. That's something I wanted to know. What are you doing out here?"

"It's cooler riding at night." She repeated the excuse she'd used at the wagon yard.

"I don't like it."

"What does it matter? I'm not your worry." She was nettled by his objection. "Just go on your way. I'll be all right."

He was standing close. She could see his hand when he raised it. "It's not as simple as that. Listen!"

From the back trail came the tattoo of more hoofbeats, confused this time. There were several riders in the party. "I'm being followed. This trail's not a healthy place tonight."

She remembered his precautions back at the Reid House. "If those are ranchers they're friends of mine," she reminded him.

"They're not ranchers, ma'am. I'm trying to think what's best to do with you."

"That's easy. You're wasting time here. Just forget about me and go on your way."

He ignored the interruption. "If I take you with me I'm apt to head you straight into trouble, but if we part company here there's danger they might pick up your trail instead of mine."

"That might help you. When they discovered they were following me——"

"Too risky. This outfit's likely to shoot first and ask questions later. No, that won't do. We'll ride together a spell until I figure things out." He led the way back to the trail where his horse waited, reins dangling.

When Grady left Apache he'd heard excited shouts and the clatter of horses behind him. The pursuit hadn't worried him until now. His horse was fresh and equal to the task; there were guns in his holsters again and he was headed into familiar country. Lazy B headquarters were only twenty-two miles ahead. There he'd find friends and a fresh horse, if he were pressed.

Apache was located near the lower end of the valley and about midway between the hills that hemmed it north and south. The lower or eastern end was spotted with nester fencing. To the west the hills gradually wedged it until they converged in the Scalp Creek Breaks, fifty miles beyond. From the Breaks almost to the town, the ranches still held their own. The valley floor lost its flatness as it stretched westward, began to roll, gently at first, gradually turning more rugged as it left the Apache River in its center until it reached the high boundary hills. North of the stream the Lazy B and the Forked W divided the range; everything south of it was Snake on a Rock country.

The fences had slowed him down at the start. Several times in the first dozen miles Ranger swerved to avoid crashing them in the dark. Finally Grady had circled away from the river and soon left the bothersome homesteads behind. As he rode he tried piecing together the information he'd gathered. He now knew three men who'd been present at Tom Williams' murder. The others, he felt sure, were members of the same gang. He would identify them. What worried him more was the purpose behind the sheriff's partially disclosed operations. This wasn't just a war between cowman and nester—August Lehman's stand against lawlessness had convinced him of that. He knew it was Rowden who kept the feud alive, but he couldn't be sure of the sheriff's purpose.

Sheriff Rowden was in pallid rage when he learned his prisoner had evaded the ambush. He grasped what had happened when he heard the shooting at the wagon yard and forgot himself for a few blasphemous moments before the need for action cooled him. It was more essential than ever that Grady Scott be silenced. He was thinking of that, planning the pursuit as he rounded up his forces. There'd be no unwieldy mob for this job, only trusted men who'd follow orders and keep their mouths shut. August Lehman need not know what happened.

Heinrich Unger and Kurt Pakebusch would do to trail Scott. Adolph Blucher, who'd received a bullet through his hand at the wagon yard, should ride with them to add strength to the party. It didn't bother him that none of these men was a well-seasoned fighter. He could count on them to follow orders.

"Just stick on his trail but don't press him," he said. "I don't want him riding too fast. The Lazy B is the nearest ranch. He'll head for it. Your job is to keep him moving and see that he doesn't turn back."

With the sheriff rode Frank Toomey and Pete Falkner. These were men of a different stamp, dependable when it came to burning powder. The route to the Lazy B skirted the north bank of the river. By crossing to the south with this party and riding hard, he intended to head Grady off. There was a good ford at Horseshoe Bend, seventeen miles west, often used for cattle crossings since fences blocked the one at the town. There was no need for caution by this trail and no fences to slow them. This was Snake on a Rock country, too troublesome for nesters to risk.

Rowden set the pace, an easy lope that ate up distance, as fast as he dared make it without winding the horses. At times they slowed to a walk to give the animals a breather, but never for long. The last three miles they covered in a dead run and their animals were floundering with exhaustion when they reached the ford. There was good cover along the river; live oaks, elms and some pecans edged its course. Once away from the stream there was little but grass, rolling with the contour of the mounded plains as far as the tall hills beyond. It still was too dark to see this, but the sheriff had rehearsed the scene in his mind a dozen times during the long ride. If their prey skirted the river, the ambush was simple. But there was no set trail; the whole unfenced prairie was a horseman's highway. Grady wouldn't be too far from the stream, however, as it marked the shortest path. The Lazy B headquarters were on the banks of the Apache, just a few miles ahead.

Toomey was left among the trees. For Pete and himself, Rowden chose a shallow basin cupped below a gentle swell. They spaced out a quarter of a mile apart to wait. He liked the location. There was nothing to excite suspicion—their target would ride into range before he guessed their presence. The stars had paled out; false dawn had turned the night to gray. Soon, they'd be able to distinguish the back trail. They hobbled their horses out of sight in the dip and settled down to wait. Pete Falkner sprawled in the grass at the crest to watch.

Grady had puzzled over the soft pace set by the men behind him before he met Clee. Obviously they weren't trying to overtake him, yet each time he checked to listen he could hear them at his heels. He rode easily, spared his horse for the time his speed might be needed, and tried to figure out the meaning of their tactics. Maybe they're afraid of an ambush or else they're waiting until dawn to rush me, he thought.

But that answer didn't satisfy him. Even at this pace he'd reach the Blake ranch by daylight, and he could tell that the party behind him lacked the strength for a showdown there. His failure to find a satisfying answer made him uneasy. It's too much like they're riding herd on me, he decided.

With Clee to think of, too, his worry grew. He had the feeling he was doing just what his enemies expected and wanted. He felt that was bad strategy. It was time to make a change.

He told his companion what he had in mind. "We've got to get rid of the pack behind us while it's still dark," he said. "So far things have been too easy for them. Will you follow me?"

Clee was surprised to find herself so willing to accept his leadership. It's because Rowden's behind us, she thought. She didn't want to face him again.

"Go ahead," she agreed. "I'll keep up."

He spurred his horse and she kept pace. For ten minutes they rode at top speed. He wanted a safe lead before he changed his course.

He ended the burst as abruptly as he'd started it, turned sharply to the left and held his horse to a walk for quiet. "Silence is the thing now," he warned. Hoofs sounded behind them. Their gallop had been heard and their antagonists had speeded their pace, too. But the pursuers wouldn't quickly discover what had happened in the thunder of their own progress. He dismounted and showed Clee how to hold her horse by the nostrils to prevent an untoward whinny that would reveal their whereabouts. They listened. Off on the trail, horses pounded past. The waiting pair couldn't see them in the dark but, by the sound, they knew there were three in the party. After they were gone Grady led the way to the river. He couldn't tell exactly where he was but he knew the stream well. There were few fords but, except in freshets, it was not treacherous. The water lay in blue pools unexpectedly deep in spots, but its current was gentle.

"Here's where we cross. Does swimming bother you?"

"No, I've done it often. You lead the way."

They guided their horses into the water, then swam on the lower side of them, one hand on their saddle horns. Before remounting he bathed his head and again adjusted the soaked handkerchief under his hat. Before he had finished, they heard more horsemen, on their side of the river this time and riding hard.

"Hear those horses blowing? They've held that pace too long."

"Who is it?" Clee asked. "What does it mean?"

Grady's answer came slowly. He was figuring this out. "Maybe this is the answer to why the bunch on my trail took their time," he guessed. "If their job was just to keep me moving in the right direction . . . and this second outfit rode to cut me off . . . it might have been rough. Rowden's a smart man, Miss Soames."

"He must want you mighty bad."

"Yes, he does. And I reckon you're wondering why."

"I didn't ask."

"No. A body can't help wondering, though. He's sheriff here."

For a time only the creak of leather and the soft clump of hoofs on sod broke the night's silence. Finally he drew rein. "Here's where we part. I reckon you know your way."

"This is Snake on a Rock range."

"If there's any trouble ahead, it'll be on my trail, not yours," he assured her.

"I don't even know your name."

"Grady Scott."

She turned her horse for home, then stopped. "I didn't ask what the trouble was between you and the sheriff." The harshness of her voice surprised him. "It doesn't matter. If he's your enemy, I'm on your side. Watch out for dry gulches, Grady Scott."

"I will," he promised. "I know his way of fighting now."

It was broad daylight when he pulled up at the shallow crossing south of Lazy B headquarters. The place was astir. Soames and his riders had arrived during the night.

He headed for the corral to turn out his horse and Dave Blake came to meet him. Around the bunkhouse both Lazy B and Snake on a Rock hands were clustered. Their conversation died as the two men approached. As usual, the stranger's horse was appraised first. Then Jim Evans remembered where he'd last seen the newcomer. He slapped for leather, realized his gun belt was still hanging by his bunk and whirled for the door. "He's mine," he growled. "Don't anybody else go for him. This *hombre* goes on the tally sheet for the Kid."

Grady noticed the stir at the bunkhouse, didn't realize its meaning until Evans stepped out gripping his six shooter.

"Stand clear, Blake," Jim warned. "I've got an account to reckon up with this man. He was at Scanlon's last night when they got the Kid."

Dave leaped in front of his friend. "Hold it, Jim! This is Grady Scott.

He's an old Forked W hand, too, and on our side. Put up your gun."

Evans hesitated, his pistol still ready. Grady hadn't moved. Shooting would start at a flick of his hand, he realized.

"When I talked to you last night we spoke in whispers," he said now. "I told you then I used to ride for the Forked W. Remember?"

Evans grinned as he slid his six gun into its holster and stretched out his hand. "I still got a debt to pay but it's a different kind. What happened to you? I waited outside long as I could but you didn't show up."

"I had a job to do there, but if I'd been smart I'd have come along then." He told of the sheriff's attempt to fix the shooting on him and of his arrest and escape. "They were on my heels when I left," he added. "'T wouldn't surprise me any if a posse rode in here with a warrant for me before long."

"I wish they'd try it," Evans retorted. "Seems like I never meet any of that gang at even money. They never force a showdown unless the odds are long."

"Yes," Grady reminded him, "that's the way it was with Tom Williams."

For the others, breakfast was over but John Soames and the two Blakes sat with Grady as he ate, discussed the situation. Soames favored a showdown at once. "Last night we pulled out so Grady could work it his way. Look what happened. They're spoiling for a fight. Let's give it to 'em." He thumped the table with his fist when someone reminded him of the odds. "That's just the point! We've waited too long now. If I'd had my way we'd have run 'em out a year ago, before they got so strong. The longer we wait the stronger they'll get. I'm for runnin' every nester out of the valley."

"They're not all cut out of the same piece of wool," Merrill Blake reminded him. "There are good nesters and bad nesters. What we need is to get together with the good ones to stamp out this lawlessness. It's time for action all right. I'm with you on that. But smoking up every nester in the valley isn't the answer."

Grady told how August Lehman had stood beside Jim Evans and the Kid and tried to protect them. "He didn't have much chance but his craw was plumb full of sand. Merrill's right. There are good and bad folks down there, just as there are with us. Let me handle this my way. When the gang that killed Tom Williams is tracked down, I think things will straighten out in a hurry."

"I suppose you know just how to handle that?" Soames's voice was heavy with sarcasm. "I reckon you know who was in that gang and all the rest of the answers."

"That's why I'm here," Grady replied evenly. "I know three of them already and it won't be long until I find the others. When I do—" he shrugged—"Tom Williams was the best friend I ever had. I'll get them one by one."

From outside they heard a chorus of yells, followed by a single shot. They rushed to the door to see what was happening. This was no fight. The rannies were having sport with a poorly mounted stranger, whose horse seemed better fitted to a plow than a saddle. The rider was a half-grown, gawky boy who'd already lost his hat as he tried desperately to maneuver his clumsy charger away from his tormentors. There were three of them circling him. One had pulled a pistol and fired into the air as the boy tried again to break away. The quick-footed broncs could wheel and intercept him, no matter where he floundered. They were about a hundred yards away.

"Who is it? Anybody know him?" Grady asked.

"It looks like August Lehman's boy," said Merrill Blake.

One of the cowhands had loosed his rope. It hung lazily in the air for a moment, then settled about the youngster's shoulders and he was snapped spinning from the saddle. The roper whooped in satisfaction and turned his horse toward the bunkhouse at a lope. For the first few jumps the trailing boy was utterly helpless. Finally he managed to grasp the rope with one hand, steady himself a little, get his head up. At the bunkhouse stood a waiting group of yelling men. Grady started for them at a run. The boy wouldn't last long at this cruel game.

The gallop had ended by the time he reached the scene, however. The cowmen, laughing and contemptuous, had turned the boy loose. He was bruised and shaken but not seriously hurt as he sprawled in the middle of the circle, still too frightened to rise.

"Why'd you turn him loose?" Jim Evans demanded. "I wish I'd had a nester on the end of my rope."

"Shucks, look at him! He's only a boy."

"So was the Kid. Remember?"

There was an ugly murmur at this. Grady shoved his way through the crowd, stared down into the frightened blue eyes. "What's your name, son?"

"Carl Lehman."

"You hear? This is August Lehman's boy." Grady raised his voice and turned to Evans. "Remember his father? He tried to prevent a fight last night. If he'd had his way the Kid would still be here. We haven't any quarrel with the Lehmans."

Evans nodded. "I don't forget easy." He lost his scowl.

"Where you heading, son?" Grady asked.

The boy found his courage in the presence of this unexpected friend and arose gingerly. His shirt was torn half off and his back was raw where it had burned against the grass. "I was going to the Williams ranch." He had no trace of his father's accent. "My pa sent me."

"What sort of mischief are you up to?" Soames demanded.

The boy straightened up, looked silently to Grady for support.

"Just tell us your errand, Carl. Nobody's going to bother you any more."

"My father and Tom Williams were good friends. Pa's trying to stop this fighting. He told me to tell Mrs. Williams the German farmers weren't to blame for that killing last night. It was a gunman named Grady Scott but he broke out of jail. He wants the ranchers to help find him. He wants me to tell Mrs. Williams that this is the time for all the good people to get together before it's too late."

"You see," Soames said, "what good friends of yours the Lehmans are, Grady?"

13 THE RECKONING STARTS

CARL LEHMAN stared around him, puzzled by the cowmen's laughter.

"So your father wants us to help the sheriff chase down this outlaw, does he?" Soames chuckled. "How would catching Grady Scott end this trouble?"

"My father thinks if the best men on both sides would work together they'd get somewhere. That's been the trouble, he says—everybody pulling a different way."

"Your father aims well," Grady said slowly. "I give him credit for trying, but this time he's on the wrong track. You see, I am Grady Scott."

Carl's jaw dropped. This was the man who had championed him here. The boy's bewilderment showed in his troubled blue eyes.

"Run along home, boy, and tell your pa he's barkin' up the wrong tree," Dave Blake advised. "We know the straight of what happened."

Carl shook his head. "I can't go back. I'm going to the Williams ranch."

"Why? You've already delivered your message."

The boy hesitated. "They're friends of ours and they're in trouble," he finally blurted out. "They'll be shorthanded. My father told me to stay and help, long as I was needed."

"A flat-heeled peeler won't be much help," Jim Evans scoffed. "We've already seen you ride."

"Let him alone, Jim. He means all right," said Grady. He turned to the boy. "I'm headed for the Forked W. Are you afraid to ride with a wild hand like me?"

"No, sir."

The Blakes saddled another horse for the youngster. "You can pick up yours when you come back this way," Dave told him. "That cayuse would slow Grady down considerable." The cowmen's attitude toward the youth had thawed perceptibly. This sending of a boy to help a shorthanded friend was something they understood and liked. When Carl rode away he was well mounted and equipped with a new shirt to replace his torn one.

Carl Lehman liked his riding companion. He'd expected an outlaw to be different. He puzzled over this and rode in silence, at first. Gradually he thawed as Grady chatted amiably.

There was a purpose behind Grady's questions which the boy didn't guess. They concerned the town and its changes, the nesters and their problems. Eventually they led to Heinrich Unger.

"He's no-count," said Carl. "How he lives I can't understand."

"Doesn't he have a farm?"

"Pfui!" Carl shrugged his contempt. "It's more weeds than crops. He's lazy, Unger is. Don't judge all the farmers by him. Most of them are good, hard-working people." Under careful questioning he went on to describe the unkempt cabin where Unger lived alone and how to find it on the north bank of the river, a few miles west of Apache. "I think it must be the sheriff's office that keeps him going." Carl dropped the remark artlessly. "You see him a lot with Frank Toomey."

Later Grady asked about Kurt Pakebusch. "No wonder you've got the wrong idea about nesters," Carl protested. "You know only the worthless ones. They're not all like that. My father has no use for Pakebusch. He has a good farm, too, but he only half works it. Don't judge all the nesters by him."

Before the conversation ended Grady learned much about Pakebusch too: his farm and how to find it.

Ma understood the friendship which had prompted August Lehman to send his boy here. She was touched by it and it overflowed in the kindliness of her welcome.

Curly was dubious about Carl's usefulness. They discussed it in front of the boy. He'd been raised in his father's store. He couldn't ride, he couldn't rope, but they were desperately shorthanded. "Rustlin'," Curly explained. "Last week I rode the upper range. Yearlin's are scarcer'n varmints up yonder. Someone's swingin' a wide loop with our livestock. All the hands in the valley couldn't comb a trail herd out of our hill pasture."

The Forked W was an easy ranch to work. The hills to the north and west, the river to the south formed natural barriers that simplified its operation. When a trail herd was made up extra hands were hired. The outfit threw in with its neighbors at roundup time. But Tom Williams and the Kid both were gone, and after the killing at Apache Jim Evans had hired out to the Snake on a Rock.

Ma summed up her arrangements. "Peg's quit the kitchen an' gone back to ridin' again. Now that you're back we'll manage, Grady."

"I won't be much help, Ma—not yet. I have a chore to do first."

Her eyes filled with concern. "I know how you feel. I was the same way at first." Her gaze wandered down the valley and there was bitterness in her voice. "I never wanted to kill anybody before, but when I saw Tom lyin' there where they left him, somethin' froze up in me. I reckon I'm not the Christian I thought I was.

"Now I've had time to think things out better," she continued. "There's been another killin'. That won't bring Tom back. No, nor the Kid. He was a good boy, Grady. I keep rememberin' that, too. I haven't changed the way I feel inside. I don't reckon I ever will. But where's the good of it? What can you do alone when we've even got the law agin us? I don't want you to go."

There was no evading this issue now. Grady realized it, drew a deep breath before facing her. "We'd better get this straight, right from the start. There's no law here. All right, it's time we changed that. What am I here for? You know how I felt about Tom. The men who murdered him are going to pay for it.

"No, don't stop me." He held up his hand when she tried to interrupt. "There won't be any more foolishness like that fight at Scanlon's. Sure, I'm on the prod, but I'm not picking quarrels with just anybody. I aim to hunt down the men who killed Tom, one by one. I'm not wasting time on anything else. I'm not quarreling with the nesters either, except those that were in this thing. The way I figure, there have to be a few funerals here before things mend. Don't try to stop me. No one can. I know what I have to do and how I'll go about doing it."

Ma didn't lose her anxious look but she dropped the subject. It was decided that Carl should stay. He could help with the chores around headquarters until he caught on to things.

"I'll keep my eyes open," Grady promised. "Maybe I can find a waddy or two. If I do I'll send 'em out."

Grady slept all day. He needed the rest, and so did Ranger. It lacked an hour of sundown when he awoke and he spent the time until supper seated on the edge of his bunk with a file. Both of these six guns were new to him and he worked on their trigger action until he had them adjusted to suit him. When he went to the house at dusk only Ma and Carl were there. The others had not come in yet.

Ma mentioned Grady's errand only once. He stopped her. "I've been figuring out what Tom would say about this, Ma. He was a fair man and you know he never picked a quarrel in his life. He wouldn't have run away from one, though, if he thought it was right, and I know I'm right. Tom would tell me to go ahead."

Even when he rode away she only said, "Be careful, Grady. I'll be mighty worried."

"Shucks, Ma, don't fret. I've learned how to take care of myself." With sudden tenderness he kissed her on the cheek.

He traveled the south bank of the river, paused at intervals to locate landmarks along its bank. The night was clear and pale with starlight. He stared across at Lazy B headquarters when he passed but didn't ride in. He was playing a lone hand now. He'd been nearly eight hours in the saddle when he neared Apache. Here his caution grew. There were nester cabins across the stream. Several times he rode down into the gloom of the river's trees before he found the mark he was seeking. It was a long bend where the river veered southward, just a few miles west of the town. Here he found a glade hidden among the trees; he watered his horse well before tethering him on a line long enough for grazing. He wouldn't be back soon. Then he searched the ground until he found a broken limb, half rotten, which he tested for buoyancy in the water. He lashed two such branches together with his whang strings to form a tiny raft on which to float his hat. In it he placed his revolvers and ammunition belts out of the wet while he swam the stream. The current was placid and the night warm. He had no difficulty in the crossing and enjoyed the feel of the cool water after the long ride.

There was little cover in this nester country. The homesteads followed water and their fields marched right down to the stream, with the brush cleared from along its banks. Day was close. Already lights burned yellow in cabins uncomfortably near. To the east the sky's blush was spreading. With Carl's directions to guide him, Grady wanted to spot Unger's homestead and scout its possibilities before the community was astir. Kurt Pakebusch was Unger's neighbor. When one was found, they'd both be located.

The first farm Grady came onto was neatly laid out and when he glided noiselessly into the cabin yard, he knew it wasn't the place. The order of the barn lot and the trim fence rows didn't fit the description he'd been given. Still he knew he was close. He turned Indian in his caution, walked on bare feet with his boots slung over his shoulder, moved with the stealthy silence of long training. There was no mistaking the Unger farm when he found it. It was a weedy, littered place, the barn ramshackle and empty of oxen. Even the corral was makeshift. There were two rooms to the cabin, one a lean-to filled with the stale odor of cooking. He searched the place thoroughly but there was no one around. Unger had left a wide thicket uncut at the river's edge, untidy to match his land, and a couple of cottonwoods rustled their leaves over the water there. It was the best cover in the neighborhood, Grady decided. It offered a shelter where he could watch unseen. He was slow in reaching it and was thankful for Unger's neglected fence rows, for the sun already was hunting out the long slanting shadows and in the next field a yoke of oxen was early to work. He readied himself for a long wait. The brush grew thickest along the lip of the bank. He crept into the densest thicket, hollowed out a clearing in its heart, where he felt secure from discovery. He'd been all night in the saddle, wanted rest. He liked the spot. By rising to his knees, he could peer through the foliage at Unger's cabin and see the field beyond where the oxen were busy. On the other side he overlooked the river. Here the water stood in a wide pool shaded by the trees, lazy and blue with depth. He stretched out on the leafy carpet and soon was asleep.

Ohmie Pakebusch trudged to the end of another furrow, glanced at the sun to gauge the time. Her arms ached from the struggle with the unwieldy plow. Dust was gray on her shapeless homespun dress. The same plow had filmed her eyelashes, penciled them with grime and streaked her cheeks where the sweat had run. There was an hour or more of daylight left but Pa would never know what time she'd quit. He was seldom around the place any more—hadn't touched a plow in two years, not since the time his fence had been cut and O-bar-O herds stampeded across the young corn, trampling it flat. Ma said Kurt Pakebusch had been a good farmer once. She reckoned those cattle had stomped the heart out of him just like they flattened his growing crops. For a spell he'd cut wood with Heinrich Unger and hauled it to the settlement. That had been a hungry year because wood didn't fetch much and there were five young'uns in the Pakebusch cabin. When Pa still shied off the plow in the spring, Ma had yoked up the oxen and set Ohmie to work. Ohmie was the oldest—seventeen, and scrawny even

for a girl, but she'd raised a garden and six acres of corn. It helped out
a heap. Now Ohmie was a year older and she'd filled out considerably.
She still was slender—puny, Pa called her—but the plow and the hoe
had left something besides aches in her body. She'd grown lithe and
wiry even if she hadn't fattened up much. Anyway, Pa wasn't around
to notice often. Since last summer he'd been ridin' with the sheriff.
When he did come home, 't wasn't uncommon for him to have a heap
of money but that hadn't bettered his temper none. Time was when
he'd laugh as quick as anybody, Ma said. Ohmie couldn't remember.
Something had curdled him; he was tetchy as a cow with a sore teat and
mighty quick with a stick. She stepped around right sharp when he was
home. Only last week he'd hided her good for bein' late with the summer plowin'. That's why she was at it today.

Ohmie often quit this early. It gave her a chance to slip down to the
river for a bath. Always these journeys were secret. She had a suspicion
that if Pa ever caught her in the river she'd get a beating. He wouldn't
like her wastin' good daylight on such uselessness.

She'd found the pool herself, guarded its secret, feeling a little guilty
about her enjoyment of the water cool on her body at the end of a back-
breaking day. She relished its privacy, something she'd never known in
a one-room cabin with four younger brothers. Once she hadn't minded
scrubbing in a tub on the hearth. As she grew older—and the boys grew
too—she was conscious of their curiosity and resented it, took to bathing
after the others were abed till Pa put a stop to it. He didn't want her
splashin 'round in the middle of the night when decent folks were tryin'
to sleep.

Discovery of the pool had changed all that. It was on the Unger
place but Heinrich was seldom home and big cottonwoods guarded it;
thickets grew to the water's edge. Its privacy she treasured most. At first
she was timid, only splashed in the riffles, but her courage grew. Now
she'd learned to paddle all the way across the pool.

She unyoked the oxen, left the plow in the furrow, herded the beasts
ahead of her toward the river. She'd thought of this long ago. If anyone
found her missing she'd explain she'd taken them to water. They'd
worn a circle thin where she always tied them among the trees.

Her preparations were simple. When she peeled off the shapeless
dress she was bare. Ohmie waded out into the shallows. She always
washed there—the stream was warm where it sang across the rocks. She
sat down and scrubbed, buried her face in the water, splashed noisily

till she felt clean. At one place the water frothed white across a sub-merged boulder. She liked to lie there, feel the current's swish against her skin. She saved the pool for last because she liked it best. It added to her relish of the rest to know that the cool, deep water was yet to come. Self-taught, she had progressed slowly in learning to swim. She still knew a sense of triumph when she crossed the pool in safety. She lingered over her playing until the shadows warned her that the time was short. Standing for her final plunge on a ledge overlooking the pool, she stared down at her reflection on its placid surface and was amused at the way her teeth flashed back at her from its depths when she smiled. She was critical of her body. For one thing, she was dark like her Pa's folks, while her brothers were white-skinned and tow-thatched like Ma. She would have preferred that. But Pa was skinny and she was glad she took after him that way. She stared at her slim legs. Ma was so flabby. She ran her hands over her thighs. They were hard, smooth, and her stomach was flat too. Maybe it's 'cause I'm too young, she thought. But in the water she could see her breasts reflected. She stared at them. They'd been a source of embarrassment to her at home where she was conscious of the boys' curiosity but here, alone, she studied herself frankly. Her romp in the pool had relaxed her. She swam across twice before she headed for the bank.

Her barefoot approach was quiet. Grady heard nothing until her splashing startled him from a sound sleep. He peered from his hiding place to see a naked girl scrubbing her lithe, brown body. His first instinct was to escape—he hadn't come here to spy on some girl's bath. What worried him was how to get away. It would take great caution to move soundlessly through this brush and he was determined not to betray his presence. He parted the green screen carefully, edged away. A dry twig snapped. It sounded loud to him. He held his breath and waited. But the girl was lying in the rapids, and the swish of water had drowned the sound. Shucks, she's going to hear me sure, he thought. And she's bound to be a nester. If they find I'm here, Unger will be warned. I'm not harming her. She won't know I'm here and I'll never see her again. Thinking of his errand here and not wanting to risk its success, he decided against moving.

It gave him a feeling of guilt, watching a girl this way. He turned over on his back and faced the sky, resolutely determined not to look. He could hear her splashing. Once she laughed aloud—he didn't know why. He was still staring upward. He waited till after the pool grew quiet, until he was sure she was gone. Finally he peered out cautiously, and saw her standing poised at the pool's edge, staring into the water. She was directly across from his thicket, utterly unconscious of his presence, her pose so intimate that he felt guilty and confused. I've got to get out of here, he decided. Watching each twig, he progressed slowly until he heard her splashing in the water again. Then he grew less cautious. There was no other good cover short of the weeds that lined the fence, and that was forty yards distant. If he could reach that he'd avoid discovery.

Ohmie crossed the pool a final time, and stood dripping on the bank. She was reaching for her dress when she saw him only halfway to the fence. She first thought it must be Unger who had spied on her and she was furious. Hidin' in the brush to peek at me! she thought indignantly. Even then the major disaster, overshadowing her outrage, was the fact that her retreat had been discovered. She tugged the dress over her head, stooped to pick up a rock and started in pursuit, her bare feet padding silently in the grass.

There was malice in her throw. Her weight was behind it and she swung half around, almost losing her balance as she launched it. It was a miss. The rock flumped into the turf; its ricochet caught Grady in the hip.

His reaction was instant, like the release of a coiled spring. His gun whipped out as he leaped; it was ready when he whirled around to face unexpected danger, half crouched. The alert look of him, quick eyes searching, lips drawn taut, frightened her. She'd felt competent to handle the lumbering Unger; this deft stranger was something different. She drew back a step but caution didn't still the fury in her. It showed in the stormy black of her eyes and the way her teeth were clenched.

He lowered his six gun when he saw who it was. A grin smoothed out the hardness in his face. "I'm sorry you saw me, ma'am. I was tryin' to get away."

"Sneakin' round in the bresh a-gawkin' at girls!" she jeered.

He turned red. She could tell how plagued he was by the way he fumbled his gun into its holster. He wasn't so neat-handed now. "I didn't aim to pry on you, ma'am."

She snorted. "'T ain't likely! A-skulkin' round in the bresh."

"Look," he blurted. "I just holed up there to catch some sleep. You woke me up with your splashin'. If I'd had a mind to watch you, I could have stayed hidden and you'd never known I was here. You saw me tryin' to get away."

His embarrassment was as convincing as his explanation, but her suspicion was slow to die. "Sleepin' in the daytime?" She weighed that. It didn't have an honest ring. His six guns, the boots, everything he wore stamped him as a cowman and an enemy, up to some devilment probably or he wouldn't be here. His kind meant only hurt to nesters. She had good cause to know. "What you doin' here? Hidin'?"

"Yes." He decided to tell her that much of the truth, otherwise she wouldn't believe him.

She knew about the fracas at Scanlon's from Pa. There'd been a killin', between cowmen this time. There'd been a heap of talk about it. The sheriff was still a-huntin' the gunman who got away. "Maybe you're Grady Scott."

That surprised him. "Would that be so bad?"

She started to nod, but saw the laughter in his eyes and was warned. "I don't know. Folks say he's a killer."

"He wasn't to blame for the shooting at Scanlon's."

"So you are Grady Scott."

"Yes."

"Then you'd best skitter back into the bresh," she warned. "Somebody's comin' an' I think it's Pa."

He stooped, half concealed by the weeds, before he looked around. It was dusk. The approaching man, still distant, was silhouetted against the sky. Grady hoped that the trees behind him had hidden his presence. Still bending over, he headed for his shelter. The girl came, too, after her oxen.

"You'd best get goin' soon's it's dark," she warned.

"So you're not going to give me away?"

"No. I reckon I believe you. Besides, Pa'd give me a hidin' if he larned what I've been up to."

They were among the trees now, safely screened from view. She was nervous with haste and Grady helped her untie the animals.

"Ohmie! Ohmie! *Wo bist du?*"

Grady thought he remembered that high-pitched nasal whine.

The girl thwacked the nearest ox to hurry it. "*Ja,* Pa, *ja.* I'm comin'."

"So your name's Ohmie," said Grady. "What's the rest of it?"

"Pakebusch—Ohmie Pakebusch. You'd best hide—Pa's close."

He watched as she herded the oxen up the slope, saw her father cuff her. Pakebusch! He scowled. That blow didn't increase his liking for the man, but he wished he hadn't met Ohmie. Knowing Kurt's daughter complicated things some.

As soon as it was full night he returned to Unger's cabin. It was dark and the corral was empty. There was no way of telling when the nester would return but Grady had no intention of turning back. He couldn't forget Tom's familiar holster swung at Unger's thigh. There could be no mistake—it identified him with the murder. Harsh brackets cornered Grady's mouth, stretched his lips thin. Unger knew how Tom had died, could name the men who'd been there. Grady aimed to get that information.

He had his horse to think of, though. He rummaged around the barn until he found a few ears of corn, which he sacked. He was familiar with the neighborhood now and the night was a safe screen. Recrossing the river was a simple matter. Ranger heard him coming and nickered a welcome. Even that didn't disturb Grady. He felt safe here. He fed and watered the animal, found a new spot to picket him where the grass was fresh. This was a better place to wait. He stretched out along the bank, face up toward the sky. The stars there were the friendly companions of many lonely camps.

There was no sleep. His mind was too busy with all that had happened since his return to Apache. Toomey, Unger and Pakebusch— all had been present when Tom was killed. Had Rowden been there? Grady didn't know but he was sure of one thing—whatever Toomey did, the sheriff was behind him.

He thought of Clee, too. Who'd have dreamed that scrawny young'un would have grown up such a beauty? He couldn't shake off the memory of her loveliness. Headstrong, though, and hard to manage. Letty Reid was more to his liking—not quite so much for looks, maybe, but still mighty pretty. And smart, too. That's what he liked most about her. She had a head on her shoulders. He recalled how she had helped him, the risks she had taken. There was a girl a man could depend on. You'd always know right where you stood with Letty. He even had time to think of Ohmie Pakebusch. Spunky little brat! The memory of her, poised on the edge of the pool, disturbed him. He didn't blame her for being mad but he hadn't meant to pry.

Unger reached home an hour before dawn, his horse lathered and stumbling with weariness. "Vot you need iss a goot feedin' of corn."

Unger often spoke aloud when he was alone. He groped around in the dark first, without success. There was a lantern handy, hooked over a corral post. He lighted it. But still he could find no corn. He stood scowling at the empty bin. There'd been a few ears left, he was sure. There wasn't some thieving animal to blame, either, or the naked cobs would have been left behind.

He tilted the lantern and stooped to peer at the dirt floor. His own tracks, deep in its dust, obliterated any chance of discovery here, but when he turned toward the door he saw the small, sharp prints left by a cowman's boot heels. He yanked out his gun, backed uneasily away from the lantern, cursing its glow.

Gradually his panic died. After all, he'd been gone two days. There was no way of telling when his unwelcome visitor had been here. Without that light he wouldn't have found those tracks. He still held his six gun ready when he picked up the lantern and followed the boot trail, past the corral, until he lost it in the turf beyond. Whoever it was had headed toward the river. He was relieved when he turned back to hobble the horse and turn it loose to shift for itself.

Unger's uneasiness returned when he reached the house. The door stood open. He knew he hadn't left it so. Again he used the lantern to search out those telltale heel prints. There were two sets here, going and coming. The prowler had left.

Texas ways were easy. Doors weren't locked and travelers were expected to help themselves to necessities if they found a cabin's occupant absent. Nevertheless, he remained disturbed. This was enemy country for a cowman. What did he want? What was he doing here? It was hard to believe this was a casual visitor.

"If he vass lookin' for me, he'll come back," Unger decided, aloud.

He blew out the light and peered out cautiously. Already dawn was thinning out the shadows, turning them gray. He had been sleepy. Worry cured that. His eyes had turned alert. He could see as far as the barn's misty outline now. The pistol clicked as he broke open its chamber, checked its bullets. He closed it softly but didn't slip it back into the holster. Better I should vatch until daylight, he decided.

He didn't wait inside. He was careful to leave the door ajar, as he'd found it, when he slipped from the house. Thirty yards away, brush which choked the fence line where it joined the corral, offered a secure hiding place where he could watch unseen. He crept into the thorny tangle and crouched to wait, gun in hand.

Grady shivered when the dawn breeze struck his glistening body. For the swim across he'd rafted his clothes over with his weapons. After using his shirt for a towel, he dressed swiftly. As he strapped on his pistol he wondered if Unger had returned during the night. He hoped so. He'd soon know.

Around him the valley was awakening. A flock of wild turkeys disturbed by his approach, flapped noisily from its roost. Smaller birds stilled their daybreak chirping briefly, but soon resumed their music. Near by a squirrel broke into chatter. He liked these sounds in his ears as he resumed his cautious advance. If he didn't alarm these wild creatures, he didn't fear discovery by a man.

It was daylight when he neared the untidy cluster of buildings. His eyes narrowed. A hobbled horse grazed near the corral. So Unger was back. The cabin door stood open but there was no sign of its occupant. Probably asleep, Grady thought. He left the shelter of the fence, his feet still silent but his step quickened.

Halfway to the house he stopped. Something was wrong. He wasn't sure what had warned him until, straining to listen, he realized that all the familiar morning stir had hushed. It was the sudden quiet which had startled him.

He glanced back the way he had come. The thickets that hid the straggling fence had been blithe with sound until now. This must be my own doing, he thought. He turned to go on. But the answer didn't satisfy him. Whatever the cause of this silence it had happened after he left the green shelter behind.

Then he heard it. The metallic click of a cocking trigger was unmistakable. Grady knew he'd stepped into a trap. He threw himself headlong into the grass and he was slapping for his holster before he hit the ground.

A gun roared three times. Bullets whimpered overhead as they reached for him.

Unger broke from cover shouting, his six gun poised. He'd seen Grady fall and was sure of his kill.

Grady was ready. Still he held his fire. He'd come here to get some questions answered.

"Drop that pistol, Unger. You're covered."

Even then the nester was sure of himself. His enemy was down. He'd finish the job quick. The dawn sun flashed red on his gun barrel as he raised it.

Grady's pistol snarled first. Unger's final shot came too late, after his knees had sagged and his weapon was wavering.

Grady knelt over him, hoping there might be time for an answer to his questions, but already it was too late. He drew his Bowie knife deliberately. He was from a grim frontier, where scalping was a common business, and he didn't hesitate. He looked down at the holster on Unger's belt. It had belonged to Tom; he couldn't leave it here. Stooping, he freed it and thrust it in his shirt.

There was another thing he had decided to do. This must not look like any other killing in the nester-rancher feud. He wanted his justice identified. He knelt beside the body, smoothed a place in the dust with his hands. He hesitated over the message, tried several in his mind before he was satisfied. He wanted it clear. Then, with a stick, he wrote, "Tom Williams." Beneath it he added, "$6 - 1 = 5$."

It had the look of a problem on a schoolboy's slate.

Chapter 14 BEWARE!

IT WAS the scalping that shook Toomey's nerve. The sheriff needed riders that night and Frank had ridden by to pick up Unger. He was a little late, and, as he rounded the barn at a lope, he was almost unseated when his horse shied at the body sprawled there.

At first he feared a trap. He explored the buildings cautiously, satisfied himself it was safe before returning to Unger. His initial caution past, Toomey noticed the swarming flies. Their drone grew louder with his intrusion. Unger had been dead for hours. Frank's first thought was of Indians, of course, but there'd been no Comanche trouble for a long time. Then he saw the writing on the ground. He peered around again, uneasily, after he read it. He scoured his boot through the dust until all trace of the message was blotted out. The stomping relieved his tension some. Damn a man who'd take a scalp! Unger's face was a wrinkled smear. Toomey even cursed Rowden for bringing him to this frontier. Damn these blowflies too! A man couldn't think with their noisy buzz in his ears. Before he left he found a blanket to spread over the body and cheat them of their victim. When he looked back, they were a thick cloud, still noisy, turning the cover black. He rode hard for Apache with his news.

Rowden listened in silence, glanced around to see how the others were taking it. They were all here, the outfit present when Williams was killed. He had planned to use them tonight, combing out beeves on the north stretch of the Lazy B range. When Toomey told of finding the message in the dust, the sheriff glanced at Pete Falkner, squatted on his heels against the wall. There was no reading his impassive face.

"This was your fault, Pete."

The gun slinger had listened with indifference. Now his eyes turned alert. "Me, señor? How come?"

"This was Grady Scott's work," the sheriff announced.

"How can you tell?"

"Who else had a chance to learn so much? You vouched for him, Pete, so we thought he was all right. I didn't understand what he was up to before. Now he makes sense. He was here to find out who killed Tom Williams. Unger must have been careless in his talk."

"I t'ought it vass Injuns." Adolph Blucher was one of Rowden's nester recruits, with a voice oddly soft coming from his slow moving bulk. His shock of hair was the color of ripe oats. Instead of tanning, his skin had weathered red. A soiled bandage swathed one hand and he nursed it gingerly. Just now his small eyes had lost their cunning, showed trouble.

Pete Falkner nodded. "A mistake," he admitted. "But I will correct it *muy pronto* if I ever see him again." His hand slid to his holster.

"You'll see him," the sheriff promised. "I guessed that he'd learned too much. That's why I was so determined to get him before he had a chance to use his knowledge."

"Kind of like a sidewinder, ain't he?" Charlie Springer drawled. "At least he's sounded his buzzer. We know what to expect." He was the same tough breed as Falkner and showed no fear. His chair was tilted against the wall, his heels hooked in its rungs, and his jaws worked slowly as he chewed a blade of grass. "Let him come. If he jumps me or Pete he won't find the pickin's so easy." The others were less confident. Kurt Pakebusch walked the floor with quick, nervous steps. His beard's ragged stubble emphasized the bony structure of his face, shadowed its hollows, and there was fear in his eyes.

"Maybe Unger talked too much." Pakebusch came to a stop beside Falkner, as if needing the assurance of his guns. "*Ja*, dot's it. He gave himself avay. Dis killer don't know who else vass dere."

"Oh, no?" Toomey grunted. "Six minus one leaves five. Remember? Sounds to me like he knows plenty." He twisted at his mustache and scowled.

Pakebusch's voice climbed the scale toward hysteria. "Vy did ve haff to shoot Villiams? Me, I didn't know it vould giff a killin'," he blubbered. "Dere vass no sense in it."

"Aw, shut up. I'm gettin' tired of your squawks," said Springer.

Blucher sided with the other nester. "Kurt iss right. Ve didn't need to kill him."

Rowden's nervous fingers rattled on the desk as he listened to their quarreling. He was more worried than he cared for these men to know. Had Unger had time to talk before he went down? How much did

Grady Scott know? Too many things went wrong. No sooner had he mended one trouble than another faced him. There'd been no word of Clee since the other night, either. That bothered him most of all. What had changed her so? He blamed her for what had happened. She'd chosen a poor time to defy him when all his other worries had worn his patience thin. After all, he'd only taken what was his. He'd find her, straighten things out at the first opportunity. He'd had no time to plan how to handle her yet. Grady Scott was a more urgent problem. He put an end to the argument among the men. "Tom Williams knew too much. There was no other way to handle it," he said. "We won't dig him up now. He's dead and buried. I only wish I could say as much for Grady Scott. We've got to shut him up quick. If we don't we might as well throw in our cards here and I don't aim to do that—not yet."

Pete nodded. *"Buenas palabras, jefe.* Let us go get him."

They were all intent as Rowden leaned across the desk. "I know his next move. He'll walk into a trap. You and Charlie will be waiting for him, Pete."

"We tried that the night he gave us the slip here," Falkner said. "This *hombre* has plenty of *savvy.* He is plumb shy of dry gulches."

"He won't be this time. He gave his game away when he left that message at Unger's. He's on the prod for the men who killed Tom Williams." Rowden's eyes shifted to Pakebusch. "You're next on his list, Kurt."

"Me?" The nester moistened his lips. "Vot makes you t'ink dat? How vould he know I vass dere?"

"You told him yourself. I heard you, outside the jail here, when you mentioned the Williams killing."

"Vot ve goin' to do?" Pakebusch's fear-haunted eyes wavered from face to face. "He iss a killer. Und he'll scalp me too, joost like he did Unger." His shrill voice had turned squeaky. "Better I go avay. Dot's it—I'll go avay."

"Shut up!" Rowden ordered. "It's your own leaky mouth that got you in this fix. We need you here for bait. You won't be in any danger. When Scott comes for you we'll have a welcoming committee waiting with plenty of hot lead."

The sheriff told them his plan and made its arrangements clear. Falkner and Springer would reach Pakebusch's cabin by a roundabout path that afternoon. There must be no betraying horses in the corral. They would be hobbled a safe distance away. Kurt would follow later, taking the direct trail home. He was uneasy about that. "Vot if I meet him on der vay?" he protested.

"You have a pistol in your belt, haven't you?" Falkner jeered.

"He iss a killer. I vouldn't haff a chance," Kurt whimpered.

The sheriff regarded him with distaste. "It's a well-settled neighborhood. You won't be out of sight of a house all the way. Don't worry. He's cautious. He won't strike until night. You've no call to lose your nerve this way."

They had kept word of Unger's death to themselves. Now Rowden had figured a way to use it to advantage. He wanted word spread. He himself would tell August Lehman. The incident could be used to build up more tension between cowmen and nesters. "Remember Unger had a homestead and he was a German," he said. "Don't let 'em forget it. Remind them he was scalped, too. Make it bloody. I want these folks stirred up."

"Maybe dey vill be saying dat about me," Pakebusch quavered.

No one bothered to answer him.

Grady spent the day in a dry camp along the river. He intended to visit the town as soon as darkness offered a measure of safety. He'd thought things out carefully. He had identified Pakebusch—he would be next. Carl Lehman had told Grady how to find Kurt's cabin. He'd seen this man only briefly but thought he had him measured. The fellow would talk. There was a chance though that he might spook too quickly, bring on the shooting before there was time for questions, as Unger had done. That was one reason Grady wanted to visit the town first. Pakebusch and Toomey had guarded the jail the night he escaped. He had them marked. Unger had watched there too but he was dead. Grady had the sheriff identified by the dun horse, and the man he had fought at the wagon yard had a wounded hand. He wanted to learn who that was.

He decided Letty Reid could help him. He had good reason to know how observant she was. She probably could identify the man with the bandaged hand for him; she might even know who rode the saddle with the tapaderos. Also, he missed his Sharp's brass belly. Six guns were all right for close work, but in the campaign ahead he might need a weapon with longer reach. He would pick it up, too.

It was full dark when he rode out. Once away from the river, he could mark the distant town by a cluster of fallen stars that shimmered wanly on the horizon. He rode easily. The heavy turf muffled the footfalls of his horse; the creak of saddle leather was much louder. A short distance above the town he swam across to the north bank, hugged the kindly shadow of the trees until he found a shelter which satisfied him. He left Ranger there and circled the town afoot to come in from the north, behind the Reid House.

If Letty had any guests they were upstairs. It was easy to scout the place through the lighted windows. She was alone in the front room, leaning over the counter at her bookkeeping. There was a lamp in the kitchen, too, where Hallelujah was winding up the last of the evening's dishes. The dining room was dark and he entered that way, through an open window. He moved cautiously, stood back in the shadows when he spoke.

Letty looked up. Again he had the impression of her skin's whiteness in the soft lamplight. "You shouldn't have come here," she warned when he murmured his name. "There's not a man in Apache who wouldn't shoot you on sight. Even August Lehman wouldn't help you now."

"If you'd blow out that lamp I could get upstairs. I've come for my carbine."

She was frowning. "You'll probably need it before the night's over." There was an edge to her voice he hadn't noticed before.

For a moment he thought she was going to refuse. Then she picked up the lamp and walked the length of the room, turned it low, and as she bent to place it on the table half the room was thrown into shadow. "It's better this way," she said. "There's always a light burning in here. It would look strange without it."

She waited there until she heard the stairs creak under his feet.

Grady found his carbine and his bedroll where he'd left them. When he came back into the hall she was standing at the head of the stairs, a dark silhouette against the yellow glow from below.

"Have you seen a man with a bandaged hand?" he asked.

"Yes."

"Who was it?"

"I'm not going to tell you."

"I thought you were on my side?" He stepped closer, tried to peer into her face, but her back was to the light. "If you hadn't helped me before I wouldn't be here."

"Don't remind me of it." Her voice still had that sharpness. "Why did you scalp him, Grady? That's an Indian trick."

"So you've heard about Unger?"

"Who hasn't? The town's boiling over with it. And don't get the idea that I'm on your side, either. A man who takes scalps like a—a Comanche!"

The violence of her anger surprised him. He didn't understand it.

"That seems to bother you a heap more than it does me. I thought you showed a lot of *savvy* about Ranger ways. We always take scalps."

"You've been fighting Indians. They'd have scalped you if they could. This was a white man."

"Sure—and *what* a white man!" be blurted scornfully. "He ran in a pack. They were six to one when they murdered Tom Williams. Then they slunk off to hide. Toomey even claimed they wore masks. I don't know. I reckon that's just his way of covering up for 'em. Well, it won't do 'em any good to hide. I aim to track every one of 'em down."

"How do you know he was in on that?" Letty was more curious than chiding now.

Grady pulled the worn holster from his shirt, told her how he'd identified Unger.

"But you're not the law, Grady. If you had such proof why didn't you turn it over to the authorities?"

"What authorities? Toomey? I know he was there. Rowden? I'm not so sure of him except I know he's the *jefe* of this outfit. These others take their orders from him. There's no law here."

"But scalping!" She couldn't shake that from her mind. "The whole town was horrified by such savagery."

"I meant those murderers to be horrified," Grady replied. "And I didn't want it to look like just another killing over fences. That's why I left the message?"

"What message? I didn't hear about that."

He thought over this for a moment. "I reckon the town hasn't heard anything Rowden didn't want it to hear," he decided finally. "I left a message all right and it mentioned Tom Williams. I wanted everyone to know why Unger died. But no matter. The men it was intended for got it all right."

She had no answer for this. Thought of the scalping still revolted her and yet, watching him in the dim light, she could see the stubborn purpose in his face, better understand much of what had happened. It puzzled her that she should scorn the deed, yet like the man to blame for it. "You should have kept on going, Grady. It was risky coming back here."

"I'll be back here often. My job's just started." He'd recognized the change in her. "Aren't you going to tell me who's wearing a bandage on his hand?"

She hesitated over her answer. "Please don't ask me that, Grady."

He picked up his rifle.

"Let me go with you." She was afraid for him. "I can get you out just as I did the other night. I know these people. They won't suspect me." In the back of her mind lurked a disquieting thought: What was the difference between helping a killer escape and naming the man with the bandaged hand?

"You'd better stay out of this."

"I can manage it, Grady." No time for doubts now, her mind was busy with her plan. "We'll slip out the back way. Anyone who sees us will simply say Letty Reid's found herself a young man."

He grinned. "I think maybe she has. Just the same, I don't want you mixed up in this. I won't have any trouble. I aim to drop out a back window." He turned through the room where he'd met Clee, remembered her as he groped his way through the dark.

Letty followed him. "Be careful," she cautioned.

"Don't worry. They won't catch me," he promised. "I've got a job to finish." His knee was already on the window sill.

"Where are you going?" she asked. She had to know.

"To Kurt Pakebusch's."

Then the window was empty. She heard the thump of his boots below, could follow his movements briefly. His silent shadow was soon lost in the night.

Ohmie came upon the two horses hidden among the trees by her pool. Her first thought was that Grady had returned. But there were two animals. She crept cautiously into the glade, listened for voices. There was nothing to hear except the steady cropping of the horses as they browsed. Even after she searched the brush and satisfied herself no one was there, she remained uneasy. The riders would return. She dared not risk a swim today. She couldn't identify either of the animals. They didn't belong in the neighborhood, she was sure. One of the saddles was strange to her, too. She'd never seen tapaderos before. She examined the wedge-shaped hoods on the stirrups curiously.

Pa was in town so she'd slipped off early. She was disappointed, and she resented the strangers who had spoiled her fun as she trudged toward the cabin. It was out of common for the place to be so still. Most times the boys were a-kickin' up a racket. As she watched she saw Ma round the corner with a tub of clothes. Nothin' wrong, she reckoned, or Ma wouldn't be mindin' her chores so calm. What had happened to those brats to hush their tongues this way? She quickened her pace.

Ma looked up from her basket. Ohmie saw trouble in her eyes.

"Where are the boys?"

The worry lines showed plain on Ma's face. She nodded toward the cabin. "Best not go in, Ohmie. Better you go out an' hoe corn. Two hours yet till sundown."

There was something here Ohmie didn't understand. "I'm a-goin' in," she announced.

She'd seen the two strangers before. Sheriff's men, they were, who'd ridden by for Pa. They dressed in a way that made her suspicious. Like cowmen. They walked loud, too, with their leather a-creakin' an' their spurs a-clatterin'. She'd learned to mistrust that kind. No wonder things were so quiet. The boys were sprawled around to watch while the strangers played cards. They looked up when she entered.

"Come in and close the door, señorita," the dark one said. He was fixy: trinkets glittered in his leather cuffs, his soft boots were fancy with stitching, and he wore his clothes with a swagger.

"What are you doin' here?"

"Waiting for your father, *querida*. He will be along *muy pronto*."

"I reckon them's your horses hid down by the river."

"I reckon. Now be a good little *muchacha* and be quiet."

"Who you hidin' from?" she demanded.

Both men laughed. "She's got eyes in her head, Pete."

She stared at the man called Pete, waiting for an answer. Outside she could hear the sound of a horse galloping. Someone was in a powerful hurry. The men heard it too. They both smiled.

"That will be your father now," Pete said.

"And comin' in a lather." His companion guffawed. "Skeered of his shadow today, ain't he?"

Ohmie was watching the strangers when Pa rode in, still suspicious, but it was plain they were friends. Pa was glad to see them but he looked mighty queer. His face was white and his mouth hung slack, exposing the ragged stumps of his teeth.

He welcomed his visitors eagerly. "Goot—goot! I'm glad you're here already."

Ohmie found chores around the hearth, listened for an answer to the puzzling presence of these strangers. They went on with their cards, paid no heed even to her father.

Pakebusch sidled up to the table to watch, but couldn't keep his mind on the game. His eyes kept straying toward the door. "Vot kind of plans you make?" he finally asked.

"Keep your shirt on." Charlie Springer went on shuffling the cards. "We'll take care of everything now we're here. Quit fidgetin' around. Trouble with you is, you're bad spooked."

Pakebusch peered once more at the door. "*Ja, ja*—I'm scared und you joost laugh. *Ja*—but Grady Scott ain't comin' here after you mit a gun. Me, I got plenty reason to be scared."

Ohmie, lifting a kettle on the crane, stood rigid, listening.

"Take it easy, señor. What are we here for?" Pete was watching the door too, now. "If he shows up your worries are over. We will get him. He won't have a chance."

Now Ohmie understood why those horses were hidden down by the river. Her father's abject fear had left a bad taste in her mouth. It was a sort of nakedness, this panic, so bare and easy to see. She didn't like Pa, mistrusted his harsh temper. He was quick with the lash, had beaten all feeling but fear out of her long ago. Still she'd been ashamed for him before the scorn of these strangers. Mention of Grady Scott disturbed her. She liked him. She eyed the men playing cards with hatred. They were uppity—they treated Pa like he was dirt under their fancy boots. There'd been none of that about Grady. She remembered his fumbling distress when she caught him trying to get away. His shyness had helped her believe him. She started for the door, moving cautiously.

Charlie Springer stopped her. "Wait a minute, sister. You'd better stay in here till we finish this job. You know why we're here now."

"I've got milkin' to do. Time I was at it."

Pakebusch, sweating under the contempt of these men, seized a chance to assert his authority. "*Ja, ja.* Out mit you. Already you are late." He shied a kick at her. The heavy boot sent her spinning.

"Oh, let her go, Charlie." Pete shrugged. "There is no harm in her."

Ohmie limped out past the barn, her temper smoldering. She'd been hurt worse before; being kicked around in front of the disliked strangers was what infuriated her. Once safe from prying eyes, she headed for the river. She had no plan in mind. She only wanted to get away and the pool was her sanctuary.

It was easy to skirt the cabin unseen. It was late, the shadows were thickening. The windows were black when she looked back. That reminded her of the danger lurking there, sent a shiver down her spine.

Were they right? Would Grady come here? What made them think he aimed to kill Pa? That was hard for her to believe until she remembered her father's terror. It was convincing.

It surprised her how clearly she could picture Grady. He was different from those other men. She had liked him right off and had believed what he told her.

She found herself listening for the sound of gunfire back at the house, straining to hear the telltale splatter of shots that would tell her Grady was dead. Terror seized her. She started to run, didn't stop till she reached the water.

She was afraid, not of the night nor of familiar sounds. The fear that haunted her lurked back at the cabin. What if Grady came another way? She realized now that her worry was for him. She must keep him from walking into that ambush. Once she decided to go back, wait nearer the cabin lest he come by the road. She even got to her feet and started before she realized the futility of such a move. She'd miss him sure up there. He had to come this way.

Hard as she listened, she didn't hear his approach. He had come as before, left his horse tethered on the south bank. He swam silently. Her first warning was the splash of water as he reached the bank, waded ashore.

"Grady?" she called. "Grady!"

The sound abruptly stopped.

"Grady," she called again.

The answer came from surprisingly close. Still she didn't see him. "Who is it?"

"Ohmie Pakebusch. The girl you saw—the girl you talked to here the other day." Her eyes strained into the blackness.

"How'd you know I'd be here?"

She located him now. He was flattened against the trunk of one of the cottonwoods, wary of ambush.

She told him what she'd heard and seen, of the men waiting in the cabin for him to come. The words poured out swiftly and her worry was in them.

"They're getting smart," he said, when she finished. "Had me figured out. Thanks, Ohmie. I was getting careless."

"You believe me, don't you?" She still was anxious. "You're not going up there?"

"No—not tonight." His fingers touched her arm, groped till they found her hand. Their pressure was firm and friendly, gave her confidence. "You're a good friend, Ohmie. I won't forget this."

She tried to follow his movements in the dark. The first few splashes as he entered the water were easy. There was a little ripple of sound when he started swimming. Then everything turned quiet. He was gone.

15 CONCERNING WORMY APPLES

CLEE rode in to the ranch wearily. She had started with strength spent, her emotions drained, so that she had spanned the early miles mechanically, drugged by the turmoil in her mind. Two thoughts kept her going—an urge to get away and a desire to hide what had happened from her father. She had resented the meeting with Grady, felt a dull anger at the intrusion, but had submitted to his guidance in the emergency, too dazed to make her own decisions. She was confused about him. Too much had happened since their first meeting for the memory to remain clear. Mostly, he'd ridden in silence. She'd welcomed that. It suited her mood. She had a mixed-up feeling: shame, hatred, mistrust, all badly tangled and she was too confused to straighten them out. She was shamed by the memory of her trysts with Rowden. She'd been such a fool, so easy, so trusting, so free with her love. And it had turned into such a shabby thing. Remembering that, she was disgusted—most of all, with herself.

When Grady had pointed out their danger, she'd sensed it dimly, followed his directions without question. She resented that, too, after she left him. What was wrong with her anyway, blindly obeying the orders of some stranger? It added to her self-contempt even though it had turned out well.

Her face was turning puffy now, she found, when she explored it with tenderly probing fingers. She must look a sight. She was thankful Jack hadn't seen her like this. She knew her father. He'd have kept after her, might have wormed the truth out of her tonight. He'd have killed Will Rowden, of course. Then everyone would have known what happened.

She wanted to get home. She clung to that thought as she clutched the saddle horn with aching fingers to keep from falling. The last hour of the ride was ghoulish. She had to fight to keep awake, fight to stay in the saddle, fight to remember where she was and what she was doing here. She was going home. That was it. And there was the ranch yonder with its corrals spread crazily and lights already burning in the bunkhouse. Queer how plainly she could see at night. Then she realized it was morning. The sky had bleached and her head hurt and shame was so bitter in her mouth that it tasted like blood.

Then she was awake, impatient, once she was alert again, of the morbid dreams that had haunted her ride. She planned what she must do. No one must see her like this. She pulled her hat low to shield her bruised face. She rode wide of the corral, headed straight for the house. Someone heard her. The bunkhouse door opened, released a shaft of light. They'd recognize her mare, of course. Maybe they'd wonder why she didn't stop. This is no time to feel sorry for yourself, she thought. Act natural.

She turned in the saddle, lifted an arm toward the figure in the doorway and rode on. At the house she took time to unsaddle the mare before loosing her, and when she walked up the steps she moved deliberately, still determined that her actions should look natural if someone were watching. Once the door was shut behind her it didn't matter. She dropped across the bed, drugged by exhaustion, slept.

It was late afternoon when she awoke, uncomfortable in the clothes she hadn't bothered to remove, but rested. For a few drowsy moments she lingered comfortably on the border of consciousness. When she rolled over her bruised cheek hurt where it pressed her arm. Then she remembered.

Her thoughts were ordered; the bewildered confusion of last night was gone. She was hard-eyed when she thought of Will Rowden. His finery, the suavity of his manners and his glibness were no longer attractive. I was easy, she thought. Her contempt was for herself; she had let him fool her with his sham.

She crossed the room, stared into the mirror. One cheek was swollen and discolored, her bruised lips were puffed. Her inspection was critical. Nothing that couldn't have happened in a fall from a horse, she decided. That story would do for everyone but her father. He knew her ability in the saddle—he would want particulars. She shrank from the concoction of such a story. There had been too much of deception with him already. It was best not to face him yet. She'd go away for a few days. Not back to town. That was out of the question. Why not the Forked W? Her father wouldn't mind if she visited Ma Williams. She made ready swiftly, packed a duffel bag, left a note. Fortunately, it wasn't suppertime yet and the kitchen was deserted, so there was no need to explain the bruises. Someone had caught up her dun mare, left it in the corral. She'd have preferred another horse but it was the only one there and she was in no mood for delay. She wanted to get away before the hands rode in. Her father might be with them. It was twenty miles to Forked W headquarters, but there still were three hours of daylight. She wouldn't be too late.

Ohmie didn't go back to the cabin. She started to, then remembered the guns waiting for Grady Scott. How could they tell her from him in the dark? She spent the night in the thicket by the river. Even after daylight came she stayed away, fearful of those strangers. No telling what they'd do if they guessed she'd seen and warned Grady. She crouched in the brush, watched silently when they came for their horses, and didn't creep out until they were gone.

Ma was worried over Ohmie. "Somet'ing's happened. You got to find her, Kurt."

The cabin was snug with watchfulness. Pete's six guns gave Pakebusch courage here but thought of venturing out put ague in his spine. Ma's fretting didn't help.

"I have been avay too much," he growled uneasily. "Und you let her run vild. I ain't blind. Vot you t'inkin' of, lettin' her sneak out to scrabble in de bresh mit de boys?"

"She ain't." 'T wasn't like Ma to flare up but Pa shouldn't say such things in front of these strangers.

This brashness surprised Kurt. His jaw sagged. His fright must show through. Bad, he thought, if even women saw it. He'd watched the contempt in Rowden's eyes, and Falkner's. That was something he couldn't help. This was different, from someone he didn't fear.

He lashed out, struck her across the mouth, saw the terror in her eyes now, took savage delight in it. He wasn't the only coward. She staggered back, whimpering. He'd never beaten her before. The sound goaded him on. He flailed at her with both fists. The way she cowered made him forget his own terror. He felt fierce and strong, until Pete Falkner hauled him off.

"Let her alone," he warned. "Only a *cobarde* beats women."

He felt better after that, braver. He still didn't venture out in search of Ohmie but when Ma whimpered, he roared, "*Stille!*" at her and his voice rasped with threat.

He fretted over Ohmie's absence, too, as the wait dragged endlessly and still Grady Scott didn't come. It wasn't worry over her. He was too concerned with his own problems for that. In his uneasy mind everything was suspicious. He wondered if her disappearance had any connection with the failure of their trap. Long before day grayed the sky he was sure Grady wouldn't come. He tried to argue with himself. How could Ohmie know Grady Scott? She was his daughter—she'd be on his side, wouldn't she? 'T wasn't fittin' she should turn against her own pa. He went over the argument in his mind again and again, used it to quiet his fears but he couldn't still his suspicion.

Falkner wanted to leave at daylight. "*Vomonos,* Charlie. He'd be here by now if he was coming."

Pakebusch delayed their departure. "Not mitout breakfast," he urged, and bellowed threats at Ma so that she fumbled over familiar chores. When there were no further excuses for delay he watched them gallop off, from a crack in the door, and there was palsy in his hands.

Ma's fear of Kurt was new. Her eyes followed him furtively. She kept out of his way, tried to puzzle out what had changed him. They'd been happy enough in the early days here. There was sap in the cabin's logs then, the raw fields were scrubby. Still they didn't want much. Kurt's crops had never matched his neighbors', but there was a plodding patience in him that extended from his chores to his family. Maybe he wasn't so much, for a fussy woman, but he was easy to live with.

That was before O-bar-O herds had driven through his fences and flattened out his fields. Other farmers had mended their boundaries, planted again. Not Kurt. Something went out of him as he stared at the trampled corn. "Vot's der use?" he'd said. "I make better cuttin' vood, somet'ing der cattle can't stomp out."

His old, easy nature changed. At first he reserved his hatred for cowmen. It smoldered in his eyes when he saw one pass, spurs jingling. In time he stared at growing crops with the same malice. He resented the prosperity he saw around him, convinced that only misfortune prevented him from sharing it. "Dey are fools to vork so hard," he'd say. "Some morning dey'll vake up und find ever't'ing ruined." When nothing happened to mar a harvest he brooded over it. "Joost luck, dat's all. I vork as hard as Otto Schneider und look at his fields. Mit me, it couldn't happen."

Otto Schneider was thrifty and he had three sons, nearly grown, to share his toil. No weeds choked their furrows. "Dem Schneiders, dey t'ink dey're too goot for us," Kurt told Ma, and spat contemptuously.

His temper with his family grew short, too. Nothing pleased him around home any more.

Kurt Pakebusch liked Will Rowden right from the first, in spite of his fine clothes. This elegant stranger understood how a man could hate. He promised a reckoning with the O-bar-O. Kurt followed him hesitantly at first. The other nesters who listened to Rowden's talk of vengeance struck Kurt as being as undependable as he himself was. Rowden guessed that. One day he showed them some shooting. Falkner was with him, and Frank Toomey and Charlie Springer. When Kurt saw their magic with six guns his belief in the promises mounted. The trap for old Luke Nesbit and his O-bar-O riders didn't sound fantastic when he learned these deadly marksmen would be there to bolster the nester scatter-guns.

Kurt exulted in that first success. After he saw how cleverly Rowden could manipulate such things anything seemed possible to him. He lost his surliness around the house. Ma was too happy over the return of his good spirits to question the cause.

He hadn't liked it when Toomey had tried to cajole the Schneiders into joining in the massacre. "Of course, dey vouldn't help us," he told Rowden. "Too big for der britches, dem Schneiders! Now maybe dey vill talk."

Rowden promised him they wouldn't. "We need someone to blame for what happened. They'll do as well as any."

Kurt liked the smoothness of it. His admiration for Rowden grew. It was he who borrowed Schneider's scatter-gun and left it at the scene for Rowden's posse to find. Schneider had no chance to explain that before the bullets cut him down.

Kurt felt strong. There was security in Rowden's leadership. He was seldom home any more, but when he was there, he walked with a swagger; his pockets were stuffed with money; he was quick with his laughter.

That was before they found Unger's scalped body and the message scrawled beside it. He'd ridden to the burying with the others and all his new courage had oozed away at sight of his dead friend. What security had Rowden given Unger?

He tried to hide his panic but he could read the same watery fear in other eyes as well. That didn't help. The terror followed him home, made him irritable, and he gave Ohmie a beating for being late with her chores. The girl twisted and dodged but she was helpless in his grasp. That made him feel strong, for a little while.

His dread grew. He tried to fight it at the outset, knew he'd failed by the scorn he saw in Rowden's eyes, and Falkner's. At times he avoided them, but when he was away he yearned for the safety of their weapons.

Always he rode at a gallop now when alone. If he came home he arrived on a lathered horse, dodged quickly into the cabin. He looked forward to these trips. It soothed him to see how he, himself, was feared here. The children slipped in and out, avoided his path. Here he was a man again. What rankled most was that he couldn't hide his disintegration from himself. He was aware of it but there was nothing he could do to check it.

He'd picked up some faint hope when Rowden outlined his plan to trap Grady Scott. Pete Falkner and Charlie Springer couldn't miss. Their blazing guns would end the terror. But the scheme had failed. Now they were riding away and he was trembling again.

He didn't hear Ohmie coming, the creak of the door was his first warning. He lunged for his scatter-gun before he saw who it was. "Where you been?" He intended to roar it but his voice squeaked out. That added to his anger.

Ohmie didn't answer; she didn't know what to say. She sidled toward the hearth where Ma stood, the boys huddled around her.

"Shoo those brats out," Pa ordered. When they didn't move, he started toward them and they scurried for the door like frightened rabbits. He slammed it behind them, threw the heavy bar in place, before he took the ox goad down from its pegs. Not trusting his voice again, he advanced silently. Suspicion and fear made his mind woolly; all his anger was centered on Ohmie.

The thick stick frightened her. When she tried to dodge, he jabbed her with the steel prod on its tip. She winced away. The sharp point snagged in her dress, tore it across the waist so that her flesh gleamed through. Ma saw the red welt there. It gave her courage.

"Nein, nein, Kurt! You don't handle girls like cattle." She sprang between them.

He was striking at Ohmie, didn't aim the blow for Ma, but the flat of the stick caught her on the head, sent her sprawling.

Ohmie, terrified now, darted the other way in an effort to reach the door. Again the point jabbed her, a straight thrust this time and deeper, but it didn't turn her back. She reached the opening, fumbled at the latch before he caught her. This time he clutched her. There'd be no more dodging. Pakebusch used the flat of the club now. It tingled in his fingers as each blow fell. The cringing girl was helpless. His mastery soothed him. This was like last night, with Ma. He was beating down his own fears.

She screamed at first. He didn't realize when she stopped. He only noticed that she was on the floor, quiet, and she no longer winced when the goad struck. He stared down uncertainly. "Get up!" he ordered. "You hear me?" he shrilled when she didn't move. He jabbed her with the point again before he realized she was unconscious.

He glared around the room. Ma was sitting up now, looked dazed, but she kept her mouth shut. They were afraid of him—all of them. He wished for Falkner to see him now. He was strong and the fear had gone out of him. It was a good feeling. He decided to go to town, show Pete and the others that he wasn't scared any more. He opened the door, stepped outside, still telling himself he wasn't afraid. He went to the corral, saddled his horse, but came back for his scatter-gun before he rode off.

When Ohmie woke up, Ma was bending over her anxiously. She felt wet, wondered if it was blood, even while her frightened eyes scoured the room for Pa. "Where is he?"

"Don't vorry. He rode off."

"I'm all wet."

"*Ja.* I t'rowed vasser on you. I vass scared, *liebchen.*"

Ohmie sat up, winced from the pain of it but scrambled to her feet. She lifted her dress, twisted to look at herself. Where the prod had broken the skin there were trickles of blood, but these didn't hurt so much as the bruises already beginning to turn blue. Ma moaned at sight of them. "Always before Kurt vass a goot man by me. Vot can ve do?"

"I know what I'm going to do, Ma. I'm going to get out of here before he comes back."

Her mother clutched at her. "*Nein, nein,*" she moaned over and over, helplessly.

Ohmie pushed away. "I've got to, Ma."

She wouldn't even wait for her mother to cook something, as she wanted. She was fearful of her father's return, determined to be out of sight by then.

When she slipped from the house she saw the boys lurking behind the barn, peering around at her fearfully. "Go on in the house," she called. "Ma wants you."

Still they hesitated until she reassured them. "It's all right now. Go on in." Nothing for them to worry about, she thought. They were little. Pa never bothered them much.

She'd made no plan. First she'd go to the river, but she headed in another direction until she'd passed the brambly fence of Unger's place. There she looked back to make sure she wasn't followed before she slipped down to the pool. This place was peculiarly hers. She felt a pang at leaving it. She shrugged off her dress, slipped in the water. It felt good against her bruised body, eased some of the soreness. And while she lazed in the shallows she wondered where she'd go. Apache was no good. Pa would find her there and bring her back. It would be the same if she went to some neighboring farm, and he'd beat her worse than ever next time. The one place he wouldn't follow, she decided, was the ranch country to the west. That's where she'd have to go. The decision frightened her a little. She'd grown up on the fringe of the O-bar-O where cowmen were dreaded. Thought of Grady Scott reassured her—he was her friend. All this had happened because of him. He would help her. Besides, I'll work, she argued to herself. I'm grown, I can earn my keep.

When she quit the pool she headed west, kept in the shelter of the river's bank until she'd left the German settlements behind. She had a nester fear of the cattle country but it offered the only haven from her father. Rocks along the bank were cruel to bare feet. Once the last cabin was left behind she abandoned caution, took to the prairie where the grass was soft, trudged steadily onward.

At the outset Carl was assigned no definite task at the Forked W. Quite aside from his lack of experience, there were no definite tasks at the ranch right then, with three trying to do the work of six. Ma did a man's share. Peg couldn't be spared from the saddle to cook. He and Ma divided kitchen chores between them after long days on the range.

Carl had a blundering earnestness they liked. The tasks were new to him but he attacked them with determination. His potato peelings that first night were unwieldy slabs. Peg soberly placed the parings in a kettle on the stove, prepared to throw out the rest.

"No, no," Carl protested. "These are the potatoes here."

"Shucks, them's just the cores. What you wanta save 'em for?" Peg pretended to grumble. "Not enough hyar to bother 'bout."

Because they liked him, they tried their humor on him. Peg waited until bedtime and Ma was gone. Carl was readying his bunk at the far end of the room. "Goin' to be kind of tough on the young'un when he rides his first bronc tomorrow." Peg's tone was confidential but he made sure his voice carried.

Curly caught the twinkle in his eye. "You ain't figurin' on puttin' a burr under his saddle, are you? Be quite a show. Take that paint hoss, Loppy, now. He'll pitch from hell to breakfast, give him any sech encouragement."

"Sh-h-h!" Peg's whisper was loud. "Don't let on but that's exactly what I got in mind."

"He'll wish he had some glue on the seat of his pants, time Old Paint starts pinwheelin' round the corral." Both men chuckled softly.

"Glue? Say, that's an idee, Curly. We don't want him findin' the glue. It'd spile all the fun. Why, I've seen a greener ride to beat hell with glue in his pants, and there's a sack of glue in the kitchen. Reckon I'd better hide it before I go to bed. We don't want this kid turnin' the tables on us."

They set their stage carefully. Curly pretended to be asleep when Peg lit a lantern and explained with elaborate carelessness that he had an errand over in the kitchen. This was in a separate building, a lean-to against the long, log dining room. Once outside, he made sure he was being followed. Then, grinning to himself, he entered the kitchen. He hung his lanter on a peg, so that each movement was clearly discernible from the window, but was careful not to look in that direction. There was an old sack of dried glue here somewhere, he remembered. When he finally found it he made a great show of hiding it behind the stove. He left the lantern by the door before blowing it out. The kid'll need a light, he decided. And he took his time returning to the bunkhouse. When he came in he found the kid sitting on his bed.

Peg was suddenly sleepy, stretched his arms in a prodigious yawn. "I'm goin' to turn in. I'm dog-tired. Reckon I'll be asleep the minute I lay down."

"Me too," said Carl. But Peg noticed he still had his boots on when he blew out the lamp.

Peg's snores started in a matter of minutes—long, rackety convincing snores that soon were echoed from Curly's bunk. The floor creaked and the door opened silently, but the whisper of fresh air betrayed Carl's movements. The snoring stopped after he left. Both men were watching from the window when the lantern was lighted in the kitchen, and there was considerable quiet laughter when they returned to their beds.

"Glue makes an awful mess," said Curly.

"Do him good," Peg chuckled. "Shucks, I wouldn't take all this trouble if I didn't like the young'un."

Carl had seen glue cooked at home. He built up a fire in the stove, spilled the hard, brown flakes into a pan half filled with water, stirred the concoction when it started to boil. The chips disintegrated into a brown, gooey mess. The smell of the evil brew bothered him. It seemed to fill the place. Before he left he opened the window, hoping the odor would be gone by morning. He didn't want them to guess what he'd done.

· They were up before dawn. Early as they were, Carl was the first one out. "I'll get the fire going in the kitchen," he volunteered. The two old veterans enjoyed another laugh after he hurried out.

The condition of the glue dismayed Carl. It had hardened during the night, and when he heated it the stench filled the room again. There was no help for it though. He wanted a place to hide it until after breakfast—the telltale pan might betray him. On the shelf he found an empty jug with a lid that would shut the odor in. When he replaced it, he was pleased with its appearance. Even if they smelled glue now they wouldn't find it, he was satisfied. When he took the pan in which he'd cooked the mess outside and hid it, the odor wasn't so bad and he left the door open hopefully.

Peg sniffed when he entered the kitchen and grinned as if he found the stench of glue pleasing. He whistled cheerfully as he started his breakfast chores. Ma was the last to arrive but nobody sat down until she reached the table. Then Peg stumped in with a steaming platter of flapjacks.

"What's the matter, Carl? Ain't you hungry?" Ma demanded. "Dig into these flapjacks. Time you spend a day in the saddle you'll need victuals that'll stick to your ribs." She helped herself to molasses from the jug.

"I smell glue," she announced, sniffing suspiciously. Peg was standing behind Carl. He screwed his face into a prodigious wink and pointed at the boy. Ma gave another sniff but held her peace. "Eat up, eat up," she admonished again, and helped herself to a hearty bite.

Her startled eyes warned Carl. Curly saw her face turn red, thought she was choking. Peg thought she understood the joke, and was holding back her laughter.

She gagged and leaped sputtering from the table. "GLUE!" she yelped. "Hell's bells, they're feedin' me glue!" as she headed for the door.

Carl sat in stunned misery. Curly glared at him accusingly. "Did you do that?" he demanded.

Carl nodded.

The old cowman held the jug up to the light. The glue was about the color of blackstrap molasses and of much the same sticky consistency. He spilled the stuff over Carl's plate. "Then damned if you don't eat it, son. You've got to larn that in this spread we don't play jokes on Ma."

"I-I-I didn't aim it as a joke." Carl stammered out his explanation.

"You aimed to put that stuff in your *pants?*" Ma had returned in time to hear the story. She started to laugh—a chuckle that grew in volume and infected them all with its merriment. Their guffaws filled the room and Ma's laughter was the heartiest of all.

Later, when they led out the Old Paint for Carl to ride he glanced around sheepishly. "I wish I had that glue now."

"You've got to ride him just as is," Ma decided. "That's your punishment, son. Hold that hoss, boys. Give him a fair break. Let him get set in the saddle before you turn the bronc loose."

They made elaborate preparations, blindfolded the animal. Peg and Ma were at its head while Curly gave the youngster a boost into the saddle.

"All right—turn him loose!" Ma roared. They all sprang back. Carl clutched the saddlehorn with both hands, his face screwed tight with determination. He was bent on doing his best.

When nothing happened he opened his eyes to stare, bewildered at his grinning audience. Old Paint's head drooped sleepily. He'd been given the safest old horse on the place.

It was long after dark when Clee arrived at the Forked W, but they still were at the table. Hours were long here.

"Set another place, boys. We've got company for supper," Ma announced. "Hell's bells, 't ain't every day you set down with a girl as pretty as Clee." Nothing escaped her sharp eyes. "If you was one of my hands, I'd say you'd bellied up to the bar at Scanlon's once too often an' got into a ruckus."

Clee had rehearsed her story. "Oh, that?" She touched the bruises. "I was breaking a green pony and got a fall."

"Must have been some hoss," said Curly. "I've seen you ride."

"The girt' broke," she explained.

Ma wondered, but she kept her thoughts to herself. For one thing, she noticed there were no scratches on Clee's arms. She thought there would have been with a broken girth. And then there was a reserve about Clee she hadn't noticed before, a guardedness of manner. Like she was afraid of saying too much, maybe.

Ma liked having her here. Woman company was rare and pleasant. And she had a yearning gentleness hidden under her bluff manner that was soothed by the thought that in trouble the girl had turned to her. She didn't let Clee guess this. Surest way to scare her off is to let on, she decided. If she's got somethin' on her chest, she'll tell me in good time. What she needs most is somethin' to keep her so busy she won't have time to think of herself. I'll bring her in so tired she won't be bothered by nothin' but a bed. Ma had proved this remedy often.

"You won't mind if I'm too busy for daytime visitin'," she said next morning, her manner brusque. "We're so shorthanded I'm workin' along with the boys. Or maybe you'd like to come along today. It sure would help me out a lot."

"Of course I will." Clee welcomed the thought of doing Ma a favor. There was no ranch skill she hadn't learned, but she'd never practiced them as she did now. It was hard work for she did a man's part. They were behind with their tasks. Many calves still were unbranded and the range was being combed for mavericks. Wherever a few were gathered a fire was built, Peg handling the branding irons. Carl held the herd while the others did the cutting. Clee's rope was as quick as any. Carl watched in awe when she shooed a calf toward the fire and let her loop fly. Always her rope tightened at the last minute, the calf was thrown a few feet away. His clumsiness bothered him when he watched her. He practiced at every opportunity, but he tried to pick his time when she wasn't around.

One day on the range she rode out of a draw and found him at it. He'd found a couple of dogies and was experimenting on them as he hazed them toward the branding fire. He missed his throw before he saw her, turned red when he realized she was watching.

"I wish you hadn't seen that," he confessed. "You're so good at it and I'm so awkward."

"I've been at it all my life, that's all." She was surprised at his discomfiture. She hadn't given him much thought before. Staring at his flushed face she guessed how important this was to him. "La, you'd make a monkey out of me in a store, Carl. That's something I wouldn't know. Maybe I can help you. Here, let me show you how it's done." She set her pony at a gallop, twisted the noose deftly. It settled over the calf's shoulders with precision. "One thing, you're too anxious," she said after watching him try. "You build your loop all right but you turn it loose too quick. Take it easy. There's a lot of timing in it."

She spent half an hour with him, trying to correct his faults. She was patient. He was so happy when his throws did catch that she promised there would be other lessons.

Clee stayed on. She had intended remaining only a few days, until the bruises on her face were healed, but she enjoyed the feeling of being needed. With her to help and with Carl improving, they were getting things in shape. She was more accustomed to the work, too, no longer rode in at dusk exhausted. And where at first Ma often found her silent, she now was the first to laugh at the minor mishaps that kept the branding camps in an uproar. They talked a lot these days, she and Ma.

"The trouble with me is, I don't know much about men," Clee said once. "I know there are bound to be all kinds, of course, but how do you tell the good from the bad? When they're smart, the bad ones take more pains to cover up. I mean young men, of course. When they're old they're pretty well marked by what they are." She glanced across at Curly Stark riding in. "Like him," she said. "That's a real man. Everyone can see it now. But what was he like when he was young? Why couldn't some girl tell it then and put her brand on him?"

Ma took her time about replying. "Me, I like apples," she said. "When I can get 'em. Course anybody can tell a rotten apple when he sees one. But sometimes you run into a wormy one, nice an' red on the outside, if you don't look too close. Once Tom brought me home a bag of 'em an' I was pleased as punch. I bit into the first one I saw, big an' red an' juicy-lookin'. Well, sir, there was a worm in it. Hell's bells, I spit it out faster than I took it in. No, sir, I didn't like it. But that didn't spoil my taste for apples. It just made me cautious. Now I look for wormholes before I take a bite.

"Shucks, anybody's entitled to one mistake, Clee. It's them that don't learn by it that I lose patience with. The signs are there if you'll just take the pains to look."

Clee thought of that conversation often. I was just fool enough to bite into a wormy apple, she told herself. Ma's right. The important thing is not to make the same mistake twice.

She'd been there nearly a week when, one morning after breakfast, Grady rode in. She was over at the big house with Ma, saw him from the window as he turned his horse into the corral. She frowned. The way he'd worn his guns, fighting fashion, hadn't seemed out of place in Apache. It did here. She remembered him, too, in connection with her flight home, a night she'd rather forget. She wished he hadn't come. "There's a stranger in the corral," she announced.

Ma's spurs rattled as she crossed the room to peer out. "A stranger? Hell's bells, that's my boy!"

Clee wanted to question her but there was no time. Ma clattered out, shouting a welcome.

This was puzzling. Clee tried to figure out how Ma could have a son of whom she'd never heard. She had no memory of him and she'd visited here several times since she was grown. She was still suspicious. Couldn't Ma see he was a gun slinger? It's like Ma said, she thought. You can tell a wormy apple if you'll look close enough. She felt a little sorry for Ma, having a boy like that.

Grady had been in the saddle all night. Clee didn't like the sound of that either, but it gave her a chance to ask Ma about him when they rode the range that day. Grady stayed home to get some sleep. Her opinion changed as she listened. "A Texas Ranger? No wonder he looks like a fighting man."

"The Frontier Battalion," Ma added proudly. "No better Indian fighter in Texas. 'T ain't surprisin'. He had a score to settle an' I reckon he's more'n evened it up by now." She told the story of how they'd first found Grady.

Clee confessed her first suspicion. "And he'd been riding at night," she added. "That made me surer than ever that something was wrong."

"He's got good reason for ridin' at night." The kindness had faded from Ma's eyes. They had turned bleak. "He's hidin' from Will Rowden an' his crew."

Clee stiffened in her saddle. "Why?"

Ma explained Grady's mission here.

"There were six in the gang that killed Tom. If Rowden's backing them, there are more than that. What can just one man do?"

"Didn't I tell you how he trained himself to fight Comanches every day of his boyhood?" Ma retorted. "Grady ain't just any man."

Chapter 16 CLEE FINDS A WAY OUT

SHERIFF ROWDEN intended for the eastern end of the valley to be stirred over the killing of Heinrich Unger. He had Toomey, Pakebusch and Adolph Blucher spread the story. The fact that Unger had been a nester himself, and a German, was accented. The scalping seemed particularly ruthless to these farm people. "I want them mad," Rowden told his lieutenants. They spread the name of Grady Scott, too. The sheriff, they said, had shrewdly traced the killer. It was the same hardened desperado who had shot the Kid at Scanlon's.

Rowden felt doubly sure of the Germans now, was confident he'd twisted the incident around to his advantage. The only trouble was, the task was done too well. The poison fermented in minds already inflamed. The nesters grew sullen, demanded action. This bitterness overflowed against the sheriff, too.

"When you goin' to get Grady Scott?" was the inevitable question of every nester Rowden met. He gauged their sullen resentment carefully, was worried by it and guessed the reason for August Lehman's visit when the little merchant came to his office.

"What iss it keeps you from catching Grady Scott?" he demanded. "That iss the only talk I hear in my store. It iss not good, sheriff, if you lose the confidence of these people."

"Don't worry. I'll get him, Lehman. What bothers me, Grady Scott is an old hand at this. I've set two traps for him and both times he slipped through my fingers. But the next time it'll be different."

The worried merchant plucked at the tuft on his chin and pointed at the hitch rail in front of the office. "Six horses tied out there, Sheriff. You have plenty of men. Why don't you go after him? That iss the talk I hear."

"So they think I've got too many deputies, do they?" There was a growl in the question.

"Not if you use them. That iss what they're for. But so many well-armed men just to sit in Apache—that iss not good."

"Now see here, Lehman. I can talk plainly to you. Scott's in with the ranch people. You know how they stick together. That's the only reason I haven't gone out there after him. I'm not aiming to start another war."

"I've known the cattlemen a long time," the merchant retorted. "If it iss murder they won't protect him."

Rowden shrugged. "All right. I hope you've guessed them right. I'll go after him." As long as he was going, he decided it was smart to make the merchant think his influence was responsible. "I'm glad you came to me, Mr. Lehman. After all, we're both interested in what's best for the valley." He added a word of caution against revealing the plan. "I'll have a better chance for success if nobody knows what I'm doing."

"Of course. That iss smart," Lehman agreed.

Another consideration influenced Rowden's decision. He'd had no word from Clee. That preyed on his mind. Several times he'd ridden to their old meeting places, hoping to see her, but without success. He found he couldn't consider her calmly, plan a course of action as with his other problems. That baffled him. One day he'd be in a fury. She couldn't flout him this way. He thought he'd shown her that. Next day he'd be hungry for her and his anger would be gone. He couldn't believe she was through with him. Too many memories of their hours together haunted him.

He would see Clee. Once he talked to her their difficulties would be settled. He was sure of that. Their last frenzied hour was more her fault than his. She shouldn't have denied him. When she understood his need for her, they'd recapture their first happiness.

Letty Reid wasn't sure just how she felt about Grady Scott. This confusion nettled her. She liked things neatly classified, her mind as ordered as her housekeeping. Her first liking had made his image surprisingly clear. She even remembered the sound of his voice, the sure, easy way he walked; he had a sort of competence that went with the weapons he wore. He was a Ranger. It pleased her that she'd been right about that, and she understood his purpose in going after Tom Williams' murderers. The scalping she couldn't comprehend. That had filled her with repugnance. She'd decided he was half savage and she should forget him. But she hadn't. The talk she heard made her uneasy. His name was mentioned often here, always angrily. Each morning at the store she asked August Lehman for word of him. He chatted with every customer, always had the latest news.

"No, he iss not caught yet," the merchant said this morning.

"It worries me, all this talk I hear. What's Rowden doing—anything?"

"Now, now, Letty. Don't you worry your pretty head. Soon everything iss all right."

His smiling confidence alarmed her. "How do you mean?"

He had promised Rowden secrecy and had said nothing to anyone. With Letty it was different. He trusted her. "I have talked to Rowden." He lowered his voice. "He iss going after this gunman now. It iss a secret, of course. He doesn't want it known but he'll hunt him down. Don't fret about it. I have confidence in the sheriff."

Letty was worried. Grady could take care of himself, she tried to reason. But she remembered Rowden's reputation and the hard-eyed men who rode with him and couldn't still her uneasiness. They were too many for Grady. If he were warned he'd have time to get out. That was the answer of course. He should quit the valley, go back to fighting Indians. That's where a man who took scalps belonged. It wasn't an easy decision for her. She summed up the arguments against it, all the way back to the Reid House. This was trouble he'd invited. He was no fool—he'd expect to be hunted by Rowden and his posse. How would it look for her to go riding up the valley with a warning? Even while she was packing a lunch for the long ride, she found more arguments against going. "But he thinks he's right" was her invariable answer. "Tom Williams was his best friend."

She told Hallelujah she was going to visit Ma Williams for a day or two. There was nothing unusual in that. It still lacked an hour of noon when she left the town, headed her pony up the valley at a brisk gait. She covered the distance to Lazy B headquarters by midafternoon. Grady had friends here who would take him word of danger, she knew. But there was no one home but the cook and she couldn't bring herself to tell him her errand. I'm not going to have him thinking I've lost my head over Grady Scott, she thought. Why else would a girl take a ride like this?

She got a fresh horse there, after the friendly custom of the country. Her own would be waiting and rested when she came back. She rode harder this last sixteen miles, held to a steady lope except for intervals to breathe her horse, and could see the friendly lights of the Forked W in the distance by the time it turned dark.

They heard her coming. Welcoming shafts of yellow light outlined the opened doors. Clee, wearing a pair of Ma's faded denim pants stuffed in her boots, like a boy, surprised her.

Ma saw Letty's astonishment. "Clee's helpin' out," she explained. "Best hand on the place. Shucks, no time for fancy doodads when you're wrastlin' calves."

Letty, a little shocked, tried not to look at Clee's legs. She understood, of course, but she'd never seen a girl dressed like that before. Her eyes quested around the room. Carl was here and Curly and Peg but no one else. She was disappointed until Peg laid a plate for her at the table. She noticed then that there were seven places. She stared at the vacant one.

Ma noticed it. "Grady'll be back. When we heard your horse we didn't know who 't was. He was snakin' his horse out of the corral."

"It might have been Rowden or one of his men," Carl volunteered.

"Where is the sheriff?" Curly asked pointedly.

It was a good opportunity to tell her reason for coming but Letty decided against it. What she had to say she'd say to Grady alone. "He was in town when I left this morning."

Grady returned then, slipped quietly into his place as if nothing had happened to interrupt his meal. She liked him better than she remembered. He seemed easier here, quicker with his smile. Letty was glad she'd come. She was impatient to deliver her message but after dinner they all sat round the table talking, while Carl helped Peg in the kitchen. The wait made her nervous. She resented the time wasted. He should be in the saddle and on his way by now. Yet she was unwilling to make her errand obvious.

When finally they scraped their chairs back from the table she managed to be at his side. "I've got to see you," she muttered.

He looked surprised. "Something wrong?"

She thought of a subterfuge then. "My horse was limping when I rode in." She spoke loud enough for everyone to hear. "I wish you'd look at him, Grady."

He lifted a lantern from its hook. "Come on," he said.

"Now what you reckon's on her mind?" Curly wondered aloud after they'd gone.

Clee wondered too. She'd heard that horse lope in and there'd been nothing gimpy about its gait.

Ma grinned. "Plain to see Letty's a town girl. She doesn't manage her excuses very well in cow country, does she?"

Grady knew it was an excuse, too. He didn't let down the bars when he reached the corral. Instead, he leaned against them, set the lantern down. "Well?"

"You've got to get out of here, Grady—now, tonight."

"How come?"

"Rowden's coming after you with a posse. He aims to hunt you down. I just heard of it this morning."

"And you rode all the way out here to tell me?"

His surprise was so obvious it made her task easier.

"Of course. I was afraid they might surprise you."

He grinned. "I wasn't here when you rode in, was I?"

"That was different. I wasn't trying to sneak up on you, Grady."

"I've got a heap of friends between here and Apache. 'T isn't likely he'll get through without my hearing of it. Thanks for telling me though." He hesitated. "I'd sort of got the idea that you weren't on my side any more. Now I know better."

"I didn't like you talking scalps."

"And you wouldn't tell me who was wearing a bandage on his hand."

"So you could kill him?" she exclaimed angrily.

"So I'd know another of Tom's murderers. Listen, Letty. I didn't think it mattered whether you understood or not, at first, but it does. I reckon I think you're about the nicest girl I ever met. Your comin' here to warn me just proves what I already thought. That's why I'd like you to see this the way I do. Sure, I'm here to get the men who killed Tom. I won't rest easy till that's done. But remember this—Unger had his chance. That's more than they gave Tom. It was a fair fight. 'T isn't my way to dry-gulch a man or stab him in the back."

"I understand what you're trying to do," she answered slowly. "But there's no time for that now. There are too many of them, Grady. You've got to get out of here."

He shook his head. "This is a big country and I know every foot of it. Don't you fret about me."

She turned angry then. "You're just stubborn. All these plans of yours won't do a dead man much good."

"I don't aim to be killed."

"If you're so bent on doing this, Grady, you could come back later, after this has blown over. You've got to listen to me."

"You get right stubborn yourself when somebody crosses you, Letty. Do folks always do just what you want 'em to?"

"I'm sorry I came," she flared. "There's no use talking to you."

"I reckon not," he agreed. "But I'm glad you came. Now I know you're just like I thought you were, right from the start. And that's pretty nice. Come on, let's go back to the house before they get to wondering what's happened to us." He took her by the arm and steered her toward the distant lights.

She was wrong in thinking that Grady hadn't taken her warning seriously, though. She discovered this later when Ma took her aside to thank her for coming. "Why didn't you tell me what was on your mind?" Ma demanded. "Hell's bells, I knew something was wrong by the way your horse was lathered up."

"It didn't do any good. He wouldn't listen to me, Ma."

"Of course he listened. He's out with Curly now, scoutin' round to see how things are."

"But he won't go away."

"I reckon he knew what he was bitin' off 'fore he started. You can't quit a job just 'cause it's tough."

"But this will be the first place they'll look for him, Ma."

"If they come he won't be here. He'll camp down by the river tonight. Don't fret about Grady. He knows all the tricks. Nobody's goin' to catch him asleep."

Letty felt better after that. She noticed when Grady returned that they sat on the porch in the dark and that Curly didn't rejoin them for a long time. When he did appear he was mounted, riding in from the trail and he called as he approached.

"What is it, Curly?"

"Couple of horsemen comin'. Nothin' snaky 'bout 'em though. Ridin' free an' easy an' headin' straight in. Reckon it's all right but you cain't always be shore."

When Grady didn't answer, Letty turned to look at him, discovered he was gone. He'd vanished so silently it made her wonder and she counted the figures waiting in the dark before she could be sure.

They hadn't long to wait. They could all hear the horses now, coming up the rise from the river. One rider called the house.

"Merrill Blake," said Ma. "I'd know his voice anywhere."

She lifted her voice. "Who's with you, Merrill?"

"A friend of Grady's."

Ma bustled into the house. "Come on in. The boys'll take your horses." She struck a light, reappeared in the doorway, holding the lamp over her head. In its glow they could see Blake's companion—a girl, awkward in the saddle. Ma looked bewildered.

"A friend of Grady's," she repeated, louder than necessary. Letty guessed this was meant for him to hear. "Why, she's just a child! What's your name, girl?"

When the girl didn't answer, Blake spoke up. "I couldn't get much out of her either, except that she was a friend of Grady's and was lookin' for him. I found her on our range, about fifteen miles this side of Apache, and walkin'. One thing's sure. She'd had hard treatment. Her legs are black and blue from a beating. I thought I'd better get her to a woman, Ma, so I put her on a horse and struck out."

"An' a good thing too," Ma agreed.

Grady returned as silently as he'd disappeared. They were clustered around the girl so that he didn't see her at once. Ma made way for him. "You know this child, Grady?"

"Why, it's Ohmie—Ohmie Pakebusch. What are you doing here?"

Ohmie found her tongue then. "I ran away. There was no place else to go where Pa wouldn't find me." She still looked frightened.

"What you running away for, Ohmie?"

"Pa found out I told you 'bout the men waitin' to kill you. He beat me most to death." She hoisted her skirt to show the welts, and high on her leg blood caked an ugly cut left by the goad.

Ma swore. "Come on in here an' I'll get out the liniment. You need some doctorin'."

"You hain't aimin' to send me back?"

"Hell's bells, you're home a'ready, child. Nobody's goin' to bother you here." She hustled Ohmie into the house.

"I'm a good worker," said Ohmie. "I can plow an' scrub an' do most anything. I'll earn my keep."

Letty was glad Ma had taken the lamp in. She wanted the dark to hide in. Her resentment of Ohmie might show in her face. How well did Grady know this nester girl? In trouble, she'd come straight to him. Letty didn't like the idea of her being here. After I've gone back that girl will be here, seeing him every day, she thought. She was surprised by the violence of her feeling about it.

Clee wondered, too. It puzzled her what these girls saw in Grady Scott. First Letty, always so critical where men were concerned, riding all the way from Apache, and her flimsy excuse of a lame horse to see him alone; now this bedraggled nester girl who'd left home because of him. Too many girls, she thought suspiciously. He must have a slick way with him. It didn't fit her impression of him. He'd always been slightly awkward around her, friendly enough, but ill at ease. After Rowden's smoothness she had found this appealing.

"You never told us about this trap, Grady. What happened?" she demanded.

"Nothing to tell. Ohmie gave you the whole story. She warned me and I got away."

"Who was it? You know that, don't you?"

"Ohmie didn't know their names but from what she said I recognized Pete Falkner as one of them. They baited the snare with one of the men who killed Tom. It would have worked if it hadn't been for that girl."

Clee held her breath, waited, but he added nothing more. Pete Falkner was a Rowden man. The smoothness of the trap sounded like Rowden, too. It's because I distrust him so, she thought. I see his hand in everything. This is foolish. She couldn't still her doubt of the sheriff though. She was uneasy with it.

Next morning Ma declared a holiday. There was company and the work was well caught up now. Letty must stay over. Ma wouldn't listen to anything else and the girl proved easy to persuade. Merrill Blake agreed to wait over a day, too. "We'll kill us a beef," Ma decided. "It'll be like old times."

All hands joined in the preparations. Ranch-fashion, they turned a big chore into a fiesta. By noon the beef was dressed, half of it roasting over a pit of embers Peg had prepared, and the hide was stretched back of the bunkhouse. The only one missing was Curly. He'd ridden out early, headed down the river. "I'll have a look-see around," he told Grady.

"I'll go along."

Curly shook his head. "This is yor comp'ny mostly. One pair o' eyes is plenty. Besides, this way I get out o' some chores."

Ma went on a baking spree. "The rest of you get out," she ordered. "I don't want you under foot whilst I'm a-makin' pies."

Ohmie wouldn't leave. She was pathetically determined to prove her worth and had been busy in the big house since breakfast. Once it gleamed to her satisfaction, she'd started for the bunkhouse with bucket and mop but Peg stopped her at the door. "This hyar's a man's hang-out," he announced firmly. "An' I don't aim to have it sp'iled. If I ever catch you in hyar I'll give you what-for, gal. Now git."

She invaded the kitchen though, dogged Ma's footsteps, fed the stove so much wood Ma had to protest. "Hell's bells, you'll frizzle them pies to a crisp!"

Carl suggested the ride up the river. He had discovered a waterfall above the rapids, a couple of miles distant, and wanted to show it. Peg stayed behind to keep the beef turning and when Merrill Blake counted the horses being saddled at the corral, he decided against going, too. "Fiesta days I aim to stay off a horse," he announced.

"What's got into you anyway?" Ma demanded.

He nodded toward the mounted group, and grinned. "Two girls, two boys. I'd just be in the way. Reckon I'll just laze around and swap lies with Peg."

Letty managed to be beside Grady when they started out. Carl fell in beside Clee. "Let's ride ahead," he suggested.

"What's the hurry?"

He nodded toward the others, grinned. "Looks to me like Letty's horse has gone lame again."

Clee kicked her mount out then and they raced ahead. "How long's that been going on?" she asked presently. "I didn't know Grady was such a hand with the girls."

"Don't get the wrong idea about him." Carl's loyalty was quick. "Grady's not the soft sawderin' kind with a wheedlin' way. I think this is her idea."

Clee laughed. "Don't get the wrong idea of Letty, either. I've never seen her set her cap for a man before."

"I always thought she was smart. Now I know it." There was hero worship in Carl's young eyes. "I've learned a lot about Grady Scott since I've been out here. I wish I was like him."

"Why? Because those girls are running after him? First Letty, then Ohmie——"

"That's not it at all," he broke in impatiently. "It's because he does everything better than anybody else. He can draw quicker, shoot faster——"

"I hear Pete Falkner's pretty fast with a gun, too. You wouldn't want to be like him, would you, Carl?"

"But that's different. Grady learned to be an Indian fighter because of his folks, so he made himself the best there was. He's that way about everything. You've never seen ridin' till you've watched him top a green bronc. Curly says there's no one like him on a trail, either. Smarter'n an Indian when it comes to readin' signs."

"You really do admire him, don't you?"

"I wish I was like him," he repeated.

"I think you're pretty nice just the way you are, Carl. You don't need to change."

Carl was too fair to tan. His days at the ranch had merely baked him red. But his flush showed through. "You really mean that, Clee? Golly, I . . . I've been wanting to tell you how I felt but—well, I guess I was scared."

His earnestness startled her. Her eyes widened and for an instant they showed panic. "I've always wished I had a brother, Carl—someone I could talk to, like this. Maybe we wouldn't have become such good friends if you'd been older——"

"I'm 'most eighteen," he broke in.

"Just the right age for a brother."

"But Clee——" He looked bewildered.

She didn't stare at him. There was too much misery in his face. "If you'd been a few years older we might have thought we were falling in love. That would have spoiled everything. It's nicest just as it is."

"You're not so old," he protested miserably. "There's not much difference in our ages."

She laughed, but there was gentleness in it. "Several years," she reminded him. "It's a good thing, too, for I might fall head over heels in love with you, and then where would I be? This way I'll always have you for a friend I can depend on and trust. I value that a lot, Carl."

He was quiet the rest of the afternoon but when they gathered round the supper table for their feast, Clee chose the place beside him and her mood was so gay that soon she had him chattering like his old self.

Ohmie's presence continued to bother Letty. She was silent and thoughtful through most of the meal. Of course, Grady couldn't be interested in this tangle-headed nester girl. She'd watched them together, guardedly, found nothing but friendliness in Grady's manner. She was critical of the way the girl followed him with her eyes, though. Letty didn't admit, even to herself, that she was jealous. It was just poor management to leave the child here where she'd be underfoot every time he rode in. There must be a way to handle this.

The solution proved so simple that she chuckled when she thought of it. "I need help at the Reid House, Ohmie," she began. "How about coming there to work for me?"

Ohmie was bringing in the pie. She halted, her wide eyes turned on Ma.

Letty was too engrossed in her own plan to notice the girl's terror. "I'll pay you good wages, besides your keep."

"Pa would find me in Apache, right off."

"Fiddlesticks! I won't let him bother you. When I tell folks how he beat you——"

"He'd take me home."

"Ohmie stays here," Ma announced firmly.

"Just another mouth for you to feed," Letty objected. "And she'd be a real help to me."

Ma stared up and down the table. "I don't see any shortage of victuals. Grub's one thing we've got plenty of. Can't you see how the very idea of going to town scares the child? She stays here. That's settled!"

When Ma used that tone of finality the argument was ended. Letty recognized it reluctantly.

The tension brought on by the warning against Rowden was gone. Curly had returned from his scout; he'd ridden halfway to the Lazy B and seen nothing. They sat a long time at the table. Most of their talk was of the past, other gatherings when they'd been merry. Even the hard days, gentled by distance, took on a mellow look when remembered now. Occasionally present problems would be mentioned. Ma was always ready with an anecdote to guide the conversation back to other times. Curly brought out a battered harmonica at her suggestion, wheezed out melodies on it until they all were tapping their feet.

"First time I ever saw a fiesta here that didn't wind up in a dance," said Ma. "Why don't you boys shove the table back?"

There fell an awkward silence. Ma ignored it. "Many's the time I've been the only woman here an' had to dance the rounds," she went on. "Tonight we've got a whole passel of girls."

"Do you think we should?" Letty voiced the doubt that had silenced the others.

Ma fixed her eyes on Curly's harmonica. "Play," she ordered. "You're thinkin' of Tom, but this is the way he'd want it. He had a lot of fun in him, Tom did. He wouldn't want to be remembered by folks sittin' round wearin' long faces. That never was his way. He'd like to hear the trompin' of a reel. An' that's the way I want it, too. Now push that table back."

Curly struck up the Virginia Reel and they lined up. Clee chose Carl for a partner. Letty turned to Grady and Merrill Blake took Ma's arm. Ohmie would have backed out but Peg grabbed her by the wrist.

"But I don't know how," she protested.

"Fiddlesticks!" Ma scoffed. "You'll catch on soon enough with Peg for a partner. Now don't 'cause me any trouble. Get in line."

They stood facing one another, the women on one side, the men on the other. Ma and Merrill Blake led off. By the time they reached the "Grand right and left" they all were spinning merrily, the strain ended, the clump of boots almost drowning out Curly's thin melody. Peg was spry and an old hand at this. Ohmie learned fast. When it came their turn to head the line she followed his lead, until it came time for him to swing his partner. The rough plank floor hadn't bothered them until now, when a look of bewilderment crossed Peg's face. He hesitated only an instant. Then clasping his partner tighter, he kept on whirling in the same place.

The others were slow to realize what had happened. "Turn her loose!" someone shouted. "Keep moving, Peg."

Ma let out a bellow. "He can't. Hell's bells, he's stuck!" She pointed at the floor where the wooden shaft of Peg's leg had slipped through a knothole and wedged.

Peg twisted in a circle, prancing manfully on his one good leg, twirled his partner to a noisy chorus of encouragement.

"Cotton-eyed Joe" came next, a Texas favorite. They changed partners for this. Clee was with Grady now. "Heel, toe—one, two, three; heel, toe—one, two, three." The dishes on the table rattled to the prancing until Curly brought the music to a halt. The din stopped and in that breathless moment they heard the galloping of horses.

Rowden took four men with him on his ride—Toomey, Falkner, Charlie Springer and Adolph Blucher. He wanted no more. A few men could move faster and with greater secrecy. These were tried men.

If Grady Scott were taken alive, there'd be no troublesome explanations should he disappear on the way back. Rowden had another reason, too. He hoped to spend some time at Snake on a Rock headquarters, and a small force could be more easily accommodated there. They rode out at night, unseen, avoided the usual trail by crossing to the south bank of the river, headed straight for the Snake on a Rock range.

They found Soames at breakfast next morning. The sheriff glanced around, was disappointed to find no trace of Clee.

"You're out early, Rowden. What's on your mind?"

"We're hunting Grady Scott. Have you seen him?"

"What do you want him for?"

"Several things. The murder of Heinrich Unger was the last."

Soames shrugged. "This ain't his range. You won't find him around here."

Rowden hesitated. He didn't want to antagonize Clee's father any more than necessary. "Haven't heard anything of him lately, have you, Mr. Soames?"

"No. I've already told you he ain't here. Will you take my word or do you want to search the place?"

The sheriff was tempted. A search would find Clee and that was his real reason for being here. Instead he smiled. "Your word's good enough for me, of course." His eyes strayed out toward the corral, where a dozen Snake on a Rock hands loitered expectantly. Clee's dun mare wasn't out there.

He tried again. "I'm only doing what I have to do. I reckon you understand that."

"I'm not hinderin' you." The cowman's hostility did not thaw.

Rowden walked to the door. From there he could see the big house, its door shut, no sign of life about. He turned back, irritated by the antagonism he found here, determined to force the issue. "How's Miss Clee?"

"Fine."

"I'd like to pay my respects while I'm here," he persisted, controlling his temper with an effort.

"She's not home," said Soames. "I'll tell her you've been here."

Rowden walked out to his waiting horse, convinced that Soames had lied to him. He was seething with resentment. He choked back an insane impulse to go see for himself. This wasn't the time. Soames had too many riders around, alert, watchful. They outnumbered him badly.

He swung into the saddle, turned away. "Not here," he said. "We'll try the Forked W next."

He rode in silence, his temper savage. He had hoped for much from a meeting with Clee. He still was determined to see her. But how? He could think of no way and his frustration whetted his anger. It turned on Grady. He'd find him. He wouldn't be disappointed in that, too. He turned the problem over in his mind. The Forked W was twenty miles away, almost due north. His presence in this area was unknown except at the Snake on a Rock, and he was in a position to intercept a messenger from there. There was no need for haste now. It would be better to strike at night, catch the ranch off guard. He set a slow pace, made camp in the afternoon to rest the horses and outlined his plan to the others. "We'll cross the river below their headquarters, move quietly so they won't guess our presence until the last minute. Then we'll close in fast, have the place surrounded. Nobody's going to get away."

They laughed at these precautions later. It was surprisingly easy to surround the place. They could hear the merriment of the dance in the dining room as they approached.

"Move in at a gallop when the music stops" was Rowden's final order. "If anybody tries to get away, shoot."

Grady started for the door when he heard them. Curly pushed him back. "Don't make a target of yorself agin the light."

"That's it—the lamps!" cried Ma. She blew out one, Peg snuffed out the other, plunged the room in darkness.

Grady moved into the kitchen, opened the back door, peered out. It was too early for the moon, and clouds blanketed the stars. Inside it was black, outside shadows smudged the buildings and hung thickly under the trees, but there was a dim visibility in the open. He groped on the shelves, found a cup, gave it a gentle toss. It fell lightly in the grass twenty feet away.

A gun blast tore open the silence, its lightning red against the night.

Curly was at his elbow. "Looks bad," he whispered. "We'll have to shoot our way out of this one, son."

"I don't like it," Grady said. "I'm thinking of Ma and the girls."

"We might bust out the back, make our fight in the open."

"With us on foot and them mounted? No, Curly, we wouldn't have a chance."

"Hello in there!" someone shouted. Clee recognized Will Rowden's voice.

"Who is it?" Ma demanded. "What do you want?"

"This is the sheriff's posse. We are after Grady Scott. Tell him to come out with his hands up and there won't be any trouble."

"Maybe I'd better," Grady muttered.

"No, you don't!" Ma grabbed him by the sleeve. "That's how Tom died, after he surrendered to one of Rowden's men."

"But I can't fight here, Ma. Too many womenfolks around."

"The place is surrounded," Rowden called again. "You don't have a chance. Come on out, Scott."

"What makes you think he's here?" Ma was sparring for time.

"Light your lamps and open up," the sheriff ordered. "If he's not here, you've nothing to worry about."

"I'm not so sure," she retorted. "That'll stand some considerin'." Ma turned from the door, lowered her voice. "We'll fight, first," she muttered. "Anybody got any ideas?"

"Shore, I've got it figgered out," Curly announced. "Right now we're surrounded. Even Grady couldn't slip through. I'll sneak out the back, throw a little lead, enough to draw their fire. They'll gang up on me if they think I'm makin' a break. That's all Grady needs, time to hit them shadders whilst they're busy with me."

"Easy," Grady retorted ironically. "I high-tail it for the brush while they're finishing you off."

"Looky hyar, Grady, you know I'll take keer o' myself. Oncet I've drawed 'em all my way, I'll give up. They got nothin' agin me."

"How are they going to tell you from me in the dark? No, it won't work."

"My mind's made up. You can't stop me."

"Listen, Curly, if you go out shootin', I'll be right at your side. It'd be a waste, that way. They'd get us both."

Clee listened in panic, remembered the trap set for Grady at Pakebusch's. Those had been Rowden men there. There was no doubt in her mind what would happen if Grady gave himself up. She couldn't let that happen.

"How much time would you need if there was a way open out of here?" She spoke in a whisper. It was better that way; her inner sickness wouldn't show in her voice.

"Thirty seconds would take me across the open. Once in the trees, I'd lose myself quick. It'd be easy to reach the river then."

"Thutty seconds!" Curly echoed angrily. "Ain't I showed you how we could work it?"

"I know a better way, Curly." Clee knew what she must do now. Will Rowden would listen to her. She shrank from the thought of facing him again but she could see no other way.

"Let me see what I can do," she whispered. "I know Will Rowden."

"You'd better keep out of this, Clee."

"Be quiet, Grady!" Ma snapped. "Let her try."

"I'll ask him to see me alone, out in front." She was pleased that no strain sounded in her voice. "That's closest to the trees. If it works I'll keep him busy till you've had your chance."

Grady still demurred. "I don't trust him."

"Neither do I, but let me try. Don't make a move until you hear me call 'Will.' That will be the signal."

"I'll go with you." Letty pushed forward. She was puzzled by all this. She resented the part Clee was playing, wondered if Grady was interested in her. If Rowden could be managed she wanted a hand in it.

"This is my job, Letty. I'll have to go alone."

Letty still would have objected but Ma stopped her. "Let Clee be. I reckon she knows what she's doing. Anyway it's worth a try.

"Go on, Clee. See what you can do."

Clee moistened her lips as she edged toward the door. "Is that you, Will?" she called.

Rowden was slow to answer. He thought his ears were playing him tricks.

"This is Clee Soames. I want to see you. I'm coming out."

"Yes," he answered. "Yes, come on out."

She found she was trembling when she stepped through the door and was ashamed of it. She leaned against the wall, clenched her teeth against the wave of loathing that choked her.

He hadn't seen her yet. "Clee! Aren't you coming?"

She fought back her bitterness. "Yes, I'm coming."

From the foot of the steps she saw his dun horse, a pale wraith in the night as he moved forward. She walked to meet him, slowly.

He swung down beside her. There was a bite to his grip as he took her by the shoulders. "I've just come from the Snake on a Rock, Clee. I thought your father lied when he said you weren't there. I had to see you."

"Why?"

"I have to know what's happened to you. What's changed you so? No, you haven't changed. You can't. Neither can I. We belong to each other, Clee."

He pulled her toward him. She resisted a wild impulse to hammer at him with her fists. She knew what she must do. This was a part of it. She was shaking again but the physical panic didn't touch her mind. "Not here—not now——" she argued shrewdly. "Your men are watching."

"You're trembling, darling." His hold turned tender. "I knew you hadn't changed. It's been so long——"

"Not in front of your men," she warned again.

He was sure of himself now. All he needed was the opportunity and she'd be back in his arms, their differences forgotten. "There's only one man out here with me. The rest are surrounding the place."

"Send him away."

He was reckless with success, raised his voice guardedly. "Frank!" he called. Toomey came out of the trees.

"Go round in back with Pete. I'll take care of this side."

She watched until the deputy faded into the gloom.

"Oh, Will." Her voice rose shrilly. "Will!"

Grady, waiting in the porch shadows, heard the signal. He moved at a crouch, his pistol ready in his hand. He'd taken off his boots for this, wore them slung around his neck. Bare feet were more silent. He could see the blur of Rowden's horse, nothing more, as he headed for the trees. He listened but heard no voice.

Past the trees now, he felt secure. The river was ahead and he knew every foot of its brushy course. Clee had managed it, he didn't know how. He had reached the water before he heard her voice raised shrilly and the sheriff's angry shout. He stopped to listen but couldn't distinguish what was said. It didn't trouble him. She knew Rowden, didn't she? Besides, Curly, Ma and the others were back there to take care of things. He headed down the river.

ROWDEN reached for her. They were alone now. Clee stepped back, repeated her signal. There was no way of telling if Grady had heard. A hand closed on her arm, held her fast. "Why, Clee, you're trembling!" His arms tightened around her. There was no escape now. She clenched her fists, burrowed her face in Rowden's shoulder to escape his kisses, waited. How long did Grady say—thirty seconds? It seemed like hours. Surely he was safe by now. She couldn't be sure; she dared not stir yet. She held her breath, tried to count the seconds.

The possessive hands grew caressing. She shuddered, raised her arms. Rowden was confident; he misunderstood the gesture and bent over her.

Clee struck with all her strength and caught him in the face with both fists. Surprise helped. She felt his grip on her body loosen, twisted free and started to run.

"I hate you!" she gasped.

He lunged after her in fury. "Why, damn you——"

She heard his feet pounding after her. The hysteria so long held back overtook her now. It was in the shrill terror of her voice. "Ma! Ma! Open the door!"

The porch shadows were just ahead. Only a step or two and she'd be safe. She felt his tug on her dress, sobbed as she tried to wrench loose. The pull of his grip snapped her bodice taut, trapped her, hurt where the sleeves bit into her arms.

He had her! His fingers tightened on the thin fabric. He felt the frenzy of her struggle, exulted in it. There was a rasp of shredding cloth. She ripped free, sprawled across the porch. Before he could lunge after her a figure moved between them, out of the shadows.

"Git back."

"You all right, Clee?" Ma's voice was anxious.

"She'd better be," Curly growled.

Rowden's anger frothed up, blinding him to caution. "Don't be a fool!"

he blurted. "She came to me of her own accord, didn't she?" A savage craving to humble her before these friends lashed him on. "She won't thank you tomorrow for intervening. You know how lovers' quarrels are."

"That's a lie."

"Why don't you ask her?" he jeered. "Tell them, Clee. Tell them how often we've——"

The muzzle of a six gun was jammed into his ribs. "One more word an' I'll let you have it. I don't give a damn how many men you've got with you."

"What is it, *jefe?*" Pete Falkner eased around the corner of the building. He'd heard voices, had come to investigate. "*Mi pistola está lista.*"

The pressure of the gun had sobered Rowden. "Never mind, Pete. Put your six gun down. We don't want any shooting here if we can help it."

Ma grunted. "Specially not when you've got Curly's gun in your belly. What do you want, Sheriff?"

"I've told you. We're after Grady Scott."

"What's the charge?"

"Murder. We have a warrant for him."

"All nice an' legal. How about the gang that killed Tom? Got any warrants out for them?" She was merely playing for time, to give Grady a longer start, but she couldn't keep the bitterness from her voice.

"Name me the men and I'll serve the warrants," Rowden growled. "We've been over all this before. I'm here to enforce the law, Mrs. Williams. Right now we're after Grady Scott and we aim to get him."

"He's not here."

He hesitated, thinking she was lying. Curly's gun still prodded him. "If you had nothing to hide why did you blow out the lamps when we rode up?"

"Thar's been aplenty trouble round hyar," Curly retorted. "We ain't takin' chances. That's how come we've lasted so long."

"Now you know me, you shouldn't mind striking a light—unless you're hiding somebody."

"Make mighty easy targets of us, wouldn't it?"

"Never mind, Curly. We'll have the sheriff with us," Ma decided. "If there's any shootin' starts, I reckon he knows we'll get him first. Light the lamps."

Clee hadn't realized the damage to her dress until now. It was torn from her shoulders. She clutched it together in front to shield her breasts and shrank back against the wall as the lights flickered up, miserably aware of how her appearance supported Rowden's coarse innuendos. There was speculation in Letty's surprised look, she thought. The men had noticed, too. She could tell by their awkwardness, the way they kept their eyes averted. Only Rowden stared. She saw the mockery in his eyes. He knew how he'd shamed her before her friends.

Ma moved over, her manner casual, but Clee found herself in shadow and was grateful.

Rowden had felt certain of his prey; he was enraged when he could find no trace of Grady. He had every building ransacked, just to make sure, although by now he suspected what had happened. Falkner and Adolph Blucher were with him when he stalked back into the dining room. He ignored the others, stopped in front of Clee. "Now I know what you were up to." His voice was low but it rasped with anger. "Is Grady Scott your lover now?"

Pete's guns already were out. Their slow arc checked the Forked W hands. Curly began to swear softly.

"Oh, I know he was here. That's why you wanted to see me alone, wasn't it? . . . Wasn't it?" he bellowed.

When still she didn't answer, Rowden turned away. "When a man's wenching, he loses his watchfulness. She counted on that."

Carl forgot Pete's guns, but Ma grabbed him as he started to leap.

Curly's eyes never left those leveled barrels but they didn't stop his voice. "You won't live long in this valley, Rowden. Your mouth's too big. An' too dirty."

The sheriff turned to stare at him, his face livid with anger, but inscrutable. He didn't answer.

"That's the same Rowden that called Tom Williams a cow thief," Ma added. "Hell's bells, I reckon he's the biggest liar ever to ride these parts."

"I could shut them up *pronto, jefe,*" Falkner offered.

The sheriff turned toward the door. "The hell with it. We're going after Grady Scott. He won't get far."

The deputies followed more carefully, backing out, guns ready.

Rowden's savagery was slow to wear off. It rankled that Clee had turned against him. He'd been so sure of her, so confident that she'd come creeping back to his arms, once he found her again. That's why he'd been so easy for her to fool, he thought bitterly. Now he'd slammed the door on that part of his life. He'd paid her off and was glad of it.

He remembered her stricken look as she faced him. Even while he gloated over her hurt, he remembered how she'd clutched at her shredded dress, tried to cover her body. She'd stirred him even then, when he knew her deceit. Would he never get her out of his system? He overheard Falkner, riding ahead, as Pete questioned Blucher.

"Who was the old *pelado* back there?"

"Vot's dat? I don't know Spanish."

"Peeled one. The *hombre* with the head as bald as a *cebolla. Muy bravo,* that one. I liked him."

"Dat vass Curly Stark, an old Indian fighter. Goot t'ing you had him covered, Pete."

Rowden's lips twisted mockingly. Even Curly's threats revealed how deeply those taunts had cut.

It was hours before his rage cooled enough for him to realize that he'd gone too far. He'd made implacable enemies, not only at the Forked W but at the Snake on a Rock and the Lazy B as well, for Merrill Blake had been present too. The cattle country would be against him to a man. He weighed the situation shrewdly. Damn Clee! She had wrecked his carefully built schemes. If it hadn't been for her, the operations here could have been prolonged indefinitely. Now it was time to get out. The ranges still were crowded with beeves, though. He wished for just a little more time to strip them. Then he wouldn't mind leaving. He blamed the nesters for part of his troubles. They were too peaceable, most of them. If he could get them mixed into it, he'd have plenty of time. He smiled at the thought; his mind grew active. That was it! The nesters were the answer. Provoke them into a fight and the ranches would be too busy for anything else. He'd get his opportunity for a final cleanup, after all.

He didn't confide his plan to anyone. He wouldn't risk their leaving before he was ready, but he issued careful instructions. The nesters already were stirred up over the Unger killing. "Keep harping on that," he ordered. "Rile them up plenty. This time I won't stop them if they want to fight."

He knew what was needed. If it took a murder to rouse these Germans to shooting pitch, he'd provide one. Scalping and all, he thought. It'll look like some more of Grady Scott's work.

"Steady ever'body," Curly warned when Rowden left. "Don't try followin' now. They're watchin' for that. Our time will come but this ain't it."

They waited motionless until the rattle of hoofs informed them the intruders had left. Ma glanced at Clee and, seeing the misery on her flushed face, was tempted to hold her tongue. She decided against it. This needed prompt handling. "You pulled us out of a bad mess, Clee." Her manner was brusque. "They'd have got Grady sure if it hadn't been for you."

The girl started for the door without replying. Ma followed, caught her by the arm.

"Please don't." Half moan, half whisper, Clee's voice was pitched too low for the others to hear. "Oh, Ma, I'm so ashamed."

"Of saving a man's life?"

"Not that. You heard what Rowden said."

"Hmpf!" Ma turned a warning glare back at the others. "Rowden! He's such a liar nobody here would believe him on oath. It beats hell the things a man like that can think up. But mind this. If he said something was black I'd know damned well 't was white. An' that goes for all of us."

Clee's chin lifted. Her eyes, still doubtful, turned questioningly from Ma to the others.

"Shucks, Miss Clee." Curly shuffled his weight from one foot to the other uneasily. "Thar's always a stink to a polecat. I've already forgot what he said. Just one thing sticks in my mind an' that's how you got Grady through. I'm plumb proud to be ridin' with you, ma'am."

"That's how we all feel." Ma's voice boomed. She didn't want this dragged out longer, so she pushed Clee ahead of her through the door.

Curly stopped the others. "Just one more thing before we hit the blankets. Who was the feller with the bandage on his hand?"

Letty knew why he asked, but couldn't bring herself to answer.

"I know him," Carl spoke up. "That's Adolph Blucher."

Curly nodded grimly. He expected to see Grady later. This was something he'd want to know.

Grady didn't go far. There might be trouble here yet. With him away it wasn't likely but he wanted to be on hand if anything happened. He found the spot where an old cottonwood leaned across the water. The bank was high here and overhanging, so that its ledge formed a shallow cave, its face screened by brush. It had been one of Grady's favorite hide-outs when he was a boy. Still moving noiselessly, he crept into the hidden cavity and waited. He heard the horsemen pass before he ventured out, still cautious, for this might be a trap. The ranch buildings were dark. That reassured him. If there was danger here, Curly'd find a way to warn him. He moved to the corral, groped for his saddle on the rail, but couldn't find it.

"You're already saddled up, Grady."

He whirled at the sound, gun ready, before he realized it was Curly talking.

"I figgered you'd be ready to move. You'll find a sack of jerky an' yor bedroll on the saddle an' yor carbine's in its boot. Ever'thing's ready." He led the way to the far side of the corral.

Grady stopped. "You've got two horses saddled."

"Shore. I aim to go along. This is my war too, specially after tonight. I've got a tally to settle with Rowden."

He told of Clee's humiliation. "The lyin' son-of-a-bitch was mad clean through 'cause you got away an' he took it out on her. I couldn't do nothin' then. Falkner had us covered. But I promised myself I'd wipe the lies off his mouth first chancet. This is it."

"This is my score." Grady's voice had lost its steadiness. "I'll settle it." Curly argued stubbornly.

"One of us has got to be here," Grady pointed out, "or they'll steal Ma blind."

That was the only argument Curly would heed. He yielded reluctantly; Ma's need came first. "But mind, he spread his lies on the Forked W, Grady. Don't forget it's our move."

"I won't forget," Grady promised.

Before he left, Curly identified the man with the bandaged hand for him, too.

Rowden had taken the main trail along the north bank of the river. Grady crossed over to the south side. It was a longer route but his horse was fresh. He was confident he could beat the sheriff to Apache. They wouldn't be looking for him there. At first, stirred by Curly's story, he could think of no one but the sheriff, but the long ride gave his judgment time to assert itself. It was Rowden who held the gang together. If he died they would scatter. There was a chance that Tom's murderers might escape. No, his original plan was better. First, he'd track them down, one by one. Rowden's turn would come but it must wait. He knew Pakebusch's guilt but they were expecting him there. He was wary of traps. Frank Toomey was on his list but he doubted if the deputy would talk easily. He wanted a victim from whom he could ferret out names—and he liked the sound of Adolph Blucher. There was as yet no proof that he'd been in on Tom's killing, but that telltale bandage marked him as a member of the gang. He wasn't a professional gun slinger, either—he would be more likely to talk.

This decision necessitated a change of plans. He didn't know where Blucher lived, would have to trail him. When Grady came to his old river camp, the one he'd used when hunting Unger, he turned in and bedded down for the day.

Adolph Blucher was worried. He hesitated to admit it to Rowden. He'd seen the contempt with which the others had watched Pakebusch's terror and had shared it at first, but when Grady Scott eluded the trap set for him at Pakebusch's, his fear began to grow. Then, yesterday at the Forked W, he'd seen Curly Stark's hostility, too. All the cowmen were against them. "'T ain't dat I'm really vorried," he finally blurted out. "But I'm hurt und I can't shoot so goot mit dis bandage on de hand."

Rowden's eyes narrowed. "That's only a scratch. Prop a rifle in the window. Then all you'll have to do is squeeze the trigger."

"Besides, you didn't shoot off your mouth," Toomey pointed out. "How could Scott find out that you were with us when Williams was killed?"

"How can ve tell how much dis man knows?" Blucher protested. "De sheriff himself says he ain't sure."

That started a new line of thought for Toomey. He was skilled with weapons and no coward. If Scott came looking for him he wouldn't meet a cowering Kurt Pakebusch, he assured himself grimly. But he remembered that everyone knew he was present when Williams died. It made him a marked man. It was one thing to meet an antagonist in a fair fight, he told himself, and quite another to have an unknown enemy lurking in the dark, ready to strike when least expected. He grew uneasy, but tried to hide it under his usual heartiness.

"Look, Adolph, if you're worried I'll ride home with you." He laughed when he saw Rowden's eyes on him. "Me, I'd like to run into this fellow Scott. Yeah, then we'd have nothing more to worry about. I can promise you that." He chortled again, a little louder than before, because he was uneasy under the sheriff's stare.

"Grady Scott's smarter than I thought." Rowden studied his deputy with cold eyes. "I thought he'd overplayed his hand when he scalped Unger. It gave me something to use to stir up the nesters. I see I was wrong. He's got every one of you wondering who's going to lose his hair next."

"Not me." Toomey bristled and slapped his holster. "It just made me mad. Yeah, I'll remember that scalping all right. It'll just make me shoot straighter if I ever catch up with that fellow."

Blucher held up his bandage. " 'T ain't I'm really scairt, not like Kurt. Mit dis I can't shoot so goot."

"Go on with him." The sheriff waved abruptly toward the door. "But keep this in mind—by the time a man's scalped he's past feeling anything. It's nothing to worry about."

Toomey laughed and thumped Blucher on the back. "Yeah, Adolph, any time you're scalped you won't feel it."

The sheriff frowned after them when they left. He didn't like Toomey's heartiness—there was a false note to it.

Both riders felt better when they left the town behind. It was twelve miles to Blucher's cabin. By the time they'd reached it, Toomey half regretted he had come. His uneasiness had worn off. The only thing that lingered was the shamed suspicion that Will Rowden had guessed it. He ought to know me better than that, he thought once. Yeah, we've been through tight places together before and I've always been ready with my guns.

He had worked himself into a resentful anger toward the chief by the time they loosed their horses in Blucher's corral. It roughened his patience with his companion. "Got any grain for these broncs? I aim to be riding at sunrise."

"I've got hay."

"Well, rustle some up. That's one trouble with you, Adolph. You don't know how to mind a horse."

Blucher found a lantern in the barn, and lighted it to see his way about the chore. Toomey didn't help.

They were headed for the house when Blucher asked: "Vot does a man look like ven he iss scalped?"

"You're as bad as Kurt. Can't get that out of your mind, can you?" Then, because he was angry and because he remembered so well, he described with savage relish how he'd found Unger. " 'T ain't pretty. It does something to a man's face. It sags, sort of. Why, when I found Unger——"

Blucher interrupted him hastily. "Don't!" he said. "I don't vant to hear it."

Before they went to bed Blucher got out his shotgun, gave it a double charge of slugs and propped it beside his bunk.

There was a light burning in the jail, and several horses were tied in front. Grady was tempted to creep up and listen, but decided against it. From here he could watch with little chance of detection. He had rested all day, slipped into town after dark. In the rear of Scanlon's the gloom was thick and from there his view of the sheriff's office was unobstructed. He saw the door open. In its light he recognized Frank Toomey. With him stood a stranger with his right hand bandaged. Blucher! They passed so close he could hear a snatch of their conversation.

"Kurt's a coward!" Toomey broke out angrily. Grady tried to hear the answer but couldn't.

He thought they were headed for Scanlon's but they didn't stop at the saloon. Instead, they found their horses at the hitch rail and mounted. Grady moved closer while they were occupied with this.

Ranger was too far away for use. There were a dozen horses at the rail. He could see them in the glow of Scanlon's windows. Boldness was his best course. Grady glanced up and down the street. It was deserted except for the two horsemen who were a hundred yards away by now, traveling at an easy jog. He tugged his hat well over his eyes, pulled his six guns half from their holsters, let them slide back gently so they'd be eased and ready. Then he stepped into the light and headed for the nearest horse.

He rode slowly. There was danger that the men ahead might wait if they heard him coming. Once the town was cleared, he checked and waited until they'd gained more distance. They were lost in the blur ahead but he could hear them still. They were riding at an easy lope. He liked that. The noise of their horses would deaden the sound of his own pursuit. The trail led past nester cabins and was packed by the tread of oxen. He rode to the side as much as possible, hunting sod to deaden hoofbeats. The riders ahead were careless. He could hear them a long way and he dropped farther and farther behind. Then the sounds ahead ended. That worried him. He couldn't be sure whether his quarry had stopped or abandoned the road for a trail across the prairie turf. He increased his gait slightly but he didn't forget his caution. After several hundred yards he pulled aside and stopped to listen. At first he heard nothing. Then, far off to the right, he picked up the sound again, faint now. He turned and followed.

The lantern warned Grady. Once on the soft turf he had closed up on the horsemen ahead as much as he dared; he increased his prudence, too. They were riding eastward into the lower end of the valley and the homesteads grew fewer and more scattered. It was thirty minutes since he'd passed a fence. Often he paused to listen ahead. That was the trouble with a night trail. If he could hear them they might hear him, if they became suspicious. Once they checked their gait and he rode too close before discovering it. It was their voices which warned him then and he waited until the sounds were barely distinguishable before moving on.

The lantern simplified things. He watched from a safe distance until it bobbed toward the house. Against its gleam the men threw spidery shadows. Grady was in no hurry. For what he had in mind, daylight would serve him best.

He scouted the place carefully after the cabin was dark. There was a creek about forty yards east of the house, explaining its location. The creek gave him cover for his horse, which he tethered a safe distance downstream. The ground was almost flat, offering no shelter. The barn was scarcely larger than a lean-to adjoining the corral and, like many of the nester buildings he had seen, was of wattle; it was framed of logs, with the interstices formed by a rickrack of slender poles daubed over with mud. He decided on the barn. Here they couldn't reach their horses without being seen. Grady burrowed a comfortable hollow in the hay and settled down to wait.

Blucher came out first. It was early; the sun still was red. Grady heard the rattle of his bucket and watched as he filled it from the creek. Later, the pungency of coffee and frying meat reminded him of his own hunger. He swung his arms to get the stiffness out, rubbed his hands to warm them and flexed his fingers to limber them, too. The two men wouldn't be long in coming and he wanted to be ready.

They started for the corral together, Toomey in the lead. There were two six guns in his holsters. Blucher wore a pistol, too, and carried a shotgun cradled in his left arm. Grady frowned at sight of that. It bothered him more than the odds. He watched as they headed for the corral, waited until Blucher reached his saddle. Toomey slid through the corral gate, trailing his rope after him as he started for the horses. Blucher propped his shotgun against the barn as he picked up his saddle and followed. Grady eased out the door and stepped toward them quietly, still unnoticed. The horses retreated into a corner. Toomey edged them in and readied his rope for the throw. Blucher put down his saddle in the center of the corral and waited his turn. Grady stepped between them and the gate. He hadn't touched his guns yet but he was balanced for it, his right hand waist-high, elbow crooked. From here he could watch both men and his eyes never wavered.

"Let the horses go," he said.

Toomey wheeled, let the rope slide through his fingers. He didn't go for his gun, not yet. Experience had taught him the signs of a draw. He knew Grady was poised and a false move would invite a bullet. Curiously, the nervousness he had felt last night was gone. He was calculating his chances calmly. There are two of us, he thought. If he goes for Adolph first I'll kill him. He stood motionless, waited for the split-second diversion that would give him his chance.

Blucher dropped his saddle, started to whimper. "Vot makes you t'ink I had anyt'ing to do mit de killin' of Tom Villiams?"

"You seem to know why I'm here." The whine told Grady much. Toomey was the one to watch. "You've changed your tune," he prodded. "You were mighty quick to throw lead the other night when you thought I didn't have a gun."

Blucher sucked in his breath audibly. "You shot me in de hand," he gasped. "You know I haffn't got a chance."

"Go ahead and draw," Grady invited. "I'll give you more chance than you gave Tom."

Blucher's face turned a sickly yellow. "I didn't know dey vass goin' to kill him. Ja, I vass dere but I didn't know——"

Toomey was waiting for a break. Maybe this was it. Blucher's sniveling sickened him but it might have its use. It wouldn't take much to stampede him. One second's diversion was all he needed. "Shut up your blubbering, Adolph! You're in this as much as anybody."

"No, no!" The nester shouted shrilly.

The cry spooked the horses. They whooshed from their corner with a clatter of hoofs, and as they whisked past, Blucher broke for the barn. Grady's glance wavered.

Toomey slapped leather but Grady was alert for the move. His hand flashed; his six gun roared. Toomey sagged in the middle, struggled to complete his draw, but his speed was gone and his eyes were glazed. The second shot sent him toppling.

Grady turned to find Blucher. The shooting had kept the horses galloping, swirled up the dust in a blinding cloud. He darted toward the right, searching for his enemy, and saw that the shotgun was gone.

Grady hugged the barn wall, took time to reload his pistol as he edged along it toward the door. The scatter-gun worried him. It sprayed its lead—even a wobbly hand could point it at close range. "Come on out," he called. "You're cornered. You can't get away."

Blucher had found some of his courage now that he was safely in the barn. He liked the feel of the shotgun. "You can't get avay eider," he called. His tone turned crafty. "Maybe ve could make a trade. I vill tell you de names of de men mit Toomey ven Tom Villiams vass kilt und you go avay, eh?"

Grady had wanted to question his first victim, but Unger had been too quick on the draw. There still were things he wanted to know but Blucher set too high a price on his information.

"No deal. You were there. That's enough for me. I'm coming in after you."

Grady sent a bullet through the crack of the door. His opponent had a devastating weapon but it had only one shot. If he could draw an answering fire the way would be cleared for a rush. There was no reply. Again he sent a bullet into the door, but the nester seemed to have guessed his purpose and still held his fire.

Grady slipped around the corner of the barn. Here there was no break in its wall. Toomey's rope lay where he'd dropped it almost within reach. Grady pumped another bullet at the door to keep the nester under cover while he pulled the rope in. The tall corral fence reached to the eaves of the low barn. He freed a heavy rail from the pen and looped an end of the rope around it, before climbing to the roof. Silently now, he crept to the ridgepole directly above the door.

He took his time with this task, pulled the rope in slowly so that the rail was nudged along the ground a few inches at a time. He wanted the man inside to hear that stealthy approach.

Fear was running from Blucher's pores; it made his hands clammy. He wiped them on his pants, gripped his shotgun tighter and held his breath to listen. There was a faint ribbon of sound, outside, along the wall. He cursed the wattle that made the barn so snug. With logs, he could have peered through a chink and watched. He heard the sound again, closer this time, nearing the door. He was sure he knew its meaning. He raised his weapon, leveled it, waited. Even its tremor, from the ague in his hands, didn't bother him. He couldn't miss at this distance.

Not with a scatter-gun. Here it was better than all the pistol trickery in the world.

Grady peered down. The rail was only a couple of feet from the door. If the ruse had worked, now was the time to draw Blucher's fire. Leaning out, he paved the way for the last yank with a well-aimed shot. Then, tugging hard, he brought the log crashing against the door and was rewarded with an answering blast from the shotgun.

Heedless of sound now, Grady scrambled for the eaves, dropped off and darted for the door. Blucher had no time to reload the scatter-gun. Instead he had his pistol out. It flashed as the door swung open—too fast, for in his terror he hadn't waited for a target. The answering bullet caught him before he could move again.

Grady smoothed the dust beside each man and scrawled his message. "Tom Williams. $5 - 2 = 3$."

Then he drew his knife. He had knelt beside Toomey before he remembered Letty's horror of the other scalping and he hesitated. Such squeamishness was hard for him to understand. In Indian fighting no one thought twice of such a thing. He intended it as a warning for the others he was hunting. If it seemed ruthless to them, so much the better. But he couldn't forget Letty. I'm a fool for listening to her, he told himself, but he put up his knife.

Clee dressed slowly. She had awakened wondering about Grady. Was he safe? Or had Rowden been able to pick up his trail? Remembering all she'd heard of Grady's prowess, she thought not. It fitted her growing estimate of him. No, he was more than a match for his antagonists. Only there were so many of them—that worried her.

She didn't wonder at this interest in Grady. It seemed natural to her. They shared the same enemy. He was on her side and the task he'd set himself was perilous. There was much she didn't understand. Why had Rowden come to Apache? What was his purpose here? Why was he surrounded by such men as Pete Falkner and Frank Toomey? She didn't know, except that everything about him now filled her with distrust.

She flushed at memory of the way he had humiliated her last night; she wished she might avoid facing her friends at breakfast. She was able to appraise the scene better now, though. Wouldn't Will Rowden be pleased if he knew how I felt? she thought. That's what he wanted. It's his way of getting even with me—that turned her stubborn—nobody's going to guess I care. There was no other way to help Grady and I took it. If anyone wants to believe Rowden, they can—her lips tightened and she raised her chin—they can go plumb to the devil.

Ma was waiting, her manner so casual that Clee guessed something was wrong.

"Any word from Grady?"

"Curly saw him last night. He's all right."

"Then what's the matter?"

Ma's eyes were sharp. "Nothing, I hope. I was troubled about you. Last night you were pretty much upset. You ain't figurin' on goin' home, are you?"

Clee shook her head.

"Good." Ma grinned. "Sometimes folks think runnin' away will solve things. Me, I always figured it had a guilty look. I didn't want you makin' any mistakes." She linked an arm through the girl's. "Come on, breakfast's waitin'."

Clee didn't mind Ma's concern; she dreaded facing it in the others. They'd be waiting, she knew. She stiffened a little outside the door, wore a crust of indifference as she entered the room. She resented the way they avoided her eyes when she came in, even though she understood their kindly intention. This touchiness bolstered her.

Only regard for her had made them awkward. Her thorny shell helped. Then she was swept into the current of familiar ranch talk and easy chaff. She lost her strain in this friendliness.

Carl was the only one who forgot Ma's warning. He couldn't keep his concern from showing. Clee saw it, puckering his face, when he followed her to the corral after breakfast. Poor kid, she thought, he still thinks he's in love. If I'm not careful this will be bad. She was gentle with him but firm in her guidance of the conversation.

"Now that there's a girl your age here, I'm surprised you waste time on me." She glanced toward the kitchen where Ohmie was bustling about and smiled. "She's pretty, isn't she?"

"I hadn't noticed. How could I with you around? You know how I feel about you, Clee."

She swung a saddle over her horse, reached under his belly for the girth. "I thought we settled all this once before. I'm too old for you. You were going to be my best friend—remember?"

"I wanted to see you last night," he plunged on. "I wanted you to know——"

"Sort of a busy evening, wasn't it?" she broke in, her voice still matter-of-fact. "I saw you dancing with Ohmie. You make a nice couple, Carl, and you have a lot in common. Her family's German like yours, too."

He turned sulky. "You keep trying to change the subject."

She straightened up, the girth finally secured. "It's something we've already settled. There's no point in bringing it up again."

"That was before last night."

"Now wait a minute, Carl. Nothing has happened to change the way we feel about each other. We had to get Grady out of here and we did. Rowden didn't like it and said some pretty harsh things, I guess. What of it? Words aren't bullets. They don't rub off on you. They can't hurt you unless you let them." She gave him a friendly thump on the back. "Now forget it, as I have."

She was so matter-of-fact about it, Carl could think of nothing to say. He felt vaguely disappointed, cheated of the heroics he'd expected. She was in the saddle and gone before he found his tongue.

He was disappointed in Clee, too, the way she'd called his attention to Ohmie. How could she think him so fickle, when he'd been blind to everyone but her? He couldn't even remember how the Pakebusch girl looked and was faintly surprised that Clee thought her pretty. Before leaving, he rode by the kitchen just to see if she was right. He spurred his bronc into a caper when he caught Ohmie's glance.

He had set himself a chore for that morning. Letty was going home. She would ride as far as the Lazy B with Merrill Blake. He was disturbed by that and had planned to join them. Letty was a disappointment too. He'd always liked her, had been pleased at her thinly disguised efforts at managing Grady. He thought it an appropriate match. What disturbed his ardent loyalty was the thought of her riding off with another man, particularly Blake. He liked Blake. That was the trouble. He considered him too likely a rival for Grady and decided against leaving them alone. All the way to the Lazy B he regaled them both with stories he'd heard of Grady. Letty had no chance to forget him. Carl saw to that.

Clee had Carl on her mind. So far she'd been able to steer him gently, but he was beginning to show more persistence. For the plan she was considering she needed Ma's co-operation. She told her about it that day. "Why can't he fall in love with Ohmie, Ma? I don't want him hurt and she's his age. She'd be pretty, too, if we fixed her up. That's where I need your help."

"Kind of like fightin' a prairie fire, ain't it?" Ma chuckled. "You build a backfire, one you can steer, an' first thing you know you've got the whole thing under control. What you want me to do?"

"If we rode in early we'd have Ohmie all trigged out before Carl got back. With a few tucks here and there, she could wear some of my clothes. Nobody's ever showed her how to do her hair. We ought to fix her up some, anyway. After all, she saved Grady's life, didn't she?"

"Well!" Ma's voice boomed heartily. "I'm glad to see you're beginnin' to wake up an' do a little managin' yourself."

Clee's eyes widened. "It's good managing, isn't it?"

"Sure—for somebody else. I want you to do a little on your own account. It's made my hackles rise the way you've sat around helplesslike while Letty outmanaged you every turn of the wheel."

Clee laughed. "It's pretty plain how Letty feels about Grady, isn't it?"

"Oh, he could do worse, I reckon," Ma grudgingly admitted. "But she's the outmanagin'est female I ever clapped eyes on. I don't like it, the way you let her outsmart you. What's wrong with you, honey?"

Clee thought this over. "I reckon I'm not interested enough in any man to start managing for him."

"Hell's bells! You like him, don't you?"

"Of course I like him. He's a lot like you, Ma. It's just that—well, I guess I'm not interested in any man that way."

"High time you was, then." Ma gave her hat a jerk down over her eyes. "Come on, we'd best be headin' for home. We've got a job to do on Ohmie."

The girl was bewildered at first. No one had ever taken such trouble with her. Starting with her hair, they tried it several ways before they were satisfied. Ohmie liked it knotted in the back, the way they tried it first—she imagined it made her look desirably older. Her mentors were on a spree though—they had to try everything. After several experiments, they decided on braids twisted around her head. Ma was anxious to make some contribution but her clothes were too ample. Clee had a dress that would do without too much altering. They even insisted on shoes although Ohmie limped in them. She'd never worn anything on her feet except coarse boots in winter, against the cold. When they saw her discomfort, they agreed that she might leave them off till suppertime but she promised to be wearing them when the men rode in.

The new finery delighted Ohmie. She strutted about the room for their inspection. Rid of her shapeless homespun, she was startlingly changed. "You look mighty thin though," Ma decided. "I'll have to feed you up." That gave her an idea. She brought out a voluminous petticoat reserved for special occasion. Pinned around the girl's hips, it gave her skirt a flare they all liked. Ma grinned. "That's better. I knew I'd find something of my own she could wear."

They were so pleased with the result that Ma decided to cook supper herself. "I don't want you all mussed up beforehand." She silenced Ohmie's protest. "You can set the table."

Clee made careful preparations, too. She had thought this out. When Carl rode in, she was wearing the old pants Ma had loaned her for use in the saddle, and her bright hair was stuffed out of sight under a battered hat. She looked as if she'd ridden hard that day.

All the men noticed the change in Ohmie. "The grub here's doin' you good, girl," Peg commented, not suspecting Ma's hidden petticoat that added the flare to her hips.

"Still skinny in the middle though." Curly eyed her narrow waist. "Trig as a bird. I like you that way."

Carl said nothing but his eyes were rounder than any. He twisted his neck each time she swished to and from the kitchen, and after supper he volunteered to help her with the dishes, a chore she had assumed since her arrival.

There was considerable chatter in the kitchen. Once, when they both broke into laughter, Clee looked across the table at Ma and winked.

THE killings at Blucher's were discovered by Hans Biedermann, a thrifty nester whose homestead lay in that end of the valley. He loaded the bodies into his wagon and brought them to town. This time the sheriff had no chance to suppress the identifying message Grady had left behind. Biedermann repeated his story many times—at the sheriff's office, at Lehman's Store, at Scanlon's, at the wagon yard and at the Reid House. As the word spread the town began to fill. Some of the nesters trudged in alone, heavy-browed men with scatter-guns under their arms; others, too thrifty to waste the journey, plodded beside their oxcarts, their families with them; a few of the more prosperous rode. The wagon yard was stifled in dust, its corral choked with animals and circled by parked wagons, where each family had its cook fire at mealtime. The haze of coarse home-grown tobacco was thick at Scanlon's, the bar was jammed and the place was filled with an angry, guttural din. At Lehman's, women used to loneliness forgot their silence and the clatter was shrill.

There were no ranchmen here. The only spurs to jingle in the town were in the office of the sheriff where Will Rowden held a council with Pete Falkner, Charlie Springer and Kurt Pakebusch.

"If this keeps up we can hold our next meeting in the pocket of my *chaleco*" was Falkner's laconic remark when he heard the news.

Terror was growing in Pakebusch. Its marks showed in his dilated eyes and in the tremulous fumbling of his fingers as he tried to roll a cigarette. The tobacco spilled over; when he tried again the paper tore. He gave up the effort, looked up to see the others watching him.

"Just three of us left," said Falkner.

"T'ree?"

"Sure. You don't count any more, Pakebusch. You've lost your nerve, if you ever had any."

"Iff ve could get avay——"

"Don't start that again," Springer warned.

Rowden couldn't keep his fingers still. Their flutter made a ceaseless patter on the worn desk. He was pleased. He'd wanted just such an incident and Grady had given it to him. There'd be no trouble rousing the nesters to fighting pitch now. Handled right, they'd provide him with his war. He decided the time for secrecy was passed. He would reveal his plan.

"For once Pakebusch is right." Rowden saw Springer's surprise, Falkner's angry flush. "Don't get the wrong idea," he continued. "We're not through here yet. We're going to stir up more trouble than a sack of snakes and we're going to make a killing before we ride out of here. This has been a good stand but we knew it wouldn't last forever.

"Both sides have got their horns sharpened for trouble now. There'll be smoke up the valley before this is over. That's what I want. The worse it is, the better I'll like it. While they're shooting it out we'll be gathering cattle, pushing them into the Scalp Creek Breaks where we'll build our trail herd and keep moving. By the time the smoke clears we'll be long gone and so will their steers."

"I'd like to meet up with Grady Scott before I leave these parts," Pete Falkner remarked.

"You'll probably get your chance. I hope so." The sheriff explained the plan he had formulated. The killings provided a pretext for trouble. The nesters already were aroused. He would form a strong posse, lead them himself in an invasion of the western valley. "All nice and legal," he added. "I'm the sheriff."

"What about August Lehman? He'll try to stop you."

"I'm not worried about him any more. It was different when we planned to stay here. Once he realized what was going on he'd be as bothersome as Grady Scott. Even more, maybe, because the nesters listen to him. In the long run he'll have his way and this will be an unhealthy place for men like us." Rowden shrugged. "But we'll be gone by then. No, we'll build a fire under the nesters quick, and to hell with Lehman now. Once the powder-burning starts not even he can stop it."

"How much time have we got?"

"Let's see." Rowden narrowed his eyes as he calculated. "There was a new moon last night. That means it'll be full in two weeks. That's just about the time we need for what we've got to do. If I head the nesters out on the warpath today, it shouldn't take us long to stir up a fight. Tomorrow maybe. How many riders have you got up on Scalp Creek, Pete?"

"Eleven. All *veteranos* and with short triggers. If there is shooting ahead that is their *pasatiempo*."

The sheriff shook his head. "If they're seen down here it might give away our plans. Besides, I want them in the Breaks to hold the herd together. We had better than twelve hundred head of steers up there at last count. No, they'll be needed where they are and so will we. Once the fighting starts we'll have our hands full."

Rowden figured the time carefully, fixed his dates. Twenty-four hours were allowed to organize and bring on the opening fight. "And we'll have to be on hand then to make sure it comes off." He allowed two more days for the cowmen to gather their forces and get moving. Once the feud broke into open warfare there was no telling where it would stop, or when. He felt safe in allowing himself two weeks. "That gives us plenty of time to build our herd," he continued. "And we'll have a full moon when we drive 'em out, two weeks from tonight. That's going to be the toughest part of the job. We'll have to take 'em west over the hills through Little Scalp Pass and I'm counting on driving a big herd."

He gave each man careful instructions. They were to mingle with the crowds, build up feeling. "Buy a few drinks," he urged. "Don't be afraid to spend money. There's plenty more where that came from. This town's going to be hell with the hide off in two hours if you do your jobs right. Remember, once they're smoking up each other nobody's going to have time to bother us."

August Lehman smelled trouble. His store was crowded but there were no men there and there was little buying. It was easy to gauge the temper of the men he met on the streets. Even the more conservative of them, friends who usually followed his lead, were short of temper.

"Ja, August, killing iss a bad t'ing," Hans Biedermann agreed. "Alvays I listen to you und vant you should be right. 'Vait,' you say, 'de goot people vill settle dis.' Comes a time now ven ve vait too long, August. Because ve are patient dey t'ink ve are afraid. Comes time now for ot'er t'ings. My scatter-gun iss in der vagon."

Everywhere he went he encountered this same dogged determination. He found the sheriff at Scanlon's.

"The people have lost their heads," he told Rowden. "But I can stop them if you will help me."

"I don't want to stop them, Mr. Lehman. That's the trouble here. Too much worry about what will happen, everyone expecting me to head off trouble. These cowmen don't understand that kind of treatment. This time I'm going to take action."

"What kind of action?"

"I'm organizing a posse and going after the murderer and I'll take with me every man who'll go. If you're wise you'll join me."

"All these nesters? Now—while they're stirred up?"

"Haven't they a right to be?"

"Yess." Lehman's face clouded. "But what happens if they run into some cowmen when they're worked up like thiss? What happens at the Lazy B, when they see this many armed nesters coming? Trouble! I don't like it. One excited man pulls a trigger and we have war. The whole valley will be in it. Where will it stop?"

"It's the only way to end these killings."

"Please, Mister Rowden, listen to me. A few good men can track one murderer down. When you lead thiss many angry men into hostile country you are inviting worse trouble. There will be bloodshed."

Rowden wouldn't listen. The merchant's interference angered him. August's worried speculation was too close to the purpose in the sheriff's mind. "Keep out of this, Lehman. I know what I'm doing. The time for talk is past."

A few men listened and were as concerned as Lehman over the situation, but they couldn't make themselves heard above the growing din. Whenever Lehman found one of these conservative friends he made an appointment to meet him at the Reid House where they could talk. Fourteen of them gathered there just before noon.

"If the sheriff rides these men into the ranch country the cowmen will fight," Lehman promised. "It iss our job to make them understand that. They are good people, hard-working and honest, but something hass got into them. Why won't they realize this iss war? It can bring no good— nothing but trouble and bloodshed. We must stop it."

A sense of helplessness pervaded the meeting. If the homesteaders wouldn't listen to August Lehman, it was useless for others to try. Their despair baffled the merchant. He refused to give up. "There are Texas Rangers at Menardville," he said. "They can stop this. I will send for them."

"Dey are for fighting Indians—dey vouldn't come."

"Menardville iss t'ree days avay. Even iff dey came it vould be too late."

He listened to the protests but his mind was set. "I would go myself but it iss better I stay here. Sometimes they will listen to me." He called for a volunteer to make the ride. Hans Agold stepped forward.

"T'ree days But I von't stop at night. I vill get dere in two."

Some of the little audience took hope. Agold had a good saddle horse. A prosperous neighbor lent him another, for it was decided he would need two on such a journey. Another friend offered him a pistol but this he declined.

"It iss Indian country, Hans."

"Still I don't know how to shoot it." His blue eyes twinkled. "Do you vant I should hurt mineself mit it? Chust giff me horses vot can run fast. Dat's more my style."

Letty heard their discussion. She had arrived back the night before. When Agold was ready to leave she met him at the door with a bundle. "You'll need something to eat on the way," she told him.

Rowden saw his departure and was puzzled by it. He didn't want the ranches warned of what was afoot.

"He's headed north," Falkner pointed out. "He can't do us any harm in that direction."

"He's no fool. He knows we'd stop him if he started west. Follow him, Pete. Make sure he doesn't circle when he leaves town. If he tries anything like that—well, you know what to do."

Falkner patted his holster as he loosed his horse. "Don't worry about him. He won't make us any trouble."

Letty was sure the killings were Grady's doing, even before she heard of the message found scratched beside the bodies. Toomey's was one of the three names he'd given her and Blucher's bandaged hand had betrayed him. She listened for the details with dread. It was Unger's scalping, not his death, that had revolted her. Men often died violently here and the motive that impelled a man to quit the Rangers to track down the murderers of a friend was easy for her to understand. Twice she heard the story, waited at the end for more. Toomey had drawn his six gun, they said. She remembered what Grady had told her of Unger's death. "It was a fair fight. He had his chance. That's more than they gave Tom."

Toomey was deputy sheriff and had a reputation with a gun. He'd had his chance, too. She found it curious that she should be so relieved to hear it. And Blucher had fired first. They'd found his empty shotgun beside him. "And this time there were two of them," she found herself repeating.

"Were they scalped?" she finally asked when the wait for more news grew unbearable. When she learned they weren't, all her grisly worry vanished and secretly she reconstructed the scene in her mind. Grady had tackled two of them this time. The odds had been against him.

After Agold rode off she went to the store. Her sympathies were mixed. She was on Grady's side. Most of the cowmen were her friends but so were August Lehman and the men who had met at her hotel. So were many of the other nesters now too inflamed for sober judgment. She had no definite plan in mind except that she knew she'd find the women at the store. Everything else had failed. Perhaps an appeal to them might help. Her sense of impending tragedy deepened as she hurried along the street. Most of the men she passed gripped scatter-guns and their purpose was evident in flushed, angry faces. They would meet men equally determined. She knew that. And unless something were done to stop it, and quickly, this would end in plenty of bloodshed.

She stood in the doorway at Lehman's and watched the women there. If they could be made to realize what was about to happen they'd do something.

Letty elbowed her way to the counter. "How much lint have you got?" she demanded loudly. August was behind the counter. He didn't understand and she raised her voice. "Lint! Lint for bandages. We must be ready to take care of the wounded."

The women near her fell silent, listened in surprise. "A lot of these men will be badly hurt when they come back." Letty's voice could be heard clearly in the curious hush now. "Those that come back," she added.

"Some of you women must help me. We can rig up a hospital at the hotel. You know how it is. It's a woman's job to take care of those who are hurt. We can't help the dead but we can make the wounded comfortable."

Lehman guessed her purpose. He shook his head sadly. "I'm afraid there iss not enough, Letty. But mostly it iss nails you'll need—for coffins. There iss lots of fighting ahead, before thiss iss over."

"Vot iss dis talk of vounded?" Work-roughened hands clutched at Letty's sleeve.

"Und coffins! Dat's vot Herr Lehman said—coffins!"

The room's clamor began again but there was an anxious note to it now.

"Of course I said dead." Letty shouted against the din. "They're going out to fight, aren't they? What are those shotguns for? You know the cowmen. Do you think they won't fight back? This is war. Do you hear me? War!"

Rowden had seventy men ready to ride. Falkner had rejoined them with a report on Hans Agold. "He is not going to warn anybody, *jefe*. He is just plain *prudente*. Headed due north and riding hard. We do not need to bother about him."

Charlie Springer and Kurt Pakebusch were there, too. The sheriff needed them to keep up the mob's spirit. The rest were nesters, but a mixed lot. The ne'er-do-wells and the shiftless, men of Pakebusch's stamp, mingled with the more prosperous homesteaders who usually looked to Lehman for leadership. The posse was mounting when the women came surging down the street with Letty at their head. The sheriff didn't realize what it meant until worried wives invaded his ranks in search of their husbands. Angry family altercations broke out. A few men shamefacedly dismounted.

"Hey, what's going on here?" Rowden saw his posse was dwindling. "Mount up, men. It's time we were riding."

When the confusion continued he singled out Letty Reid as their leader. "What's the matter with these womenfolks?"

"They know there's going to be shooting and they'd rather have their menfolks safe at home."

"Confound it! This is a posse. There's been murder done. We have to preserve law and order."

"Which murder are you working on?" Letty demanded. "Tom Williams?"

Rowden's eyes narrowed. "Which side are you on?"

"These are my friends. I don't want to see them led into trouble."

The sheriff looked out over the crowd, measured its uneasy reaction to this. "The trouble with this girl is she's got too many friends on both sides. She beat us to the Forked W where Grady Scott was hiding.

He got away. If it hadn't been for that these last killings wouldn't have happened."

Letty was trapped and realized it. She turned crimson.

"You see?" Rowden laughed. "No wonder she wants to stop you. She's a friend of Grady Scott's."

She wouldn't give up. "Whose quarrel is this?" she cried. "Remember that message beside the bodies? Someone's avenging the killing of Tom Williams. Were you in on that? If you weren't, this isn't your fight. There's no reason you should die over it."

Rowden saw that more of his men were dismounted now. "Don't pay her any mind. She's on the cowman's side."

"No, listen! Listen!" A woman cried, and others took up the chant. "Listen! Listen! Listen!"

The sheriff didn't dare wait longer. He must move fast before the disaffection spread. "Come on!" he shouted. "Let's get moving."

Some of the horsemen moved with him. Others had trouble extricating themselves from their wives. Still a third group already were afoot. More might have followed, the sheriff thought, had he been able to put spurs to his horse, move out fast, but that was impossible. He had to pick his way through the crowd. When he looked back to count his strength at the edge of town, he found he had only thirty-eight men left. No matter. That was enough to get things started. After that, the others would have to fight.

Chapter 20 WAR

GRADY was in no hurry to leave Blucher's. Fighting had been his grim business too long for the two bodies to worry him. His mind was busy with the problems ahead. It would be unwise to travel that neighborhood by daylight. He turned the horses from the corral so they could shift for themselves. Then, remembering the coffee he had smelled earlier, he visited the house.

He didn't like the squalor of the cabin. It had the animal smell of a close-shut place. The floor was unswept, the fragments of breakfast littered the table. He found what he needed, made his own camp in the lee of the barn and while the fire was kindling scoured the blackened utensils with sand at the creek. He was still there, breakfast just finished, when Hans Biedermann drove by, stopped to investigate when his "Hello" went unanswered.

Grady slipped into the barn where he could watch unseen, and his guns were ready until he satisfied himself about the stranger. A neighbor, he decided, a nester whom he hadn't seen before. He had no quarrel with this man. He made himself a hiding place in the mounded hay, waited in silence until the wagon's rattle told him it was safe to come out.

The news wouldn't be long in spreading now, he knew. He stomped out the fire and made ready to move. He had never known this end of the valley well and it had changed. Homesteads were thick along the river to the south. That didn't trouble him greatly. He wasn't known there. He decided to find a crossing, keep south of the water until he'd passed the town and was back in familiar territory. He brought his horse up to the barn, fed him well before he rode off.

The grass had cured brown. There was no trouble marking the river's course. It was a meandering green belt across the flat valley. As he neared it he could discern the patchwork of nester fields and wattle cabins whose plastered walls were bright in the sun. Fences shut him off from the river. He turned aside to find a path, heard the pounding of a horse and watched as its rider on the distant road halted briefly at a cabin before hurrying on. The fences irritated him. He rode three miles before he found a break.

The road, so recently almost deserted, had turned busy by the time he reached it. He turned left, away from the traffic. His eye reached ahead; each farm made its contribution to the steady flow—sometimes a man who walked alone, elsewhere a family that marched beside its oxen. There were few horsemen. All moved in the same direction, toward Apache, and Grady thought he understood when he noticed that each man carried a scatter-gun. That rider who'd galloped so fast had brought news of the fight at Blucher's. The nesters were gathering. He was sure of this when he met the first group. The farmer strode beside his oxen, his weapon nursed in one arm, and his scowl didn't lessen when Grady lifted an arm in silent greeting. There was a woman in the cart and two half-grown boys followed in its dust. Each eyed him in the same sullen way.

He met two horsemen next; he liked their appearance. They rode like farmers but were better-dressed than most. They had a sound, substantial look that reminded him of August Lehman. He smiled his greeting this time, checked his horse in pleasant Texas fashion. The strangers nodded curtly but rode on.

Grady halted his horse in the middle of the road at the next encounter. There were three men in this group, all afoot, their boots already dusty. He could read the dislike in their eyes before they stopped.

"I'm looking for a way to cross the river," he began. "How much farther do these fences last?"

They regarded him in awkward silence. "Der's a ford back of Mueller's," one finally admitted reluctantly. "Dat's de t'ird house."

"But Mueller vouldn't vant a cowman ridin' t'rough his pasture, leavin' open de gates," the leader of the trio interrupted sullenly. "Better you don't go t'rough his fields."

The third nester remained silent but he had taken his scatter-gun from his shoulder.

"And if I don't cut through Mueller's, how far do I ride before I reach a crossing?"

"Six miles und dat's vere you cross. I told you—you don't go t'rough Mueller's."

The surly tone irritated Grady but he held his temper. He wanted no trouble with these men. "I'll ask Mueller. I don't see why he'd mind."

"Vy you vant to cross in such a hurry?" The heavy-set nester in the middle had elected himself their spokesman. "Maybe you run away from somet'ing, eh?" He reached for the bridle. Grady saw the move but didn't try to check it. Instead, he let the reins fall across the horn, stiffened in the saddle so that his left shoulder was thrust forward and his left arm dropped out of the way. His right hand was poised about two inches above the horn. A saddle draw was a cross draw, and he was ready. This was all foreign to the nester; he didn't recognize the danger signs.

"You said the wrong thing, mister. I don't run from anybody."

The hairy hand didn't free its grip on the reins. "Pouf! Big talk. Cowboy talk. Now ve get tired of it und ve'll change t'ings round here. *Ja,* I t'ink maybe ve take you mit us joost to see vy you vant to cross de river in so much hurry. How you like dat, cowboy? Ve let you valk mit us for a vhile."

"Don't try to pick a quarrel," Grady replied. "I've nothing against you."

The mild tone made the nester underestimate Grady, and he kept up his bluster. "I'll do de decidin', cowboy, und I say get off de horse."

"Drop those reins and step clear!" Grady's voice turned crisp. "And don't make a move to raise those guns either."

"Dere are t'ree of us und ve haff guns."

"Don't be a fool. You wouldn't live to raise one of those clumsy things. You're just begging for trouble but I don't want to kill you. Now turn loose of the horse."

Slowly the hand loosed its grip. The three men stepped back, still looking bewildered and uncertain.

"Now start moving and don't look back." Grady sat motionless, watched until they were beyond gunshot before he turned away. He didn't want a bullet in his back.

There was no one at home at the third house. When his call went unanswered, he let himself through the gate and found the ford as described without difficulty. There were more farms on the south bank here but he quickly left them behind when he headed away from the water, and he had no further encounters with nesters. It was afternoon when he reached the thicket where he'd left Ranger and turned loose his borrowed animal. He spread out his bed roll. This was a safe camp. From here on, he'd travel after dark.

Word of the excitement in Apache had reached the Lazy B. Merrill Blake was concerned by it. "This spells trouble," he told his brother.

"It's only the beginning," Dave reminded him. "I know Grady. There were six men in on Tom Williams' murder and he'll get 'em all before he's through."

"That's not what worries me. It's the way the nesters are being stirred up that I don't like. This isn't their quarrel, but if they get the idea that it is, there'll be hell to pay."

Dave didn't agree. "Sometimes things have to get worse before they get better. When Grady finishes this job maybe we'll be rid of the troublemakers."

It had been Merrill's idea to end the quarrel by appealing to August Lehman and the better class of nesters. He had been outvoted but he still clung to the idea. The more he considered it, the better he liked it. He had confidence in the little German merchant, felt that an understanding with him would bring about co-operation. The brothers had established a patrol to guard their range because of the recent thefts. After the noon meal Dave rode off to find his riders and see if they had anything to report. Merrill watched him go without hinting at the plan he was turning over in his mind. He had determined to visit Lehman. Nothing else would head off open warfare, he felt sure.

He rode alone. It was better that way. He didn't want any show of force. That would only invite trouble.

Two Lazy B riders had a camp at the Horseshoe Bend crossing. Dave had insisted that the men ride in pairs, ready for trouble, and they had agreed that this ford might be one of the spots used by the rustlers in driving cattle. They weren't in camp but Merrill sighted them three miles beyond and checked until they rode up. Red Hepburn and Andy Smith were top hands, had been with the outfit for years. He could tell something was wrong by Andy's expression. "What is it—rustlers?"

"Nope. You ain't headin' into Apache are you, Merrill?"

"I thought I'd ride down that way." Merrill didn't want these men to guess his errand.

"Best not. Toomey's been killed, along with a nester named Blucher. Must have been some powder-burnin' too 'cause they both had time to draw." He grinned. "Grady Scott's work, sure, 'cause he left a message remindin' 'em of Tom Williams. That's three of the gang and I'd hate to be in the boots of the others. I wouldn't be s'prised if they ain't decided by now that cold-blooded murder's right unhealthy round here."

"But the town's riled up," Red put in. "Don't go ridin' in there to-day."

They had the news from the nester homesteads on the eastern fringes of their range.

Merrill suggested that they scout the river above the ford for sign of other crossings before they parted. That would take them out of his way, avoid further questions about his destination. He watched until they were out of sight beyond a river bend before he again turned toward the town, unaware that once they were out of view the two men had dismounted and were watching him from the river's scrub.

"What you reckon he's up to?" Andy asked.

"I don't know but I reckon we'd better deal ourselves a hand, pard-ner," Red replied.

Rowden headed his posse west but kept well away from the river. He felt reasonably sure that no word of his coming had reached the ranches but he was taking every precaution. The stream offered too easy a screen for ambush. He didn't like the situation too well. Nearly half his force had been left behind, and for the most part the remaining men were not the best. It was the better element he'd wanted, the prosperous farmers. They lacked experience but they had determination. Most of the crew at his back were too much like Pakebusch, the shiftless and easily led. Except for Falkner and Springer there wasn't a real fighter in the lot. It would have to do, he decided. At least he had numbers. There must be a fight. He was confident that once the shooting started nothing could stop its spread. The ranchers could be depended on to retaliate, and under cover of the struggle he would gain the time he needed for his final operations.

Falkner spied the rider first, a lone man half a mile away between them and the stream. "I hope it's Grady Scott," he said, as they changed their course, fanned out toward the river and set their horses at a lope.

Merrill Blake had seen them and had turned for the shelter of the trees, hoping to escape detection. He wasn't sure of their purpose, but the strength of the party made him suspicious. He watched their dust rise, knew he'd been seen and decided it was too late for concealment. He turned to face them and waited.

Red and Andy had kept to the river's screen when they followed their boss. It was rough going but Merrill was traveling at an easy pace. Nevertheless they had fallen behind and he already had stopped when they caught their first glimpse of Rowden's posse galloping up. "Come on, Andy. I reckon it's time we made our move." Red pushed his horse into the open and dug in his spurs, with Andy at his heels.

Rowden was a little disappointed when he recognized his victim. The Blakes were well liked. Some of his mob might hesitate. No matter, he thought. This is no time to choose. They were within fifty yards of Merrill when Pakebusch saw the two cowhands approaching at a dead run.

"Look!" he shouted. "More of dem comin'."

"So that's why he was trying to lead us toward the river!" the sheriff shouted. "See it, boys? They were going to trap us there."

Rowden intended the warning to infuriate his men but it didn't have the desired effect. They were scared. Most of them stopped.

Merrill couldn't hear what was said above the clatter of the horses. He nudged his animal and started toward them.

"Stand back!" Pakebusch warned. The terror of the past few days made him unreliable. He clutched his scatter-gun in panic. "Stand back!" he shrilled.

Merrill waved his empty hand and grinned at them. He recognized Pakebusch's fear, saw no menace in it. Spooked half out of his wits, he thought. This gang won't make trouble.

Rowden had his hand on the grip of his six gun but it would suit him best if the first shot came from a nester. He glanced at his riders. Falkner was watching the approaching cowman. He was a fighter and he was having no part in this since Merrill had raised his hand. The nesters waited uneasily, uncertain what to do. Only Pakebusch had his gun raised and his panic was easy to read.

"It's a trap, Kurt—a trap!" The sheriff's voice snapped.

Pakebusch pulled the trigger. He didn't take aim—he didn't need to with a scatter-gun at this range. Merrill spilled from the saddle.

Red saw it. His gun began to spit. Andy was right behind him. His bullets were singing too. One of the nesters fell. Springer's horse lunged wildly, then crumpled up, and Rowden saw Charlie kicking frantically in an effort to free himself from the saddle. Falkner's gun was smoking now. Rowden fired coolly. Some of the nesters forgot their panic, and shotguns started blasting.

The two cowhands wheeled toward the river. These odds were too great and Merrill was beyond help. Andy's horse went down but he rolled clear. Red pulled up beside him. "Grab a stirrup," he called. "We'll make the trees."

Andy clutched Red's boot and raced beside him, but their gait was slowed and behind them the pursuit was on. When the ranchmen turned even the weakest nesters had found their courage.

Red felt his horse stagger. Andy loosed his grip and slid to the grass. Red dug in his spurs, managed to get the floundering animal among the trees before he quit the saddle. There was a bullet through his shoulder. He didn't realize it until he tried to use his left arm to reload; he found it useless.

He darted to the right, broke his gun awkwardly and crouched among some bushes to reload slowly with one hand. This done, he edged his way back. He had no thought of escape now—his horse was gone. His sole determination was to fight as long as he could. He had a score to settle. The posse was spreading out along the bank. They were sure of him now; they'd just found his horse. His first shot sent a nester spinning. His teeth were bared in a savage grin as he aimed again. He managed to squeeze the trigger before their volley caught him. The scatter-guns cut him to pieces. It made the end quick. He didn't even feel it.

GRADY was awakened by a shot. He woke "all over," his eyes wide, every sense alert to danger, but motionless in the fashion of men from an Indian frontier where the slightest careless noise could mean death. An irregular volley followed. He had the sound placed now, fully half a mile away and across the river to the west. He didn't like the wham of scatter-guns mixed in with the pistol shots. The sounds ebbed while he was throwing on his saddle; they broke out again in another fierce exchange as he quit the camp and headed west at a gallop.

He rode hard with little thought of caution, depended on the growth along the river to hide him. If he didn't move fast he'd be too late. The firing ceased abruptly. He drew up, worried, and strained to listen; he located the scene by the hoarse clamor of voices. His carbine was out of its scabbard as he swung among the trees. Here he left Ranger "tied to the ground" by simply tossing the reins over his head and slithered down the bank. The same foliage that hid him concealed the men beyond. He could hear their excited voices but could see nothing. Some of them spoke German though. That identified them. There were no more shots to guide him. The fight was ended. A crossing here was fool-hardy, but the stream lost itself in a bend not far below; he turned that way, found a dead branch on which to raft his weapons and swam across. It didn't take long but he could hear men and horses moving off by the time he reached the other bank, and he counted their strength from among the trees. There were thirty-six of them and they led two horses. More important, they carried three bodies with them. It was too far for recognition of the men but he knew the sheriff's big dun horse.

He found Red first, so shattered by the scatter-guns he could only be identified by his hair. Merrill Blake and Andy lay where they had fallen. Four horses were down, too. The position of the bodies told the story well. Grady swore softly and his mouth hardened to a bitter line when he found Merrill's six shooter still in its holster.

His first thought was to lay the bodies out under the trees but he decided against it. He had no way to take them in and, barring that, he thought it better to leave them untouched so that others might read their message.

He pressed Ranger hard on the ride in. He couldn't make sense of these killings. There hadn't been a better-liked man in the valley than Merrill Blake, unless, he remembered grimly, it was Tom Williams. There was a certain pattern to both those murders, he thought: Tom had been unarmed, Merrill didn't have a chance to draw his gun. Red and Andy had fought. Guessing at the action—he couldn't figure it out precisely—he found satisfaction in the fact that they'd had a chance to use their weapons and hadn't been murdered in cold blood like the others. He tried to piece together what he'd learned. The murder of Tom Williams began to lose itself in a larger problem. The feud between nesters and ranchmen wasn't new, yet even its bitterness didn't offer a satisfactory explanation. Where did Pete Falkner and his outfit in the Scalp Creek Breaks fit in? That was a wild bunch, certainly, but rustlers were cowmen, too. Normally they ranged themselves on the rancher's side in the struggle against nesters. This was a queer alliance. Grady remembered how he'd been mistaken for a Pecos cowboy himself, from the way he wore his guns. That's when he'd been invited to join Pete. He recalled, too, that Toomey and Rowden sent orders to the Scalp Creek camp. Before he rode into Lazy B headquarters he determined to visit Scalp Creek himself.

Dave Blake flew into a murderous rage when he heard Grady's story. "Merrill was always easy with the nesters. They murdered him! Now they'll learn what killing really means!" He took his Winchester from the rack, reached for the extra cartridge belt. "We'll drive 'em out. When I'm through, Apache will be just a heap of ashes."

"Hold on, Dave. Don't send a boy on a man's errand. What can you do alone? They'd trap you just like they did the Kid or Tom Williams or Merrill. That way you're just playing their game. When it's time for a showdown I aim to be standing right beside you and my guns will be hot. But you can't rope a calf until you build your loop. Why, even your own outfit is scattered all over this end of the valley. Bring 'em in; send word to the Snake on a Rock and to the Forked W. If those murderers want war they'll get it, but don't let 'em dry-gulch you before you get a chance to draw your six guns."

The Blake outfit had eight hands left; only two were present. The others were riding the range just as Red and Andy had been. They added their arguments to Grady's before Dave would listen. Then they arrived at a plan. Dave would take a wagon for the bodies. One hand would accompany him. The other would circle the Lazy B camps with news of what had happened, bring in the riders.

"I'll head for the Forked W, gather them up and send word to Soames from there. It's a full night's job. We'd better start riding. We'll meet here sometime tomorrow, as early as possible.

Every hand the ranches could muster gathered at the Lazy B next morning. There was none of the merriment that usually marked a gathering of cowmen. They came sober-faced. There were cripples here like Peg and boys like Carl, but there was a rifle across each saddle and every man wore his six gun. Ma had wanted to keep Carl home. "There's nesters mixed up in this, boy—German folks. I don't want you goin' against your own people. 'T ain't fittin'."

"Not my people," the lad argued stoutly. "You don't think my father had a hand in this, do you?"

"Of course not. Your pa's a different breed of cats. There's good Germans an' sorry cowmen. Just the same, I don't like the idea of you mixin' up in this."

Curly decided the argument. "He's a Forked W hand," he said. "An' the Forked W is ridin'." He tied a rifle scabbard to the boy's saddle, and Ma made no further protest.

Ma was going herself—she was head of the outfit. "But you'd never know it," she complained. "Nobody's listenin' to me this mornin'." She tried to persuade Clee to stay behind, too, with no more success.

"My father and the Snake on a Rock spread will be on hand. I'll ride as far as Blake's anyway. I want to know what's going on."

"But that'd leave Ohmie here alone. I don't like it."

"Bring her along. I'm not staying behind." Clee was obstinate.

Curly and Grady both favored taking the girls as far as the Lazy B. "We don't know what's ahead." Curly rubbed his chin thoughtfully. "I'm agin leavin' women scattered round, now we got on our war paint. You're best off stickin' together."

They saddled a horse for Ohmie too.

There had been no burying. Dave waited. He wanted his neighbors to see that Merrill's gun had never been drawn from its holster before

the bodies were carried to the graves already dug between the house
and the river. Ma read the funeral service from her worn prayer book.
That came first. The meeting was held later, under the trees that shaded
the Lazy B headquarters. There were thirty-one present, not counting
the women. John Soames had brought seventeen riders. The Lazy B
still could furnish nine, counting Dave Blake, and with Grady, the
Forked W added four more.

Every cowman present was determined on a reckoning, the only differences of opinion concerned the method. Dave Blake wanted to move
directly on the town. "Don't tell me we'll ride into any traps." He
glared around him. "When it comes to tricks we've done more Injun
fightin' than they have. If they hole up in the town waitin' for us, all
the better. We can burn 'em out. There's an east wind to fan a fire.
That's my idea. Drive 'em from cover. Once we get 'em in the open
they're no match for us."

"Thar's a heap of womenfolks in Apache," Curly objected.

"We've got to get rid of 'em sooner or later. We don't want 'em
spawnin' any more of this nester breed." In his fury Dave was not quite
sane.

"We have friends in town, too," Grady reminded him. "Men like
August Lehman. And there's the hotel. Letty Reid has a good many
friends here." He looked across at Soames for support.

"No," the boss of the Snake on a Rock decided. "We can't burn the
town. But there's another way we can bring 'em out. We'll stampede
stock into their fields, break down fences and trample their crops. I'm
not softhearted where nester cabins are concerned. We'll burn 'em.
That'll bring 'em out boiling. They'll have to fight or they won't have
any homesteads left."

Grady listened, held his tongue until the others were through. He
hadn't found the answers to all his questions himself but he intended
to. Unless he could find the proper way to present his plan, he knew
it wouldn't be popular. These men wanted fast action. Soames finally
turned to him. "What's your idea, Grady?"

"In Indian fighting it's always smart not to do what they have you
figured to do."

Curly nodded agreement. So did a number of the older rannies.

"You think you know how they've got us figured?"

"You know, too," Grady retorted. "They figure every cowman in the
valley will hit the trail when he hears what happened. They're not fools.

They know we won't take this lying down. They expect us to come in there burning powder."

Soames showed his annoyance. "Any fool would know that."

"Sure." Grady was quick to agree. "And I don't like it when they take me for a fool. They knew these killings meant war. That's plain. It's like they'd sent us an invitation. I can't help asking myself why. Is it because they think they're ready for us and want a showdown now? Or have they got something else in mind? 'T ain't like nesters to invite us to a fight. They're not so handy with weapons as all that. There's something else in the wind and I think maybe I've figured it out."

He turned to Curly. "How many head of cattle have you lost lately?"

"Plenty. Thar's no way of tellin' till we run a check but I'd reckon it past a thousand head—maybe more."

"How about you, Dave?"

"We're no different from the rest. They're stealin' us blind." The question irritated him. "This is no time to talk about cow thieves. We've got a bigger job on hand."

"The way I've got it figured it's all part of the same job," Grady argued. "That's the only way this makes sense. How many hands did you leave home, Soames?"

"We're all here."

Grady nodded. "It's the same with the other outfits. Every ranny in the valley has been pulled off the range. Don't you reckon somebody planned it that way?"

He told them of Pete Falkner's invitation to join the outfit in the Scalp Creek Breaks. "Pete took me for a Pecos cowboy and I didn't argue about it. I knew Frank Toomey was on hand when Tom was killed and I had to get in with his crowd if I was going to find out what happened and who was there. I was on the right track, too, until I showed my hand the night the Kid was killed. Then I had to pound leather. But I learned something else before I left. Will Rowden gives the orders for whatever's done up on Scalp Creek. Once you know that, the rest of this begins to make sense."

"You saw those bodies," Dave objected. "Scatter-guns did that. Those are nester weapons."

"I was there. I heard them jabbering German, too," Grady agreed. "But I recognized the sheriff's big dun horse in the outfit, too. And if the nesters were bent on trouble, why did they turn back then? What was to stop them from coming on here—you had only three men at headquarters—or on up to the Forked W, where we're so shorthanded we've got women riding our range? You know what I think? Rowden was just bent on stirring up trouble and he'd already done a good job. If that was simply nester doings they would have come on, tried to clean us out quick before we had time to gather. But Rowden wanted to give us time. He wanted us to pull every man off the range and start on the warpath. He figures that while we're busy carrying the fight to the German settlements there'll be nobody to hinder his Scalp Creek outfit while it's riding our ranges, running off our beef.

"You all know me," Grady continued. "You know I'm not dodging a fight. I'm just set against anybody haltering us to lead where they want us to go. I want to call the turn myself so I'll know what I am doing. When we settle up, let's settle up with the crowd that's really doing the mischief."

Clee sat on the steps, listening, and wondered if this sounded as convincing to the somber-faced riders as it did to her. She saw her father's frown. He was more than half-persuaded, she could tell.

"To hell with all this talk," Dave Blake growled. "Let's go on to Apache. One thing at a time. We can take care of this Scalp Creek outfit later."

Soames, still scowling, turned to Grady. "What you got in mind?"

"Why, I'd let 'em think we'd fallen into their dry-gulch. I'd send a salty old hand like Curly into the settlements with enough riders to kick up a dust. A dozen men could do the job. Curly's too smart to be caught in a fight he's not planning. They'll think we're all with him. That way we'll trick Rowden into making his move. I'd split the rest of the riders between John Soames and Dave Blake, and head them up the valley to patrol the ranges. If Rowden's outfit thinks we're all away they won't be expecting trouble and they'll ride right into our trap."

"And while we're rounding up cow thieves the killers get away," Dave still objected.

"No. When we get that outfit I'm hoping we'll find Rowden and Pete Falkner with them. That's the crowd that's to blame for the killings, Dave. If anybody gets away you can count on our help. We'll run 'em down. One thing is sure—you won't find them in Apache if we ride there. They'll be busy somewhere else. This is the way to get 'em."

"You haven't counted yourself in on any of these plans," Soames pointed out.

"I aim to head for the Scalp Creek Breaks. I want to find out how much of a layout they've got. Maybe I'll locate a sizable herd of stolen cattle too."

"Alone?"

"It's better that way. If it's a rustler hide-out they won't be sitting on their gun hands. One man is best for such a scout. More would run into trouble. I want to find out exactly what we're heading into up there." The plan met general approval. Curly's force would act as a decoy, masking their other activities. Soames and Blake each would have a strong patrol to guard the ranges, while the final move would depend on Grady's discoveries. Even Dave Blake was convinced now.

Grady told Curly what he had in mind. "Stir up a fuss but stay clear of fights. No use throwing lead at poor scared nesters who've been tricked into this just as much as we have. A couple of fires would help. You could start with Unger's place, circle the town and hit Blucher's. We know they were both in this gang and there'd be no womenfolks to suffer from it at either place. I don't have to tell you to keep shy of an ambush," he added. "As long as the ranges are being patrolled there's no hurry. Your job's to keep 'em worried and make 'em think you've got every hand in the valley riding with you."

To allow plenty of time for this project and for Grady to scout out the Breaks, they arranged for all forces to meet one week later for a final drive on Scalp Creek. Spy Butte was named as the gathering point. It was a landmark they all knew, a peak that, like a straggler, stood isolated from the rugged hills farther on in the northwest stretches of the Forked W range. It could be seen for miles, with the added advantage that from there they could move swiftly into the Breaks beyond.

While the three leaders were dividing their forces, Grady turned to Ma. He suggested that she and the girls remain at Lazy B headquarters until the trouble was ended.

"Why? We'd be better off at home."

"That's closer to Scalp Creek, Ma. If we have any real fighting I think it'll be up there."

She scoffed. "An' this is closer to Apache. If there's trouble in that direction this'd be the first place hit. No, if we've got to wait we'll go back where we belong to do it."

He knew there was no use arguing. "I'll ride that far with you," he said. "I'm heading straight up the river."

When they were ready to leave Lazy B, they couldn't find Ohmie. Clee looked through the house but she wasn't there. "Find Carl," Ma

suggested. But he was absent too. Grady couldn't locate him with the
men saddling up at the corral, although his horse was there. Annoyed,
Grady turned back and cut across behind the cook shack on his way.
He stopped abruptly when he discovered he was intruding. There were
Carl and Ohmie, locked in each other's arms. They had slipped away
to say good-by. He retraced his steps quietly until out of sight, then
called Carl by name. The boy didn't come at once and when he did
his face was red.

"You're riding with Soames and he's ready to move, Carl. Better get
started."

Clee rode beside Grady when they headed for the Forked W. She
was silent for a long time. Thought of the Scalp Creek Breaks troubled
her. "You picked the hardest job of all. I'm worried, Grady, and you
should be."

"I'll move carefully when the time comes," he promised. "Right now
I feel good about the way things have worked out. I was afraid they
wouldn't listen to me back there. Now everything's going to be all
right."

"How many men are there up on Scalp Creek?"

"I don't know but I aim to find out."

"You won't be dealing with nesters this time," she warned. "They'll
be more like Pete Falkner's type."

He grinned at her. "I know. Let me do my own worrying, Clee."

It was dusk when they reached home and he stayed over until after
supper. Clee followed him out to the corral when he was ready to go and
waited in silence while he saddled up.

"You think I'm just a girl and have no business meddling," she said,
when he turned to say good-by.

"You're not meddling and you're right about what's ahead. I reckon
I'm bothered a little too, enough to look out for myself."

She liked the feel of his firm handclasp. It added to her confidence.
"I know you'll be all right but I can't help worrying a little," she confessed.

He loosed her hand then. She thought he was going. Instead, his arms
were around her, his lips pressed against hers. What surprised her most
of all was her response. She was kissing him too.

"Grady!"

"Let's not talk now."

"I've got to. There's something I want you to know."

He didn't release her. She could feel the hardness of his arms about her. Their strength was reassuring.

"It's about Will Rowden." She forced herself to go on. "He . . . I—"

"Wait! This is something I don't want to hear."

"But you've got to, Grady. I want us to start out all even. That's how I want it to be with us."

He pressed her head against his shoulder so she couldn't talk, held it there. "That's all over, isn't it?"

He felt her head nodding against him.

"But when he had me trapped here the other night, you went to meet him—gave me a chance to get away."

She pulled free. "I didn't want to face him. There was no other way."

"Seems to me that's when you made your choice between us, Clee. That's enough for me."

"How long have you known this, Grady? About Rowden and me?"

"Since that night. When I heard what happened later I guessed the rest and understood how much you'd done for me. So did Rowden. That's why he flew into such a rage. He was trying to get even with you."

"And then you felt sorry for me?" she challenged.

"No, then I realized how much I loved you. But it wasn't the start. I reckon it began the first time I saw you, that night in Apache, only I didn't have sense enough to know it then."

He kissed her again.

"Don't worry, Clee," he whispered. "I've got to come back now."

Then he swung into the saddle and she was standing there alone, her eyes straining into the night after him.

CURLY's force was twelve strong and he was careful to include several veterans like himself when he picked his men. He headed due north at first, toward the hills and away from the town and the nester homesteads. "If they don't see us they'll think thar's twicet as many of us." He grinned at Peg. The prospect of using his old skill pleased him. "We'll show Grady we ain't gone rusty."

When the flat table of grass turned rolling, he veered east and began the wide circle that would bring him among the settlers' cabins from an unexpected direction. They no longer straggled carelessly along. He had taken firm hold and had chosen their course himself. He kept a couple of riders out to watch the trail ahead from each new crest. Few words were needed; the men knew and trusted him.

Curly never rode over the hills while on such a mission. He led the way around them, to avoid being silhouetted. He'd known this country well but had avoided it since the nesters came. This was the old O-bar-O range and they kept a sharp lookout for cattle. Curly had instructed them to gather up any they found. "If we can build us a small herd it'll come in handy for stampedin' fields," he said. They found only a few strays left, wary mossy-horns that were hard to drive, but they brought them along. By late afternoon they were in nester country and hadn't been detected. Curly made a dry camp in a shallow fold of hills and waited for night. While his little force rested he crawled to the hilltop, spent most of the interval prone in the grass, squinting down at the cabins below and memorizing the location of fences that would be barriers in the dark. Grady had drawn him a rough map on which the Unger, Blucher and Pakebusch farms were located. From it he located Blucher's place and made an interesting discovery. There were fifty or sixty longhorns penned in one of Blucher's pastures. I'd shore like to have a look at them brands, he decided.

He noticed that there were no men in the fields although there was plenty of activity around the cabins. Away with Rowden, he thought grimly. They're all in this up to their necks.

When dark came the group moved straight to Blucher's, giving the cabins a wide berth. "Nothin' but women an' young'uns thar an' no sense in spreadin' the alarm yet," Curly warned. The moon was in its first quarter and already high, but their little herd was small enough to handle easily. At Blucher's they threw it in with the cattle Curly had discovered earlier. These wore the O-bar-O brand, too, revealing a part of Blucher's recent activity. "Now we got enough beef to do some damage," said Peg.

They wasted no time. Lights still marked the location of each homestead, when they littered Blucher's cabin with dry hay and set it ablaze. Then they moved out.

They ignored the roads now. Several men rode ahead and cleared a path through the fences for the others to drive the herd. Soon they reached a farm where corn still stood in the fields.

"Hyar we go," Curly announced. "Start 'em runnin', boys, an' mind, ever'body make racket enough for two. We want 'em to think we're all hyar."

There was a high torch behind them where Blucher's had stood, and the herd already was uneasy. They spooked fast, bellowed with terror when the riders crowded them, yelling and shooting. They flattened out the field as they thundered across it. At the far side stood a brush fence reinforced with rails, stout enough normally but no barrier for these terror-stricken brutes. They crashed through it, plunged on over field after field, cutting a swath of destruction across each farm. At every fence a few cattle went down; the rest fled on in terror, unable to shake the yelping men who pressed them.

The dread had spread to the cabins. No lamps marked their windows now. The flame at Blucher's was the only light that showed. Once the stampede racketed past a nester cabin, its clamor reverberating against the log walls. One steer bonged into the big soap kettle and went down. Others surged over the earth-floored porch, carried its frail posts with them in their panic. The splitting of the timbers added to the din. A child wailed behind the barred door as the riders swept past, their six guns hot as they harried on the drive. At each farm domestic animals caught the fever. Oxen and milk cows joined the flight. It lasted for miles before it lost its fury and stragglers spent its strength.

Curly wasn't through. There was Unger's cabin to visit. On the way they burned several barns to spread the terror but they left the cabins alone. "Nothin' but women in 'em," he said. "That ain't our style of fightin'." From a distance, though, the flames were effective. Neighbors couldn't tell that the dwellings had been spared. Even after the moon had died, the red path kept the night aglow.

Curly gradually veered northward with his fires to make it appear he was headed back toward the hills. He was too canny to mark his real trail. Then he doubled back and struck off at an angle for Ungers. He cautioned the men to silence now. They were through for the night. "We're lookin' for a place to hole up," he explained. "Where they ain't likely to find us."

They found Unger's cabin deserted, as they expected, and had their horses hidden among the trees along the river before daylight. Grady had marked on the map the tangled copse where he first met Ohmie. After eating cold rations, they snugged down for a day of waiting.

Kurt Pakebusch had ridden home that night. He'd felt better since the day he'd beaten Ohmie. There were times he could forget the scalping of Heinrich Unger, when he even thought he was no longer afraid. Each day that passed without word of Grady Scott bolstered his flickering courage a little. Then Toomey and Blucher were killed and the same grim warning was scrawled in the dust beside their bodies. His panic returned, more shattering than ever. He'd clung to the company of Rowden's gun slingers lately for safety; but Toomey's presence hadn't helped Blucher. He wanted to hide but didn't know where he could turn that Grady Scott wouldn't follow. Finally, with the cunning of despair, he reasoned that crowds offered the greatest security. He haunted Lehman's Store, the wagon yard and Scanlon's, felt easy only when they were jammed with nesters. His part in the Blake slaying bothered him, too. He hadn't wanted trouble, had gone only because he craved the safety of the party's well-armed numbers. And he had fired the first blast in a fit of panic. Now the town was packed with nesters; it echoed warlike talk and no longer seemed safe. Rowden openly declared he expected an attack there. Pakebusch crept home and barred his door. *"Ich bin nicht zu hause,"* he told his family. "If anybody asks tell dem I am *nach* Apache."

Word of Curly's raid exaggerated as it spread. By the time the report reached Pakebusch's everything west of there was supposed to be in charred ruins and whole families had perished in flaming cabins. Refu-

gees trudged past, all headed for Apache, each telling some new rumor
of horror. Kurt slunk out to the corral, saddled his horse.

"Vere you goin'?" Ma asked anxiously.

"If dere iss trouble I vill be needed in town." He swaggered and
barked out the words in an effort to bolster his courage.

"Don't leave me now," she pleaded. "It iss near my time." She
clutched at her swollen body. "I can't leave. It iss too late for me."

He turned his face away to keep from seeing her. "Der sheriff vill
need me. I got to go qvick."

She tried to hold him back but he shook her off, scrambled into the
saddle and left at a headlong gallop without looking around. She started
for the house, walking heavily. No matter. Pa wasn't much help anyway, such times. She'd send one of the *kinder* to the neighbor's. Last
time Frau Schultz had seen her through. She stopped at the door and
called. No one answered. Come to think of it, she hadn't seen any of
the young'uns around in quite a spell.

"Kurt! Fritz! Otto! Hans!" She shouted as loud as she could but still
there was no answer.

The boys, infected with panic, had started for Apache long ago.

Curly was ready to move as soon as it turned dark. He had a different
route mapped for tonight. If the nesters still were holed up in Apache,
this should bring them out. They started by making a torch of Unger's
cabin, then headed immediately for Pakebusch's. They'd avoided occupied cabins up to now but this was a known enemy. The place was
dark but when they surrounded it, they moved carefully. "Take cover,"
Curly warned. "Even in the hands of a scared woman a scatter-gun's
bad medicine."

He hailed the house, got no answer and decided it was abandoned.
That pleased him. He had dreaded the prospect of turning out a family.
He moved in alone and was surprised to find the door open when he
tried it. He was edging through when a moan stopped him. He flattened
against the wall, waited until he heard it again.

"Who is it?" he challenged. "What's wrong in hyar?"

"I'm sick." Ma gasped. "Send for a voman."

"You alone hyar?"

"*Ja.* Dey all run avay. Joost send for a voman."

The voice quavered with pain. It sounded convincing, but Curly was
still cautious. He fished for his block of sulphur matches, broke off sev-

eral for a brighter flare, gripped them in his left hand. His pistol was ready as he scratched a light against the wall. He dropped the six gun back in its holster when he saw the woman stretched across the bed. Even in that dim light the sweat glistened on her forehead and her lips writhed with pain. He found a lamp and lighted it. "What's the matter, ma'am?"

She pressed her abdomen with both hands. "It iss a baby I'm havin'. Joost send for a voman—but qvick."

Curly called for help and nodded toward the figure on the bed as the men crowded in. "We've got to fetch a woman hyar. She's birthin'." He sent riders off in pairs, headed in both directions. "An' take care how you approach these cabins. These folks are panicky an' apt to shoot before they know yor errand. I reckon if you let 'em know our fix you'll find a woman to come quick enough. You've got to."

The flames were high at Unger's now, warning the countryside of their presence. There was risk in waiting here, if the nesters had been drawn out of Apache to intercept them. Curly calculated the chance, threw out pickets to guard against surprise. Mrs. Pakebusch stilled her moans when the men first trooped in. She was twisted crosswise of the pallet, her arms flung wide, clutching at the mattress. Her breathing was heavy and irregular. When she started to murmur again the men looked stricken. They tiptoed out, all but Peg and Curly.

"What we goin' to do, Curly?"

"We can't leave her like this—not till we get someone for her."

The messengers were soon back. They'd found no one. Each cabin they'd visited had been deserted. The woman heard their reports. There was a whimper in her throat, growing louder. "A voman," she kept repeating. "A voman. You've got to find a voman for me."

Peg cursed softly. "I wish Ma was here. She'd know what to do."

"She ain't an' it's close on to forty miles to the Forked W. This is one time she can't help us." Curly crossed to the bed, leaned over it. "This yor first 'un, ma'am?"

She didn't try to answer but she shook her head and held up her hand, fingers outspread.

"Five. You ought to know somethin' 'bout it by now. Look, we've tried to find a woman for you but they're all gone."

Her voice rose in a wail.

"Now don't you go frettin' yorself, ma'am. We'll see yo're took care of, good an' proper. We've midwifed more calves than you can shake a big stick at. This can't be plumb diff'rent. You just tell us what to do."

She choked back another sob, her hands clutched tighter at the mattress. The sound of her panting filled the room. "You need a string to tie der cord," she said. "Und a knife."

"All right. That's easy, ma'am." Curly tried to make his voice sound confident. "Now don't you fret."

He found a towel and wiped the sweat from her face, while Peg looked for a string. Finding none in the cabin, he finally stumped out and returned triumphantly with a rawhide whang string cut from his saddle. He held it up for the woman to see and she nodded her head. He laid it on the table, his Bowie knife beside it.

Her moans grew louder and they noticed that frequently she turned to watch the door anxiously. Peg guessed what was troubling her.

"I reckon she's worried 'bout the boys. A woman nat'rally wouldn't want the whole outfit trompin' in to watch, a time like this." He shut the door, slid the bolt in place.

Her body twisted. This time she made no effort to choke back her pain; her voice shrilled with it. The baby came quickly. She showed them how to receive it, and Curly knotted the thong around the navel cord before Peg severed it with his knife. The child let out a lusty wail. Curly, holding it gingerly, thrust him into his mother's waiting arms and fled outside.

Peg followed him to the door. "Some of you rannies git a fire goin' and put some water on," he called. "Dagnab it, we've got to wash this young'un up proper." Soon the fire was crackling under the big soap pot. Peg gave the baby its first bath.

They were worried about leaving, and cooked breakfast for the mother before they saddled up. "You shore yo're all right, ma'am?" Curly asked.

"Ja. Everyt'ing now iss all right. Soon I vill be up." She stammered her thanks to them both before they rode away.

Curly had to change his plans. They'd lost much precious time and must be in the hills by dawn. They headed north, tore down fences and burned a few barns on the way, but this night's work didn't equal their previous havoc. "But shucks—" Curly grinned—"we'll do better tomorrow night if we don't have no more babies."

23 THE RANGERS ARRIVE

EACH batch of refugees that reached Apache brought new and swelling rumors. Will Rowden listened to each tale with a wintry smile. He'd chosen his own site for battle and didn't intend to be drawn out. "Wait," he counseled. "We're not hurt yet. Sooner or later they'll attack the town. We'll be ready for them. That's when we'll settle this account."

He kept the nesters busy digging a breastwork near each end of the main street, but not across it. He wanted nothing to obstruct the ranchers' coming. "Getting out will be a different matter," he promised. "They'll find lead everywhere they turn." He no longer feared Lehman's influence here. There were nearly two hundred nesters in the town. As their families crowded in, with new stories of destruction, their anger was fanned. Many, like the merchant, had tried to avoid this conflict; now that it had come they were determined to defend themselves. Their version of the latest fight was different from the ranchers'. Rowden had seen to that. "We were a posse hunting down Grady Scott for the murder of innocent farmers" was the way he told it. "And the ranchers tried to ambush us. Luckily we were too smart for them, but as it was we lost three men."

He didn't feel the confidence he voiced. He didn't understand what delayed the cowmen's coming. It was long overdue and he had no competent scout he could send to discover their movements. Falkner and Springer had ridden to Scalp Creek with instructions.

"Give the ranchmen time to gather," he'd told them. "It should take about three days. Then it will be time for you to move out. You'll not find anyone on the ranges to bother you. I'll stay in town and keep the nesters stirred up to make sure they do their part. Once the fighting starts in earnest I'll slip off and join you for the drive out." Several days had passed. The fight was overdue; the nesters were ready; still nothing had happened.

He was at Scanlon's when they brought him word the riders were coming. This was better, he thought. The cards were beginning to fall in their proper places. He gave his orders briskly, made sure the shallow trenches were manned. Every nester had been assigned his place. Each scatter-gun carried a double load of slugs. He glanced up the road where a cloud of dust was moving slowly forward. It was a good-sized force; probably that's what had caused the delay. They'd gathered help. That didn't worry him, however. Things were going even better than he'd hoped. He'd expected a night raid and here they came in broad daylight, straight into a path of fire he'd set for them.

He'd chosen an upper window of the Reid House for his own post. From here he could best watch the slaughter, and as the horsemen neared he squinted at them, tried to identify their leader. It wasn't Dave Blake or John Soames. Not Grady Scott, either. He peered at the horse, obviously a blooded animal, sleek with care, and at its rider, a dapper, slender man, dressed all in black, and trim, except that dust powdered his shoulders. The column halted a hundred yards short of the trap, within easy rifle range but too far for a scatter-gun to reach. At a sharp order a dozen men deployed on either side of the road and with rifles ready circled each of the sheriff's carefully prepared traps. Their leader waited until his men were in position, then spurred his horse forward.

"Come out of those breastworks," he ordered. "Who's your leader here?"

The nesters stared around them uneasily. Some stood up but none quit his post.

"You hear me? Where's your leader? We're Texas Rangers and there isn't going to be any trouble in Apache."

The nesters dropped their scatter-guns and came out. Will Rowden hurried down to meet the new arrivals and there was no hint of his disappointment in the bland smile with which he greeted the commander of the Rangers.

Legends already clustered about Major John B. Jones. Rowden knew the reputation of the man who had organized the Frontier Battalion of the Texas Rangers. From the Indian territory on the north to Mexico on the south his six tiny companies had scourged the Comanches back, brought peace again to the border. It was his size that surprised the sheriff. He couldn't have weighed more than one hundred and thirty-five, looked almost dainty in this setting, and his immaculate dress was more suited to a mansion than a frontier trail. He even wore a starched collar with a black bow tie tucked neatly under its corners. It seemed to match the blackness of his mustache. There was command in the flash of his eyes, confidence in his every move. He'd first earned recognition in a Confederate uniform. He had started as a private under Terry in '61, and by '63 he was adjutant of a brigade.

"Tell your people to come out, Sheriff. The fighting's over," he ordered crisply and kept his men waiting until the sheriff walked the length of the street to bring the nesters from their hiding places.

There were forty Rangers in the column, a heavy show of force for them. August Lehman's messenger had met them on the march. The major had all of "A" Company with him, thirty strong, and a detachment of ten men from "D" Company at Menardville. They wore no uniform, yet they looked curiously alike—bronzed, lean and young, most of them in their early twenties—and they wore the confidence of seasoned fighting men. These were curious veterans of the terrible war years when boys filled the shoes of absent fathers, carrying rifles taller than they. In this grim school they ripened early or soon died. There were two pistols to each belt with the holsters cut low and tied down, for they had to match anyone at the draw. The butt of a Sharp's brass belly glinted from each saddle scabbard and every man had his Bowie knife. Each wore the broad-brimmed hat of the plains, the boots and spurs of a horseman, and the animals they rode were superb.

August Lehman was standing in the street when the column reached his store. "I'm glad you're here, Major. I wass afraid we'd have a war if you didn't come."

"You must be August Lehman." There was a grave courtesy in the major's manner when he wasn't giving orders. "I'll call on you presently. First, I must make camp. We will bivouac at the river crossing."

Will Rowden didn't wait. He followed the Rangers, watching with growing uneasiness as they went about their preparations for the night. The major was aware of his presence but gave no hint of acknowledgment until each detail of his camp had been inspected personally. "Well, Sheriff, suppose you tell me about it," he invited then. "The report I get is that there's civil war in Apache Valley."

Rowden told his story swiftly. It was the familiar one of fence wars. The way he described it the ranchers were out of hand, determined to drive the nesters off. There had been murders, homesteads had been burned. They had grown so bold that he had even feared an attack on the town. "I have sympathy for the cowmen, Major. I can see their side of the quarrel. But I'm not the sort of man to be swayed by sentiment. As sheriff here it's my duty to uphold the law and I've been doing my best to protect the nesters. Of course I'm mighty glad you've come."

"Every mob has a leader. Who is it here?" Jones demanded.

"They're all in it, Major, every ranch in the valley. But I think the worst troublemaker is Grady Scott. I've traced at least three murders to him."

The major's eyes turned even blacker. "Major Reynolds!" he called, and his voice was sharp. "I want Major Reynolds."

Reynolds hurried forward, a tall, gaunt man, older than most of his comrades, with a light-brown mustache that half concealed his mouth and a frown to his eyes from following sun-scorched trails too long. He was a sergeant in D Company but, like Jones, had held officer's rank during the recent war and his old title clung to him. "Maj" his friends called him.

"Don't we have a Grady Scott in D Company?" Jones demanded.

"We did have. He resigned not long ago."

"Where was he from?"

"Somewhere around here close, Major."

"Thank you." Jones turned to the sheriff. "Now if you please, suh, we'll call on the merchant here, Mr. Lehman. I want to hear his report." He took Rowden by the arm and stepped briskly up the street.

The merchant's story was more temperate but it followed Rowden's closely in many of its details. He didn't omit the provocations on both sides: the shooting of the Kid at Scanlon's, Williams' death. The major scowled when he heard of that.

"He was a cow thief." The sheriff was quick with an explanation. "Such things are bound to happen when feeling is running high."

"If you have any more deputies who can't take care of prisoners you'd better get rid of them," Jones retorted. "I'd like to see a mob big enough to take a man from one of my Rangers."

He questioned Lehman about Grady Scott. "The sheriff tells me he's at the bottom of this trouble."

"There wass trouble before he came." The merchant frowned with his effort to be fair. "He didn't start it, but things are worse since he came. They blame him for two or three of the killings. The sheriff arrested him once, but he escaped."

"That was after he killed the Kid." The sheriff broke in. "You know he did that. You were in Scanlon's that night yourself, Mr. Lehman."

"I wass there," the merchant agreed. "It wass dark. I couldn't see. That worries me. Why would a cowman kill a boy on his own side?"

"He was here to start trouble. It's plain once you understand it," the sheriff retorted.

Major Jones had heard enough. The sheriff would have accompanied him back to camp but was turned back. "I'll keep in touch with you, Mr. Rowden. In the meantime kindly make it your business to send these nesters back to their farms. Tell them the trouble is over." Jones wanted no outsider present when he instructed his men.

"I want Grady Scott," he told them. "Most of you know him. He's on his own range here and he'll have friends, so move fast. You'll start as soon as it's dark." To the task he assigned twenty-four men, broken into eight parties of three, in order to cover the valley quickly. Their additional duty was to reassure everyone they met that the trouble was ended. "Tell them to go home and get to work, the Rangers have come," he concluded. The rest of his force would remain in Apache.

Grady's good-by kiss left Clee breathless. She stood there in the dark looking after him, long after the sound of his horse had been muffled by the night. He had crowded her thoughts ever since she'd learned his errand here. His loyalty was so fixed. She liked that. It helped her at a time when her confidence was shaken. The danger in him attracted her, too. Her interest had been entirely impersonal, she'd thought, until she found herself resenting Letty's proprietary tricks. That surprised her, and she had determined to put him out of her mind. You've already made a fool of yourself once, she told herself savagely. Haven't you learned your lesson?

He wasn't easy to dismiss. This was his home; his friends discussed him often. No matter who her riding partners happened to be, there would be tales of Grady's prowess before the day ended. Ma's anecdotes of him were ceaseless and each yarn sharpened the picture in her mind. She found she liked the stories of his boyhood best. When he came she watched him with new sharpness, but found nothing to disturb her growing opinion of him. She liked his confidence, the way men listened when he spoke. Even her father, usually so headstrong, accepted his suggestions at the Lazy B meeting. She liked her own relationship with Grady—their easiness together. Their straightforward companionship had no boy-girl blandishments in it. That suited her mood, at first. As her interest grew, this calm piqued her. I'm doing a man's work, wearing pants. He's forgotten I'm a girl, she thought. When Letty came she saw his embarrassment grow in the presence of petticoats, and she was critical. He doesn't think I matter—not that way. Well, isn't that what I want?

Then he had kissed her. She was honest—she'd wanted him to do it. She realized it when he took her in his arms and was only a little surprised. She was sure of herself now, her doubts were gone. This was the man she wanted.

There was no news of him. As the days dragged on that proved the greatest strain. Her confidence in Grady didn't falter. It was his competence which first had fascinated her. But if he found the men he was hunting in the Breaks he'd be outnumbered and there he'd meet others with his own deadly precision. Clee couldn't shake those odds from her mind. Spy Butte was a misty blue sentinel visible for miles across the Forked W range. Often she rode near and was tempted to explore its heights to see if he'd returned. She stifled the impulse. She felt a reserve about Grady she didn't clearly understand. Maybe it's because I met Rowden too often, she thought. I want this to be different.

"See any signs of life round Spy Butte?" Ma asked that evening when she rode in. "It's most time we heard from Grady."

Clee shook her head.

"Next time you're out that way, look around," Ma suggested.

Clee thought of it constantly but she didn't intend to go, even when she found herself near the mountain's base next day. She scanned its crest for a sign of smoke but there was none. That doesn't mean anything. I should have known he's too smart for that. She even started on and then, driven by worry, turned back. It's bound to be all right. Ma suggested it herself, she argued as she picked her way up the steep trail.

That parting kiss astonished Grady. He hadn't planned it. He'd thought himself in love with Letty and felt, guiltily, that he'd been disloyal to her. This was due partly to Letty herself. He hadn't been fooled by the ruses she'd contrived to be alone with him. That had amused him, and he'd been flattered by her interest so that he'd taken it for granted that there was more between them than actually existed. With Clee it had been different. Because he imagined himself interested elsewhere, he had been free of constraint with her and their friendship had ripened more naturally. He'd known too few girls to feel at ease with them, but with Clee his initial embarrassment quickly wore off. She threw a ranny's expert loop, straddled a saddle like a man, too, and her practical mood fitted these accomplishments. No foolishness about her, he thought. Their friendship fell into a comfortable, plain-spoken serenity that he liked. He thought of girls as mysterious, fragile creatures. But she had a sturdy self-reliance that surprised him, reminded him of Ma. Thought of her as a girl didn't complicate their friendship until the night she helped him escape from Rowden. He thought that typical of her resourcefulness until later, when he learned what had happened. He had the tact not to mention her humiliation, but that increased his discomfort. From then he was acutely aware of her femininity. But he still didn't realize the depth of his feeling for her until that kiss. He rode with the memory of it, a little awed to realize that she shared his feeling. And she filled his thoughts so much that he had to remind himself of his task as he slipped down into the Breaks from the hills to the north.

This was rough, broken country, its narrow valleys covered with scrub timber. He'd been here before. The Forked W had sheltered stock in its thickets during blizzard winters. It had skimpy summer pasture, however. He found beef, lots of it, and the brands were mixed. The Forked W and Lazy B predominated but there was plenty of Snake on a Rock stuff here too, together with half a dozen marks he didn't recognize, probably brands of nesters who ran only a few head of stock. He rode with vigilance, scouted each valley for cover, hugged the trees, and occasionally covered the length of a ravine to avoid skyline crossings.

He heard the rustlers at work long before he saw them, on some flats near Scalp Creek, and left his horse in the thicket to worm his way along a hillside until he reached a ledge from which he could watch. Even in these remote hills he was surprised at their boldness. They were blotting brands and worked with no thought of caution. All the familiar sounds of a cow camp came up to him: the bawling of cattle, the flurry of hoofs, the catcalls of derision when a loop fell short. Four riders held the herd. Two others were busy with their ropes cutting out the animals one by one, swinging them toward the fire before making their throw. The iron man was clearly a branding artist. Grady could tell by the quick, sure strokes with which he altered markings with his running iron. And it was a running iron, Grady could tell, long and straight, shaped like a poker with no brand at its tip. There were other irons in a fire where a tender squatted. At the cry "Hot iron" he would bring a fresh one glowing red and return the chilled tool to the flames. Grady was too distant to see how the brands were changed. He discovered that later. In the next valley all the cattle were freshly marked. The blotting had been done so skillfully it was hard to detect. The Forked W had become a Triple X. The fork in the center of the *W* naturally formed an *X* in the original brand. By crossing each of the outside arms of the letter, two more *X*'s were formed. Snake on a Rock's Benched S had been altered as simply. The S had been turned into an eight. The bench below originally was only a straight line with a short leg at either end. A line across the bottom of this had changed the bench to a box. The Lazy B had required more ingenuity but the result was startling. It had been converted into a prairie schooner. The horizontal shaft of the *B* had been lengthened, projected like a tongue at one end, while the *B*'s loops below resembled wheels. Above the shaft the silhouette of a sheeted Conestoga wagon was drawn. It was crude but had the simple look of an authentic marking and so effective that it was hard to recognize in it the *B* lying on its back.

That branding worried Grady. It could mean the rustlers were getting ready to move out with their loot. Certainly they had the makings of a big trail herd here. Warned by the branding crew's carelessness, he didn't relax his caution. They must have guards out. He discovered their camp about a mile down the creek and again he left his horse behind while he scouted. The cabin had been old when he first remembered it, probably some early hunter's abandoned dwelling. The sagging roof had been repaired and there was smoke coming from its chimney. The pole corral was new and there were two horses in it. Grady would have passed on by had he not seen the saddles resting on the top rail. One of them had tapaderos on its stirrups. He found a clump of agritas not too far distant and settled down there to wait.

It was two hours before the riders came out. He recognized them both. Charlie Springer flung the brush saddle on his horse. The other man was Pete Falkner. Too bad I couldn't have been closer, Grady thought. He was sure Pete's was the other saddle he had marked the night of the ambush.

Caution made him slow. He rode north when he quit the Breaks and sheltered in the hills for miles before turning south where Spy Butte was tall in his path.

The mountain was flat-topped and timbered. Its south approach was steep but the ascent from this side was easier and there were half a dozen game trails he could follow. Clee was expecting him from the other direction. He was almost on her before she heard his horse and turned.

She'd been waiting there an hour and her earlier anxiety had returned to trouble her. He had stiffened at sight of that dun horse. Then he saw her and swung from the saddle.

24 BETRAYAL

WITH relief Letty watched the Rangers ride into Apache. This would end the fighting, she thought. But she was worried too. The cowmen didn't know they were here. She didn't like to think what might happen because of that. And she thought of Grady, too. Would he still hunt down the men who'd murdered Tom Williams? She took a more tolerant view of that now. The sheriff called it murder but it hadn't that look to her. Three men had died but each fell with a gun in his hand. Grady abided by his frontier code—until now there had been no other law to which he might appeal. Weighing her conclusions honestly, she had wasted no sympathy on the victims. They had earned this grim justice. Her concern was for the man who faced these odds. It worried her, too, that Grady should be so constantly put in the wrong. That was the sheriff's doing and there was little she could do to combat it.

She decided he must be warned. Arrival of the Rangers had changed everything—he would understand that. The trouble was in finding a messenger. She knew of no nester who would ride on such an errand. Even August Lehman wouldn't listen, she knew. If Grady had friends here they were more apt to be in the Ranger camp. She knew Major Reynolds—had recognized him as he rode in that afternoon—and decided he might help her. At least it was worth the effort. After supper she walked to the camp beside the crossing. A sentry stopped her and, when she had explained her errand, sent for Major Jones.

"This lady wants to see Major Reynolds," he explained. "Claims he's an old friend of hers."

"I'm sorry," Jones told her. "Major Reynolds isn't here."

"But I saw him this afternoon."

"No doubt." The Major was courteous but firm. He blocked her path, determined that none should guess he'd already sent out more than half his troop. "I sent him off on an important mission, ma'am. I'm sorry. I'm sure he'll regret it, too, when he learns he missed you."

Letty was not permitted in the camp but she did get a look at the line where the horses were picketed. When she noticed how few there were she counted them—seventeen. Including the major, forty-one Rangers had ridden in that day. She turned away more troubled than ever. There was a light in Lehman's Store and she opened the door. The merchant was bent over his books.

"Most of the Rangers have already gone. Do you know where they went?"

Lehman showed his surprise. "I didn't know it."

"They must have slipped away after dark. I don't like the looks of it."

Lehman laid down his pen. "You have been worried too long. Now it iss time you stop. Let the Rangers handle it. Me, I think Major Jones knows what he iss doing and that iss enough for me. You should go home and get some rest."

"You talked to Major Jones, didn't you?"

"Yes. He wanted to know about Grady Scott. The sheriff had told him he wass to blame for the trouble."

"That's where they've gone," she declared with conviction. "They're after Grady."

"Why not? Leave this to the Rangers, Letty."

The more she considered it, the surer Letty grew that her guess was right. What chance had Grady if the Rangers were acting on the sheriff's advice? He must be warned and since there was no one to send she must go herself. The ride held no terror for her. It wasn't dangerous. Her only concern was to slip away unobserved. Could she have chosen her time she would have waited another hour. By then the town would be asleep. But the Rangers already had left. She lacked the hour to spare. She plotted her course while she was saddling the mare. The Rangers hadn't passed the hotel. From their camp the easiest way to slip out unobserved was to cross the ford and head west on the south bank of the river. She could go north until clear of the town, then head west across the open range with slight fear of interruption. As a final precaution she slipped on a black dress. It was her best and she was a little dismayed at thought of the havoc such a ride would make of it. She wore it though. There was less chance she'd be seen in it at night. She rode the back street. There were only two dwellings here between her and the town's edge, and she walked the mare carefully until these were passed. Then she spurred into a gallop and headed west.

The moon was high. It dimmed the stars and laid silver on the dry summer grass that stretched its sheen ahead of her, lighting the way. She wasn't lonely—her mind was too busy—and it didn't occur to her to be afraid in this brightness. Her first concern was felt at the Lazy B where the buildings huddled darkly under their trees and no one answered her call. She hadn't reckoned on finding it deserted. There was uneasiness in the silence here and she rode on west, lonely for the first time but more determined than ever.

The moon set shortly after that and night crowded in around her. She resisted an impulse to speed her gait. There was a long way yet to go. The Forked W was miles ahead when day broke.

Soames didn't recognize her at first. His outfit had been in the saddle all night, patrolling the range, and was headed for a hidden camp along the river for breakfast when he spied her. He pulled his men down into a shallow dingle, spread them out to wait. She rode over the hill and was among them before she guessed their presence. Their astonishment equaled hers when they recognized her.

"What you doing here, Letty?" Carl demanded.

She told them why she'd come—of the Rangers' arrival and the need to inform Grady.

"Don't fret yourself, Letty." Soames grinned his approval. "Nobody's going to surprise Grady. We'll see him in a couple of days and give him your message."

She was vexed. Part of her purpose in coming had been to see Grady. Carl guessed it.

"We're meeting him at Spy Butte tomorrow," he blurted. "He's probably waiting there now. Why don't you tell him yourself?"

"Maybe I will," she said. "The sooner he hears the better."

"Now why'd you tell her that?" Soames demanded after she rode on. "Is it smart for everyone to know our meeting place?"

"But she's his girl," Carl protested. "Why do you think she rode all this way? He'd want to see her."

Soames grinned understandingly then.

Clee's first relief at seeing Grady safe was tempered with regret. She felt trapped, sorry she had come. Will he think I'm throwing myself at him? she wondered.

He got off his horse, strode forward, grasped her by the hands. "What's wrong, Clee?"

"Nothing. We've been worried about you, that's all. I promised Ma if I came by this way I'd see if you were back."

His grip was strong. She liked the feel of it as he pulled her toward him. Still she was reserved. He kissed her. It wasn't like the other time. There was no response at first. Then he felt her arms tighten around him, the answering pressure of her lips. She looked worried when he released her. "There's a lot we don't know about each other, Grady."

He grinned. "Like what? I know all that matters. I love you."

"What about Letty Reid? Until the other night I thought she was your girl."

"I like Letty," he answered slowly. "But not this way. If you mean have I ever kissed her——"

"No, I didn't ask that."

"Well, anyway I haven't."

She lost her soberness. "I'm glad, Grady. I didn't intend to ask you that but I couldn't help wondering. I wouldn't be happy, taking you away from someone else. And I don't want a man who's just in love with girls—any girl. This is something special—you for me and no one else—me the same way about you. That's the way it's got to be."

When he kissed her again her reserve was gone and her fervor took him by surprise. Their companionship had always been so matter of fact, he wasn't prepared for it. She didn't want his kisses to stop and her arms were as tight as his.

She was too candid to be otherwise. In the days of anxious waiting she had thought of nothing else and had asked herself many searching questions. Now the last of these was answered. His mind hadn't kept up with hers. He had been occupied with his stern errand and the grim problem of survival. He was a little bewildered by her caresses but he found them delightful.

Sight of a horseman approaching far off on the plain below brought him back to reality. He frowned at the tiny figure too far distant for recognition. "Someone's headed this way. What are your plans, Clee?"

"Ma will want to know you're back. I'll ride straight for headquarters when I leave. Do you know who that is coming?"

He shook his head. "Could be a messenger."

"And it might be one of Rowden's men," she added.

"Yes," he said. "That's another good reason you'd better get out of here."

He led her to the trail by which he had come, down the north side.

By this route she wouldn't be seen. "If that rider goes on, wait till he's out of sight. If he's headed here, don't let him see you. Don't worry. I'll be waiting for him." He kissed her again before they parted.

There were many game trails down the mountain. Clee followed one of these for some distance until she reached a well-defined path which turned abruptly to the right. It led downward too and more in the direction she was going. The only drawback was that this way she might intercept the unknown rider and she knew Grady didn't want that. No use riding so far out of my way, she decided. I'll keep under cover if I find I'm too close to the other trail. In addition, the thought of seeing that horseman appealed to her. She rode slowly, picked her way, as she realized the trail was veering rapidly southward. Presently there was an abrupt turn just ahead and she stopped. Beyond she might easily be in clear view of the approaching stranger. She dismounted and peered cautiously around the mountain's shoulder.

The trails intersected not far ahead. She could see no one but from below came the scuffle of rocks. She had stopped just in time.

Clee waited silently. The approaching sounds grew until the clink of hoofs was sharp on the stony trail. Again she peered around the ledge.

Her eyes widened in recognition. She choked back an impulse to call out. Not fifty yards away on the south trail rode Letty Reid. Clee watched until horse and rider disappeared on the path above. When she drew back her face burned with anger and her fists were clenched. She struggled with the impulse to turn back. Her mind seethed with the words she would say. So there was nothing between Grady and Letty! The sickness in her grew as she remembered how convincing his words had sounded, how glad she'd been to hear them. This was no chance meeting. Apache was more than fifty miles away. This had the sorry flavor of her own meetings with Rowden. She choked back a sob as she recalled their shabby detail. No wonder he was in such a hurry to get rid of me, she thought bitterly. She brushed her mouth with the back of her hand in torment at thought of his kisses. She remembered how eager she'd been for them, too. That shamed her. She waited until the sounds above had died, almost frantic in her desire to remain hidden now. Letty must not know she had been here. Or would Grady tell her? Perhaps they'd laugh about it. She bit her lip. She mounted her horse, dug her spurs in savagely, the hurt and bewilderment submerged in her anger.

Her lost confidence in Grady disturbed her most. She had felt so

certain of him. Some day I'll learn, she thought wretchedly. I thought
he was so different from Rowden. This time I was going to be sure. But
they're all alike. I should have known. Thank God I discovered it in
time.

Her fury didn't wear itself out with riding and she galloped too fast.
The butte soon was far behind her. The mare tired and she slackened
the breakneck pace for a time. Soon she was using the spurs again but
the bitterness kept pace with her. She couldn't outdistance it.

Her thoughts were turned inward, her mind so occupied that she didn't
see the horsemen until after they had changed their course. There were
three of them. She drew rein and her eyes sharpened as she watched
their approach. Cowmen, she thought at first, and panic filled her. How
would she explain her presence here? No one must learn where she
had been. The answer was so obvious that she scoffed at herself. This
was Forked W range she was working. She belonged here. As they drew
nearer, however, she realized they were strangers. She didn't try to avoid
them. That would have been useless and she felt no fear. These were
fighting men, she realized. They were marked by the way they wore
their weapons. Like Grady, she thought. She decided they were rustlers
from Scalp Creek and waited in hostile silence until they reached her.

"Headed for the Forked W?" Their spokesman was older than the
others, his manner friendly, and he looped his hat over his saddle horn
as he spoke.

She nodded.

"Meet any riders up yonder?"

Were they looking for Grady, she wondered, or were they hunting
news of the cattlemen patrolling the ranges? She hesitated over her
answer. "Were you looking for someone?"

Her hostility was obvious. The stranger grinned. "I reckon valley
folks have grown a little cautious about talkin' to strangers," he observed. "Set your mind at rest, ma'am. The trouble here is over. We're
Texas Rangers."

She stared at them with new respect. "What are you doing here?"

"Putting things to order mostly" was the mild answer. "But there's
one trail we'd like to pick up. Do you know Grady Scott?"

She stiffened. For an instant she thought they'd guessed where she'd
been. She knew that was impossible, but mention of him was like the
flick of a lash across raw nerves. Fury welled up in her and the taste in
her mouth was bitter. "I know where he is." Even to Clee her voice had

a grating sound. She didn't care. Nothing mattered now except that the Rangers were looking for Grady and she could tell them where he was. In the same hard tone she pointed out Spy Butte. "It's about ten miles, but he can see you coming unless you wait till night."

She watched the Rangers ride on, wondered if they would find Letty Reid still with Grady when they reached the butte. She hoped so. She was savage when she wished it and there was hatred in her eyes. But they were blurred, too. She couldn't watch the three riders long.

Chapter 25 A WARNING

GRADY was bewildered by Letty's presence here. She was tired. It showed in the sag of her shoulders and in the slow way she slid from the saddle.

"What's wrong?" he asked. "How'd you find your way here?"

"Carl Lehman told me where you were. I had to warn you, Grady. There are Rangers in Apache."

He grinned. "Do you know what company? I'll have friends there."

"Does it matter?" Her voice turned edgy with impatience. "Major Jones himself brought them. And don't you go looking for friends there, Grady. It's you they're hunting."

He whistled softly. "Why?"

"Major Jones has been listening to the sheriff. He has only one side of the story. You see, Grady? You're blamed for all the trouble here now. That's why I had to warn you. You'd better get out fast."

He merely grinned again. "I don't scare as easy as that. Sit down and while you're resting tell me what happened."

"Oh, Grady, why won't you listen to me? Do you think I'd have ridden all this way if it wasn't serious? Yet you just stand there and grin."

He quit smiling but the twinkle lurked in his eyes. "I reckon I must be a trial to you, Letty. I don't manage easy, do I?"

She frowned at that, bit her lip. "Just the same you're going to listen. When the Rangers rode in I counted forty-one of them. When I went to their camp last night hunting Major Reynolds, they wouldn't let me in. I counted their horses—there were only seventeen left. That means two dozen Rangers are scouring the valley for you, Grady. You could laugh when a bunch of clodhoppers tried to chase you around, but this is different. These are Indian fighters just like you."

"So you were worried and you rode all this way to tell me. I'm sorry I laughed, Letty. I didn't mean to rile you. It's just . . . well . . . some things a man's got to decide for himself. You've helped me a lot. Now I know how things stand. But I'm still not running away. Suppose you sit down and tell me all that's happened."

As she talked, he fanned the embers of the fire with his hat and nursed a flame into some twigs. Soon they began to crackle. "Let's have some coffee. You need it." He propped a battered pot against the blaze and, while waiting for it to boil, unsaddled her horse and picketed it to graze.

She watched his preparations. "I can't stay long."

He squinted toward the sun. "Not more than an hour if you're going to reach the Forked W by dark, but you and the horse both will travel better with a little rest. Now tell me about the Rangers. What brought them to Apache?"

"It was August Lehman's idea and it was a good one." She described the scene at Apache, how Rowden had the nesters ready for battle when Major Jones rode in unexpectedly at the head of his column. "If they hadn't come there'd have been more useless killing. It was the only way to stop it."

He filled a tin with coffee, handed it to her. "Still troubled about scalps?"

She stared at him across the brim of the cup. "No. You're improving, Grady." She couldn't refrain from adding, "Did you resent a little managing by a woman when you spared Toomey and Blucher that?"

"I just remembered how you felt about scalps and decided maybe I'd picked up too many Indian ways."

"You took my advice on that. Why won't you listen to me now?"

He knew the answer. Then her opinion had mattered and he'd tried to look at his deed through her eyes. He hadn't been in love with Clee at that time. At least he hadn't realized it. That changed everything. Queer, how easy it now was to see through Letty and her efforts to make him over. It was different with Clee. She was worried but she took him as he was. When he thought of her he kept his eyes on his coffee— he didn't want Letty reading them. He wished she hadn't come. He wanted words that were warm and gentle to say, a way to thank her for all this trouble. That wouldn't do. His awareness of it made him uncomfortable. Because of that his manner turned brusque. "Forget about me from here on out, Letty. We don't see things the same way. I still aim to even up Tom Williams' tally. That's what worries you."

"It troubles me more when a man like Merrill Blake dies with his gun in his holster," she replied soberly. "I'm beginning to see things your

way, some. Is that what you wanted to know? And that's why I'm glad
the Rangers are here. They will put an end to all this."

His eyes grew somber. "Blake was murdered—just like Tom Williams.
There are a lot of scores to settle here, Letty, before we'll have peace
again. My work has just begun."

"I was afraid you'd be like this. That's why I had to see you. Things
are different now. I'll admit you were right in the beginning. There
was no law here, only mobs and murderers. We needed someone like
you. Now the Rangers have brought order back. It's their job to track
down these killers and they will do it. You've been right but it's time
to stop. You'll be on the wrong side from now on. Don't set yourself
against the law, Grady. Remember you've been a Ranger yourself."

"The trouble is the Rangers are getting only one side of the story.
You told me yourself they were listening to the sheriff."

"Give them time to find out the truth. You have many friends here.
They can tell the Rangers. You can't—not while you're a hunted man.
There's just one thing for you to do, Grady," she argued. "Get out until
this blows over. You have punished three of the murderers. If you know
the others, tell me and I'll take their names to the Rangers for you. I
want them caught, too, but let the authorities handle it. It isn't safe for
you to stay here any longer."

He shook his head. "You don't know me very well. I'm not much of
a hand at running. In my book I've done what I had to do except that
the job isn't finished. I've done what's right but if I leave now that's
not the way it'll look."

She argued with him further; and she was always halted abruptly by
the same answer: "I've done nothing wrong. I won't run away."

"You're the stubbornest man I ever knew," she exclaimed, while he
was saddling the horse for her.

"You're a little mite stubborn yourself, Letty," he reminded her.
"Quit worrying about me and the Rangers. I've been taking care of
myself for quite a spell."

She was troubled, though. Her fears followed her down the mountain
and she changed her direction, rode miles out of her way to avoid betraying where she'd been, should she be seen.

Grady watched her after she reached the valley. He recognized her
precaution and smiled at it. Her devious path wouldn't fool a man who
could follow a trail. Her news had troubled him more than he let her
guess, though. He knew the ability of the Rangers. If they'd heard only

Rowden's story they could be riding on the wrong side and that was bad. He had only met Major Jones—didn't know him well—but played with the idea of seeing him. The major would listen, he knew. There were obstacles to such a course: he had no proof for his story yet; he could not be sure he would ever reach the major. No, he must wait here until the cowmen arrived, tell them what he'd discovered. Until that was done he couldn't risk capture.

He cooked supper before sunset. From here his blaze could be seen too far at night. When the sky turned red he took a final look at the plains below. Far to the east, Letty, a diminishing speck, still followed her roundabout path. The hill shadows were long and turning purple. He stared a long time to the south and to the west without seeing anyone. When he looked for Letty again she had disappeared and the sky had lost its color. Tomorrow the cowmen would be here. He stamped out the last embers of his fire, watered his horse at the spring and washed, made ready for the night.

The moon was almost round. Good weather for a cattle drive, he thought, and remembered the branding he'd watched along Scalp Creek. There wasn't much more time, he was sure, before the rustlers and the cattle would be gone. He wondered, too, about Rowden. He wanted the sheriff there when he led the way into the Breaks. That would be the final proof of the story he'd worked out in his mind. He was still thinking of that when he went to sleep.

He didn't know what waked him. He could hear nothing now but there must have been some sound. Every sense was alert. The moon had moved westward and was bright. If he could just lift his head he'd be able to see. He listened again with no result. His saddle was his pillow. By turning cautiously he could peer over it. Slowly he shifted his weight a few inches at a time, pausing at intervals to listen.

Then he heard the sound again, a soft stir off among the trees. A deer perhaps, or some lesser animal. He didn't lose his vigilance.

"Grady!" someone called softly from off to his right. He grinned to himself. One of the cowmen surely, arrived early for the meeting. He knew that wasn't the answer before the thought was finished. A horse on the trail would have awakened him sooner. This approach had been more cautious than that. His movement still was deliberate. His hand moved guardedly toward his holster.

"Grady!" This time the call was louder.

His fingers closed on the six gun. He inched it from its holster.

"Grady, it's Maj Reynolds. I've got to talk to you."

"I hear you. Come on out into the moonlight, Maj." His gun was still poised until he recognized his friend. "What's the idea slipping up on my camp Indian style?" he complained after they gripped hands. "I might have shot without knowing who it was."

"That's why I called, and if I'd ridden in you might not have waited for me. Things are bad, Grady. Major Jones has Rangers scouring the country for you. I have two with me, both old friends of yours from D Company." He turned and called the others in.

"Suppose you tell us what's going on here," Reynolds urged after the others came up.

Grady told his story. When he finished Reynolds held out his hand.

"I'd have done the same thing if Tom Williams had been my friend," he said. "The trouble is the major has heard a different tale from Rowden. Where does he fit into this?"

"I'm not sure whether he was in on the murder or not. I think so but I can't prove it yet. He's mixed up in the rest of it. I heard him send orders to the rustler camp on Scalp Creek. I know he set the trap for me in Apache because I'd learned too much."

"What you need is time," Reynolds decided, and the others murmured their approval. "We all know the major. He's one of the greatest fighting men who ever lived but he's hard. If he thought it was his duty, he'd ride up here with a gun in each hand, even if it was his own father waiting at the top. Right now he wants you for murder. There are ten of us from Company D with him. You don't need to worry about us, but Company A's along too. How many of them do you know?"

Grady couldn't be sure.

"Then stay out of their way," Maj warned.

What Grady needed, they decided, was proof of the sheriff's role in the valley's struggle. They discussed this at length. "If you can get that, your worries are ended," Reynolds assured him. "The major's sharp. You'll need real evidence. Get that and you'll find him a fair man." Before they left, he took Grady aside for a final warning. "A woman visited you this afternoon didn't she?"

"What makes you think so?"

"We met her. She can't be trusted, Grady. Keep away from her."

"But she was a good friend. You're all wrong, Maj."

Reynolds shook his head. "How do you think we found you? Everyone knows the Rangers are on your trail. When she learned who we were she told us where to come. I thought you should know, Grady. Don't trust her again."

Grady couldn't understand that. Long after they were gone he puzzled over it. Letty had ridden long and hard to warn him. It didn't sound reasonable. Yet he couldn't doubt Maj either. He was angered at the betrayal, thought of her only with bitterness.

26 THE RANGERS MAKE A CHOICE

SOAMES had eight riders with him. They worked the north range vigilantly, resting by day, patrolling at night, for rustlers were like Indians. They liked moonlight for their task. One day the cowmen made camp in the northern hills; another they holed up in a river bend. Both had been cold camps—they weren't risking fires. Soames was disgruntled. The plan as Grady had originally outlined it sounded good. There'd been a prospect of action and that's what he wanted. Instead, there'd been nothing but grueling, fruitless rides. They hadn't sighted anyone until they met Letty Reid. They weren't sure how to take her news of the Rangers. "They're our kind of folks" was Soames's glum comment. "But we'd rather settle this our own way."

Twice that day Ranger patrols picked up their trail, followed them to camp. This was a working cow outfit. There was nothing about it to excite suspicion. Always they rode on but their questions left the cowmen uneasy.

"All hunting Grady." Carl looked worried. "I don't like the sound of it."

"Me neither," Soames growled. " 'Pears like they've been listening to the wrong people. If they're taking sides there'll be trouble."

This was their last night ride and Soames led them toward the western end of the valley as soon as it was dusk. "If we don't get action tonight we will tomorrow," he promised. "We meet at Spy Butte in the morning and I aim to have my say. There won't be any more of this delay. I'm for wadin' into the Breaks after 'em."

They worked their way westward slowly, clung to the shallow valleys, eyed the skyline for strange silhouettes. The cured grass was a reflector, making the night brighter.

Carl Lehman laid a hand on Soames's arm and pointed. Cattle were drifting across the slope ahead, many of them, and bunched, all headed west. No men were visible but the steady plodding had its meaning. There was a muffled stir among the rannies as weapons were readied.

"Easy," Soames cautioned softly. "Don't stampede 'em. It's the riders we're after. They're headed for Scalp Creek. Let's get where we can head 'em off."

They pulled back from the valley quietly, set their horses at a canter at a safe distance from the herd. Soames explained what he had in mind as they rode. The country was progressively rougher as it approached the Breaks and there still was an hour of moonlight. The rustlers would try to get the herd into the broken country by then. "Grady was right. That's where this gang hangs out. We don't want any of this bunch to get away to warn them. Never mind the cattle either. We can pick them up later."

The slopes grew steeper and scrub timber began to blot the silver of the grass. Soames chose a position where the herd must cross a dwindling valley and divided his force, half on each side. They didn't dismount. Each rider found a thicket and reined motionless in its shadow. Soon the cattle came, grown noisy and bawling as the hills' shanks crowded them into a narrow file.

Three riders rode the drag, bandannas across their faces against the herd's dust. The Breaks were close and they'd grown careless of the clatter.

"Now!" Soames shouted, and dug in his spurs. From both sides the cowmen crowded in and moonlight glittered on gun barrels. The drag riders had no chance. One tried, but three bullets dropped him before he got his gun away. The others raised their hands.

Pete Falkner had lagged behind, watching the back trail. If there was to be any trouble he expected it there. The shots ahead surprised him. He clamped his legs together, lifted his pony into a lope, started forward. There was only one volley, then silence. That warned him. "It is over. If my *cuadrilla* is on top they don't need me. If they are not I won't ride into an *emboscada*."

He circled cautiously until he reached the far side of the valley. There was little need for his caution here—the uneasy cattle were noisy. It was almost like day below. His eyes turned hard at what they saw and he was tempted to use his pistol. He decided against it. That could wait until the odds were more favorable. He must warn Rowden. Still hugging cover, he withdrew and circled again, this time heading east and riding hard.

Charlie Springer cursed under his breath. He couldn't understand it. Rowden had said he had everything worked out; all the cowmen would be pulled off the range. Charlie wondered how Pete Falkner had fared. Pete wasn't the kind to desert a friend; he'd bring help. The cowmen lashed Springer's feet under his horse. As he felt the ropes tighten he wished he'd gone for his gun too. It was better to die that way than from hemp fever. There hadn't been a chance though—he'd seen that. This way there was. He thought again of Rowden. The sheriff had planned this cleanup too carefully to let anything slip now. There were nearly three thousand head of cattle in the Breaks ready for the drive. No, Rowden would know how to handle it. "Keep your chin up," Charlie told his companion guardedly. "There's been a slip some place but the sheriff can handle it."

In camp the prisoners were bound securely and a guard was posted over them. Springer took heart from that, too. What he had feared most was a necktie party and no delay. Now there would be time for his friends to act.

The incessant tapping of Rowden's fingers wore Pakebusch's nerves raw. It had kept up all afternoon. Each time a horse clattered down the main street the sheriff stepped to the window and watched. His cold features had grown sharper with worry. There was no word from the Breaks. A fortune in cattle was penned in that wild country and he had the wild men to handle it there, too. Perhaps he'd waited too long but he'd been reluctant to quit Apache until the fighting actually started. A nester-rancher war was a perfect cover for his operations. He would have been gone by now if things had turned out right. The only flaw had been the need for handling the nesters properly. He felt Toomey's loss there—Frank was a good hand at that. With him gone the sheriff hadn't dared leave.

Something had gone wrong. The trap had been carefully baited but the cowmen hadn't sprung it. He still didn't know where they were, what they were up to. The Rangers were the final complication. He'd been only annoyed by their interference at first. After all, he was the sheriff. Major Jones had accepted his report without argument. He'd seen possibilities in that: If they arrested Grady Scott for murder, it would be almost as good as a pitched battle in stirring up excitement, good cover for the final stripping of the ranches and the drive out. But he could learn nothing. Rangers rode in and out constantly but they brought no prisoners with them.

He turned to Pakebusch. "Tonight I'm sending you to Scalp Creek. I need to know what's going on up there."

"Not me!"

"Why not? You're the only one I have to send."

Pakebusch moistened his lips and his voice raised to a whine. "You know vy. Dat's Grady Scott's country. I vouldn't haff a chance."

"Where's your guts?" The sheriff's voice was flat with contempt. "The valley's crowded with Rangers. By this time Grady Scott has either taken to the tall ridges or he's laying mighty low. Quit worrying. You've no call to be scared now."

"Dat's vot Toomey und Blucher t'ought." Pakebusch's voice had grown husky. "He got dem bot'."

Rowden's temper reached the breaking point. He didn't flare up. Instead, his eyes grew more chill, his face tightened and the pulse at his temples throbbed. "All because of the Williams murder. That worries you a lot. Let me tell you something. That's been bothering the Rangers too. Major Jones asked me about it. If he had the straight of that you'd really have something to worry about."

Kurt sat up straight. The nervous fumbling of his hands stopped. "Vot do dey know about it?"

"Nothing—yet. But they don't like the idea of mobs killing prisoners. If I should tell them what I know——"

"I didn't do it," Kurt whimpered. "*Ja,* I vass dere but I didn't do it mineself."

"Try telling the Rangers that." Rowden made no effort to hide his dislike. He lashed out the words. "How about Blake? You shot him. I can swear to that myself. So can a dozen others."

Pakebusch backed away. Fear glazed his eyes. "You vass dere, too," he shrilled.

"I'm sheriff." Rowden nodded calmly. "It was my job to be there. I did my best to stop the murder."

"But you didn't. You made me do it."

"Just your word against mine, Kurt, and don't forget I'm the sheriff." The breath went out of Pakebusch. He wilted, moistened his lips before he spoke and even then his voice was barely a whisper. "You vouldn't do dat to me, Vill—not to me."

The sheriff shrugged. "Don't force my hand. You're no use to me this

KURT PAKEBUSCH no longer whimpered. He'd been a prisoner two hours and nothing had happened yet. He still was terrified. His haunted eyes followed every move Grady made about the camp. But as time passed and he gathered hope, the raw edges of his fear no longer showed. Grady had marched him back to Spy Butte, roped him to a tree and let him wait while he tended his horse, kindled a blaze and boiled coffee. *If he's as spooked as he looks, I'll let him worry a spell,* Grady had decided.

He looked up from his coffee now. "Ready to start talkin'?"

Pakebusch chewed at his lips. "Vot you vant to know?"

"Who was with you when you murdered Tom Williams?"

"I didn't do it. Dat vasn't me."

"You were there. I heard you admit it once." The nester's first babbling had revealed his horror of scalping. Grady remembered it, pulled out his Bowie knife, nursed it in his palm. Pakebusch stared at it and started to sweat.

"*Ja*, I vass dere." He began reluctantly. Once loosened, his tongue couldn't stop. He dribbled out his story with little need for prompting. Grady memorized the names of the six who had been present: Pete Falkner, Frank Toomey, Charlie Springer, Heinrich Unger, Adolph Blucher, in addition to Pakebusch. He'd already hunted down three of them. He winced as the story reached its climax—Tom, unarmed, making a last effort to escape as the murderers closed in.

"Where was Rowden? Are you sure he wasn't there?"

"*Aber* he vass *unser* boss. Rowden sent us dere."

That led to other questions. Whenever Pakebusch hesitated, a flourish of the Bowie knife untied his tongue. Gradually Grady fitted the fragmentary pictures together, until the story took form. From the time Rowden reached the valley, he'd always lurked in the background of the violence: the cunning trap where Luke Nesbit and his O-bar-O hands had died; the way the Schneider family had been blamed for that, and their slaughter; the killing of old Sheriff Sparks and how that had paved the way for Rowden to take office.

"Who killed Merrill Blake and Red and Andy? The sheriff was there that time."

"Ja, ja, he vass dere." Pakebusch started sniffling. "Who fired de shots—dat I don't know. I don't know, I tell you. Ever'body vass shooting." That was all he would say about these murders.

Grady had finished his questioning by the time the cowmen arrived. Curly's raiders were first. Then came Soames and his rannies with their prisoners. Dave Blake had been south of the river and had farthest to come. His party was last. Grady knew what must be done. He waited for the last arrival before announcing his plan.

"I'm going into Apache," he said. "Pakebusch has talked and I'm going to give the whole story to the Rangers."

"Are you plumb loco?" Soames demanded. "They're scouring the country for you. If you get there alive nobody'll listen to you. You've been blamed for all that's happened here."

Grady nodded toward Pakebusch. "They'll listen. I'm taking my witness with me." He told them what he'd learned, fitting each incident into its place as he now understood it.

When Charlie Springer heard himself listed among Tom Williams' murderers, he turned on Pakebusch. "Did you tell 'em you're the one that shot Merrill Blake while you were spillin' your guts?" he snarled.

Dave Blake turned white. There was a growl from the Lazy B riders. "Looks like we've got a couple of murderers here," said Dave. "They're not goin' to be much use as witnesses, Grady, when we're through with them. I was willin' to wait and hold a trial for some plain cow thieves. But not now. Let's get out our ropes."

"Not yet," Grady argued. "First, let's use their evidence to clear up this whole mess. Right now they'll help us more alive than dead. We've got 'em Dave. They can't get away and they're sure to hang, no matter what court tries them."

"You're tryin' to dose me with medicine you wouldn't take yourself," Blake retorted. "How about Toomey and Blucher and Unger? You settled with them quick enough."

"Springer and Pakebusch are still on my list." Grady took a stand before the prisoners as he argued. "I haven't scratched 'em off. All I'm asking is for time. I still aim to settle my tally for Tom, but first let's use their evidence to prove our side of the story to the Rangers. That's our best bet for squaring things here."

"We can settle it ourselves, now we know how things stand," Soames grumbled. "Grady's found where Rowden's gang is holed up in the Breaks. We can clean 'em out today and then go after Rowden himself. We don't need any more evidence."

Curly moved to Grady's side. "Shore, we can handle this easy, clean out Rowden an' all his gang double-quick." He held up his hands to still the mutter of the rannies. "But we've got Ranger trouble too, now. An' whar does that leave Grady? Right now he's blamed for ever'thing that's happened hyar, an' don't fo'get that's Rowden's doin's, too. Now me, I reckon I feel the same way 'bout Tom Williams that Dave Blake feels 'bout his brother. I got a itch in my fingers when I think of it an' I don't like to wait. But this is our chancet to squar' things up, oncet an' for all. 'Pears to me like we've got us a choice between Grady Scott an' a couple o' murderers an' I choose Grady. He's my friend. Mind, we ain't lettin' these killers off. We're just waitin' a spell."

Curly had wisely given them a choice they understood. They still wrangled over it but they decided to try Grady's way, although they still wanted to accompany him on his journey to town. "Everybody's agin you, Grady," Soames pointed out. "The Rangers are huntin' you and so are the nesters. And you know what to expect if you run into any of Rowden's crowd. Why don't we all go?"

"That's a good way to run into a fight. If they saw this outfit coming, they'd think we were on the warpath sure. No, I can do this job better alone."

"Why not take me?" Carl volunteered. "All the nesters know me. I can get in and out of town any time without trouble."

Grady smiled. "Maybe you could alone but not with me. No thanks, Carl. I'll take Pakebusch along and that's all."

After providing a horse for the prisoner, they lashed him securely in the saddle with a rope binding his ankles under the horse's belly and crowded around to watch as Grady set out for Apache. It was agreed that the cowmen would await his return before their drive into the Breaks.

"We'll stay over tomorrow," said Soames. "Then if you're not here——"

"I'll be back," Grady promised. "And I'll have Rangers with me. This time they'll be on the right side."

Carl didn't confide in anyone lest they try to stop him. He slipped away quietly after Grady left, took one of the easy trails down the north side of the butte and traveled slowly. There was plenty of time. He wanted Grady to have a long start. He knew he could be helpful and was determined to go along, but Grady must not guess his presence until they neared Apache. He chose a northerly course, watched from the brow of a hill until the figures of the two horsemen ahead dwindled and faded across the horizon before he set out in pursuit.

Clee was in a savage humor when she reached headquarters. Her mood had changed several times during the long ride. When her initial fury was spent she had mocked herself for a fool, easily duped by any man. That was better than admitting the hurt she felt that turned her sick inside. When she remembered her meeting with the Rangers, she was filled with panic at what she'd done. That didn't seem real to her now. How could she betray a man she loved? The thought of Letty at Spy Butte had the same quality of unreality. Clee had met Grady at a time of lost confidence. She had been wary and her faith in him had been slow in building. It was hard to shake. She couldn't think straight right now no matter how hard she tried, and she knew it. In this turmoil nothing remained fixed. One moment she was in blazing revolt against Grady's faithlessness; the next she denied it could happen. It was like living an odious nightmare. Most of all, as her thoughts turned inward, she loathed herself for what she'd done.

Ma was at the house. The lamps were already lighted and Clee could see her stirring about. Clee didn't want to face her—not yet. Instead, she turned toward the kitchen where Ohmie's clatter foretold supper.

"What's the matter, Clee?" Ohmie stopped her work to stare.

"Nothing."

"You—you ain't been hurt?"

"No, of course not."

"Then I reckon you've had bad news. Nothin's happened to Carl, has it? If that's it, tell me quick."

Clee shook her head, and wondered if this heaviness and pain she felt deep inside would ever leave her. She'd have to brace up. If Ohmie could see through her like this, what would happen when Ma came in?

"Carl's been ridin' our range," Ohmie went on hopefully. "I thought maybe you'd seen him."

"You'd best forget Carl," Clee flared back. "Falling in love is the surest way I know for a girl to get hurt. You can't believe what men tell you."

"Not Carl."

"Oh, they're all alike," Clee stormed.

"Not Carl," Ohmie persisted. "And not Grady, either. Ain't you forgettin' him?"

Clee wanted to cry out against Grady, too, but she choked on the words.

"No, not Grady. Hell's bells, he's not cut out that way."

They'd been so absorbed in the dispute that they hadn't heard Ma enter. She glanced sharply at Clee. "Someone's comin'. I heard the horse. You'd better go wash up before they get in."

As she hurried out, Clee wondered how much Ma had heard and what those keen eyes had seen.

The visitor was Letty Reid. Ma helped her unsaddle and turn her horse into the corral. They were at table when Clee returned. She stopped in the door when she saw who it was.

"Grady's back," Ma boomed. "Letty's seen him. She's been to Spy Butte. Didn't I tell you not to waste any worry over him? He knows how to look out for himself."

Clee had been careful to compose her face before she entered. She didn't want Ma to read it. Letty's presence had taken her by surprise. Now she wasn't sure of herself. "Oh, yes, Grady'll always take care of himself," she agreed. Of one thing she was certain: she couldn't sit calmly across the table from Letty. Not tonight, not without Ma guessing too much of what had happened. "I'm not feeling so well. I don't want anything to eat."

Ma didn't protest. "Sure, you run along," she said. Clee was glad of that. But after she was gone Ma left the table. "I reckon that young'un's sick. I'd better dose her up with calomel. Go on with your supper. I'll be back."

She found Clee out by the corral, leaning against its poles. Ma rested against them, too, rolled herself a cigarette and lighted it before she said anything.

"Want to tell me about it?"

"No."

"Sometimes it helps to get these things off your chest."

"Leave me alone, Ma. I don't want to talk. Not now. Go on back and finish your supper."

Ma grunted. "Don't worry about the others. They think I'm out dosin' you up with calomel. I don't think that'd be much help for what's ailin' you."

"Ma, please let me alone."

"Not this time. I did once, when you rode in here with a story 'bout bein' throwed by a bronc. Your face was bruised up but you didn't have any scratches on your arms. Remember? I figure the less said the better, sometimes, an' that was one of 'em. Whatever was wrong you've cured it since you've been here an' I'm glad." Her cigarette glowed as she pulled on it thoughtfully. "This is different, somehow. I heard what you said to Ohmie an' I saw your face, too, Clee. There's torment in it. You know the worst mad of all is when you're mad with yourself. That don't cure so easy, honey. I'm a pretty good hand at mindin' my own business mostly, but I don't think this is the time for it. I think you'd better tell me about it."

"Oh, Ma! If anything happens to Grady, I—I don't know what I'll do."

There was so much anguish in the outburst, Ma didn't know how to answer.

"It would be my fault." Clee tried but she couldn't check the sobs that shook her. "My fault . . . my fault," she gasped over and over.

Ma took her in her arms, tried to soothe her. "Shucks, he's all right now. You heard what Letty said."

Clee had choked back her emotions too long. The violence of the storm that shook her alarmed Ma. She got the girl to bed before Letty and Ohmie were through in the kitchen. She was baffled by it, too. All her arguments met the same answer. "You don't know—you don't know," Clee would sob. Ma couldn't make sense of it.

"Clee's right sick," she told the others. "It's a fever, I think. She may have a bad time of it. Don't go in there and bother her."

Letty left next morning without seeing her. Thinking Clee was still in bed, Letty didn't guess that she had crept out of the house at dawn, saddled her mare and headed for Spy Butte.

She had no definite plan except the urge to know what had happened. If Grady had escaped she'd find him. The other alternatives were more difficult to face. If he'd been captured the Rangers would take him to Apache. She'd follow there. But Grady wasn't the kind to give up easily. That worried her most of all. What if there'd been a fight? This time he was matched against Rangers and the odds were three to one. She tried to push the outcome of such a battle from her mind but couldn't. Her dread of that was worst of all, crowding everything else from her mind. She had to know.

She didn't see Pete Falkner until she topped the hill and he was rising from the grass to face her, his six gun leveled. He was as surprised as she when he recognized her.

"*Perdóneme,* señorita. I wasn't expecting a girl." His teeth flashed pleasantly. "I do not mean you any harm but I am in trouble and I will shoot if I have to. You will get off the *caballo, por favor.*" He nodded toward his own horse stretched in the grass beyond. "I was riding hard last night and mine broke his leg. He stepped in a gopher hole. I had to shoot him." He glanced approvingly at the dun mare. "*Muy bueno,* I have seen this one before, señorita. A fine animal in spite of its bad color. That I do not like. Do you speak Spanish, señorita?"

She shook her head.

"*Bueno.* For in Mexico they have a word for this color. I would not say it if you knew its meaning. They call it *palomino.* I feel that way about it, too."

"What will I do if you leave me out here afoot?" she demanded.

"Señorita, it is just five miles that way." He pointed toward Forked W headquarters. "I am *muy triste* that you have to walk but I need this *caballo* worse than you do." He hesitated. "Maybe you will not mind so much if you know my errand. Señor Rowden is your friend as well as mine. I found this mare and bought it for him. I ride to tell him there is trouble here."

He swung into the saddle.

"Will Rowden is no friend of mine." She had turned scarlet.

"*Mucho mejor,* señorita." He grinned. "Then I am inconveniencing an enemy rather than an *amigo. Buenos dias.*" He raised an arm in salute as he galloped off.

Spy Butte was beyond reach afoot. Clee had to turn back. It wasn't loss of the dun mare that troubled her. She'd wanted to be rid of the animal for a long time. She was worried over Grady; she still didn't know what had happened up on the mountain.

Carl rode carefully, far behind Grady and Pakebusch and on a parallel course farther to the north. He reasoned there was less likelihood of being seen that way, should Grady be watching the back trail. Occasionally he rode close enough to see them in the distance. Then he would check and wait. There'd be time enough to close this interval when they approached Apache.

It was during one of these pauses that he spotted the other horseman.

Someone else was on Grady's trail, still just a distant speck, dark against the grass. He moved his horse out of sight under the hill, stretched himself prone on the brow to watch. The rider came fast. Before long he could distinguish the color of the horse. There were only two like it in the valley. If this was Rowden it meant trouble. If it was Clee, what would she be doing here? It's a good thing I came, he decided. The sheriff's discovered what Grady's up to, somehow, and is bent on stopping him.

He returned to his horse then, tried out his newly acquired knowledge as he picked a zigzag trail through the valleys to intercept the stranger. When he sighted him again the man was much closer. This wasn't the sheriff. This was a smaller man. And the horse was smaller, too. Carl's brows tightened. That was Clee's mare and must have been stolen. He abandoned caution now, rode boldly out to investigate. He loosened his holster strap as he went and was reassured by the feel of the six gun in his fingers. Pete saw him coming and reined in. Their recognition was mutual. Carl took confidence in the feel of his weapon. Falkner wasn't worried by this boy.

"Where'd you get that horse?"

"From a friend, *muchacho*."

"I recognize it." Carl lost his temper. "Clee Soames is no friend of yours."

Pete shrugged. "*Quién sabe?*"

Carl gripped his pistol tighter. "Get off," he ordered. "I'm going to take that mare back home."

"Listen, *hijo*. Do you know who I am?"

"Yes, I know. You're Pete Falkner, one of Rowden's men."

Pete stared at the pistol in the boy's hand. He still was smiling, his tone persuasive. "With a reputation as a gun slinger, *también*. Do not forget that. Ride on back home, sonny, and tell them you did not see me. I am not hunting trouble with boys."

His intention was kindly but Carl took it as a taunt. He brandished his weapon. "See this? Get off that horse!"

Falkner shrugged. "Have it your way, then." He turned his mount at an angle as he swung off. For a brief instant the animal screened him. The blast came as he hit the ground, from beneath the dun mare's neck. Carl toppled from the saddle, his weapon unfired.

"I warned you, *muchacho*," Pete said. He reloaded his six gun before he mounted and rode on.

Chapter 28 A CHANGE OF TUNE

Far back up the trail Grady heard a shot. He didn't know its meaning and was disturbed by the knowledge that he was followed so closely. Another hour on this course would find him not far north of the homesteads which straggled out from Apache. There were enough complications ahead without someone closing in behind him. Turning north, he lashed Pakebusch's horse with a rope end to make it move faster and kept at a gallop until he reached the cover of some rounded hills. From there he watched until he saw the distant horseman. It was too far to distinguish the rider but he recognized Clee's mare. It wasn't she, he knew. He puzzled over it, thought of Carl. It would be like the boy to follow but he rode a bay. It couldn't be he. Another time Grady would have investigated. Not now. He had a prisoner on his hands and a task on which too much depended. He waited until the strange rider disappeared before he ventured on.

When at last he could see the first distant farmsteads he halted again. A secure place to leave Pakebusch was his first problem. South of town, the river's screen would have served him. Here there was nothing but grass, and the hills had flattened out, their valleys mere dimples. He decided on one of these shallow cups, took Pakebusch from his horse, bound him tightly and left him in the grass. He took the animal on another mile before he hobbled it. A bronc was too easy to spot. He didn't want his prisoner found that way. It was growing dark by the time he was ready to move. He was safe from distant observation now, but he rode carefully. There were lights to warn him where each cabin stood. Occasionally he stopped to listen. The presence of Rangers had lulled the valley. He reached the town's edge unchallenged, left his horse in the familiar clump of trees back of the Reid House. He'd find Major Jones at the hotel, he felt sure, but Letty troubled him. He could no longer trust her. It was a good thing Maj Reynolds had warned him of her betrayal or he'd probably have gone straight to her for help in this emergency. He scouted the building cautiously. It was no feat. He lurked in the shadows, peered in the well-lighted windows.

Supper was long over. Hallelujah had finished her dishes and gone to her quarters. The kitchen was dark. In the front room Letty was bent over some figures at her desk. Major Jones was seated across the room and with him was Will Rowden. The sheriff did most of the talking, gesticulated often. The Ranger chief listened gravely, occasionally nodded. Grady wished that he might overhear that conversation. This wasn't the time to go in. Rowden wouldn't let him reach the major if he could help it. Grady was confident he could outmatch him in gunplay, but the major's six guns wouldn't be idle if it came to shooting. Anyway, that was hardly the introduction he wanted for this talk. He needed an opportunity to tell his story calmly, produce his proofs. There were two other men present. He knew them both—old friends in the Ranger service—but they soon came out and sauntered down the street toward Scanlon's. Grady waited on. He smiled when he saw Letty prepare the major's lamp. She gave its chimney a final whisk with wadded paper before she lighted the wick. She left the lamp on the table beside Major Jones before she disappeared in the back. She was still absent when Rowden rose to leave. The major, always formal, accompanied him to the door.

As soon as Rowden was gone Grady started in. Boldness was his best course now. The major had taken his lamp upstairs but there still was a light on the desk. Grady opened the door, was halfway to the steps when Letty came back.

"Grady Scott! What are you doing here?"

He read guilt in her face. She was pale. Her eyes were wide with fright, her hands trembled.

"Look out, you'll drop the lamp." His voice was curt.

She saw the harsh twist of his mouth, the bitter frost in his eyes. This wasn't the Grady she knew. She set the lamp down, whispered this time. "Don't you know there are Rangers staying here?"

"That's what you wanted, isn't it? Well, you're going to get your wish. I'm looking for Major Jones."

"Why? What do you want with him?" She thought she knew. Vengeance had brought him here before. She could see nothing but ruthlessness in him now. There must be a way to stop him. She slipped between him and the stairs.

"Don't try to manage me any more, Letty. Get out of the way."

"No, Grady. I can't let you do this. Go back. There's still a chance for you to escape."

He laughed. "No thanks to you."

She didn't understand that, didn't try. Her mind was too busy with the problem of stopping him. In his present temper he couldn't see that killing Major Jones would solve nothing, only make things immeasurably worse.

He took her by the shoulder to push her aside.

"Wait, Grady. If you're determined to see him I guess I'll have to help you."

"How?" he asked suspiciously.

She turned away so he wouldn't see her face and started up the steps. "You don't know which room is his. I'll point it out."

He followed her, wondering at her change of manner.

The corridor was dark but light showed under one door.

"This it?"

"No," she whispered. "He's down at the end of the hall. I'll show you."

The room was dark. "He must have gone to bed," she said. She pushed the door open and stood aside. Grady peered in.

"Major Jones!" he called.

Letty threw all her weight into the shove, caught him by surprise, sent him staggering over the threshold. Before he could turn, the door banged behind him and he heard the key click in the lock.

"Letty!" he yelled, and banged on the panels. She didn't answer but he could hear her footsteps as she raced down the hall. He threw his bulk against the door but it didn't yield.

Letty burst into the startled major's room without knocking. "Quick, Major! Get out while you can. There's a man here to kill you."

Major Jones merely lifted his eyebrows. "So? Who is it?"

"I . . . I can't tell you that but he's a dangerous man. You must get out."

"Perhaps that's what the banging down the hall's about," he suggested. "I thought it was some ranny coming home from Scanlon's." He stepped out the door and listened. But the sound had stopped. Letty made a final effort to halt him. She tugged at his sleeve, but he pushed her aside. The only preparation he made as he stalked down the hall was to pull his coattail back and loop it behind his holster to free his six gun for action.

When the door didn't yield, Grady turned to the window. He'd left this place that way before. He shoved up the sash. The major heard the sound and knocked.

"The key's on your side. You open it," Grady called.

"Who's in there?"

Grady identified himself. "Who are you?"

"I'm Major John B. Jones of the Texas Rangers. We're hunting you, Scott. Lay down your arms. I'm coming in." The key turned. Jones swung the door open with his foot and drew his six gun.

Before he could step in Letty leaped ahead of him. "Don't shoot!" Her voice rose shrilly. "Don't shoot!"

The swiftness of her movement caught both men off guard. "Here, here, girl! What are you doing?" Jones, nettled, pulled her back. "I'll not have a woman taking my risks."

"There aren't any risks, Major. I came here to find you." Grady followed them out the door. "You can have my artillery. All I want to do is talk."

Letty sobbed. "Why didn't you tell me?"

He was less brusque with her now. "I never know what to expect from you, Letty. If you thought there was going to be fireworks that was a fool thing you did. But I like you best that way."

They talked in the major's room. Grady's recital was brief but he covered every incident. The major listened in stern silence until he was through.

"An ingenious story," he finally commented. "Where are your proofs?"

"Pakebusch has confessed and I brought him with me." Grady told where he'd left the prisoner. "Let's go get him."

The Major stood up. "But of course you understand you're still my prisoner, Scott. Nothing's proved yet. Have you any other weapons besides these six guns you've handed over?"

Grady turned around. He wore his Bowie knife Ranger-fashion, at the back. "Just my blade, sir. I reckon I'm about the willingest prisoner you ever had. I'm anxious to straighten this out, too."

Jones took no men with him. "If there's anything to your story, Rowden or his men may be watching our camp. I don't want them to see you or suspect anything's afoot. Besides—" he smiled for the first time—"I don't mind admitting I half believe you already. I hope for your sake you've got proof, Scott. There's not a man in the Frontier Battalion with a record better than yours."

They were cautious in their leaving. The major borrowed Letty's horse and she went to get it herself. "Can't tell who might be watching," he said. They blew out the lamps, slipped out the back way, and soon were in the saddle and out of the town unseen.

Pakebusch was found without difficulty—Grady had marked the spot well. They tied him to his saddle and started back. "We've got to take him in sometime. Better do it while it's dark," Jones counseled. They didn't try to question the prisoner on the way.

Pakebusch rode in glum silence. Most of his early panic had left him; he had turned surly. Since early morning he had been a captive and nothing had happened. He had recognized Major Jones, knew his reputation and noticed Grady's deference to him. The major was in charge now and that gave the nester hope, too.

Their return was as stealthy as their departure had been. Again they crept in the back way. Letty, expecting them, had extinguished the lights. "Just as well Rowden doesn't guess what's going on," said Jones. Pakebusch heard and his courage revived another notch. There still was hope if they feared Rowden.

No lamp was lighted until they had regained the major's room and the blinds were drawn. Grady shoved a chair forward. "Sit down, Pakebusch."

"Dis vay? Mit my hands tied behind me?"

Grady reached for his knife but it was gone. The nester saw that, and also that the pistol holsters were empty. Jones cut the rope and pushed him toward the chair.

"Now tell Major Jones what you told me," Grady commanded.

Pakebusch chewed at his lips, still cautious. "Diss iss Grady Scott, Machor. You know dat? Dis iss de murderer you haff been lookin' for."

Jones nodded. "Suppose you tell your story now, Pakebusch. I want to get to the bottom of this."

"Den he iss a prisoner, too?"

The major nodded again.

The nester's face gaped open in a toothless grin. "Vot iss it you vant I should say? Dere iss de murderer, Machor. Grady Scott is to blame for ever't'ing."

Grady sprang up but the major waved him back. "I'm handling this now. Keep out of it, Scott."

Pakebusch grinned again. "Get der sheriff. Ask him." The major's gesture had added to his confidence. "*Ja, ja*. Get Herr Rowden here, Machor. Dat's de vay to find out ever't'ing."

"I'd rather hear it from you. Were you present when Tom Williams was killed?"

"I don't know not'ing, Machor. Frank Toomey, he knew about dat *aber* he iss dead." He leveled a grimy finger at Grady. "Und he killed him. Dat's de guilty man right dere."

It was the same with each question Jones put. Pakebusch denied everything, twisted each answer into an accusation.

"Did you or did you not make a confession of these things to Grady Scott at Spy Butte this morning? He says you did."

"Lies . . . lies . . . all lies, Machor! He iss a bad man und he iss joost tryin' to save his own skin."

Major Jones didn't lose his suavity nor raise his voice. Each question was asked in the same smooth way. Kurt Pakebusch would have understood bluster, but he was deceived by this calm and thought he'd convinced the major of his innocence.

Jones weighed the two men before him. He knew Grady Scott's past record. More convincing than that was the way fifteen of his old comrades had stepped from the ranks rather than hunt him down. It was hard to believe a liar could win such loyalty. "His story doesn't help you much, does it, Scott?"

"He's the first one of Tom's murderers I've spared," Grady retorted. "I thought if he told you the truth that would be the best way to end the trouble here. Now I'm sorry. I see it was a mistake."

Jones shook his head. "No, you were right. How'd you make him talk before?"

"He remembered what happened to the others. Unger's scalping seemed to bother him most."

The major picked Grady's Bowie knife from the table, bounced it in his palm, looked thoughtfully at Pakebusch's growing pallor. "Here's your knife back. I'm going for a walk. When I come back I expect you to have his scalp—or the truth, one." He started for the door, but was stopped by a shriek of terror.

"Don't go, Machor! Don't leave me alone mit him!"

"Are your ready to talk?"

Pakebusch rolled his eyes despairingly.

"Listen, my man. Grady Scott didn't dream up that story. It fits the facts too well. And whatever else he's done he's not a liar. You'd better come out with the truth—and pronto."

"*Ja, ja,* I'll tell you. Only keep him avay mit dat knife. I'll tell you ever't'ing, Machor—ever't'ing."

Gripped by his old terror, Pakebusch blubbered so it was hard to understand him at times, but he held nothing back. Jones got the whole story from him.

Rowden had gone to Major Jones after Pete Falkner arrived with his bad news from up the valley. "If I can get the Rangers to close in on those ranchers before they hear about this, there'll be a fight," he told Pete. "That will give us the time we need to move that herd out of the Breaks. There's a fortune there. We can't let it slip through our fingers."

He had tried. The major had listened carefully but remained unmoved by his arguments.

"They're a wild bunch, Major, and they're gathering on the Fork W range. I've just had word they killed one of my men."

"That's bad, Sheriff. What was he doing up there?"

Rowden hesitated. He wondered if Jones had heard, but decided that was impossible. Pete had just brought in the news. "He was one of my deputies, Major—hunting Grady Scott, of course."

"Strange. I've had Rangers in that area hunting Grady Scott, too. They didn't have any trouble with the cowmen."

"They will unless something's done—and quick. The only way to stop great trouble here is to move in before it starts. I thought I could make you understand."

"There isn't going to be any trouble here, Mr. Rowden. Be assured of that. I'll handle this my way."

Rowden hurried back to his office in the jail where Falkner was waiting. "I can't understand where that fellow got such a reputation as a fighter," he complained. "I couldn't stir him up. No matter what I said he stayed cool as a cucumber."

"Don't get him wrong then, *jefe*. That kind shoots the straightest."

Rowden jerked out a drawer, began emptying it of papers. "There are some records here I can't leave behind," he said. "And it's time for us to move. If we ride straight for Scalp Creek we still may be able to move out that herd before they pick up our trail."

"*Recueídese,* señor, but there is one thing we must do first. Two of my *hombres* have been caught."

The sheriff looked up. "They knew the risk they were taking, the same as we did."

"*Sí,* they knew. But one of these is my *compadre,* Charlie Springer. He is waiting for me to come, *jefe.* He knows I will help him if I can."

Rowden looked down at the litter of papers on his desk. He'd learned how stubborn Pete could be, on occasion. This was no time to argue. "Of course," he conceded. "I feel the same way you do. First we must help Charlie."

They worked swiftly but there was much to do. The papers he didn't intend to carry Rowden burned in the stove. There were letters here from his bank in St. Louis by which he might be traced later. He intended to leave no shred of evidence behind, and even Falkner couldn't be trusted with this task. They needed spare horses. It was nearly sixty miles to the Breaks and they'd be moving fast. Falkner went after these. The dun mare he'd ridden in was unfit for further use. Two hours had passed before preparations were completed. Rowden left his office lamp burning; he chuckled over that touch. "The longer start we have the better off we'll be."

Pete thought it a useless trick. "*Por qué?* It will be *mañana* before they look for us—maybe longer. We have plenty of time."

They started slowly, each leading his extra horse. There still were lights in the Reid House as they approached. Rowden glanced that way, noticed how sharply the moon lighted up the building. As they drew abreast of the hotel the door opened, flooded the porch with yellow light. Three men appeared in the door. The sheriff pulled his hat down and looked away. He wasn't anxious to be recognized now.

"Look, *jefe,*" Pete whispered.

He glanced back. The first man was Major Jones—there was no mistaking that figure. Pete thought he recognized Grady Scott but couldn't be sure. He swore when he recognized the third man—Pakebusch— cringing between the others.

"How'd Pakebusch get here?" Pete growled. "That *cobarde* will tell all he knows." He whirled his mount. But he had two to manage and the swiftness of his movement startled them. The led horse lunged.

"No, Pete, no!" Rowden warned. "Don't shoot now or they'll be right on our heels." He dug in his spurs.

The warning came too late. Pete's gun was out. The rearing horses spoiled his first shot. His second sent Pakebusch sliding down the steps. The major had drawn his weapons and returned the fire. One of the horses shrilled as it went down. Pete hunched forward along his mount's neck, went careening after Rowden.

"You'll have the Rangers on our heels now sure," Rowden exclaimed, once the town was left behind.

"*Quién sabe?* If they listened to Pakebusch our time was short, *amigo.* Did you see who else was there?"

"Grady Scott? Did you get him?"

"My horse was bucking," Pete complained. "*Quizás.* He didn't shoot back. That makes me hope."

They thundered on westward, all caution abandoned now.

Chapter 29 SHOWDOWN

GRADY dived for the floor when the bullets started singing. The major hadn't returned his weapons and Grady was helpless in the duel. He pointed at his empty holsters after Pete escaped. "Your guns are on my table." Major Jones bent over Pakebusch's body. "Go get them."

The pursuit was quickly organized. The shots had been heard at the Ranger camp. Several of the Rangers already had arrived when Grady returned, wearing his six guns, and the major had sent back orders for his full force, mounted and ready to ride.

Letty knelt beside Pakebusch. "It's no use, Major Jones. He's dead."

"I thought so." He turned to Grady. "Did you see who it was?"

"Sheriff Rowden was on the dun horse but he didn't do the shooting. I can't be sure but I think the gun was Pete Falkner's."

"And bound for Scalp Creek, I reckon. That's where their outfit is. Well, get your horse, Grady. That's where we're headed, too."

Letty tried to stop him as he turned away. "I want to tell you something, Grady."

"Not now. I'm in a hurry."

"I'll go with you after your horse."

"Tell me where your mount is, Scott. I'll fetch him," Major Reynolds volunteered. "That'll give you a little time."

Grady didn't want to face Letty. The way she'd jumped between him and Jones to prevent a shooting had won his reluctant admiration but he hadn't forgotten her betrayal. "No. I want to look after him myself. There's a hard trip ahead and he hasn't been fed."

As he strode off, he heard someone following him and was angered by it. "Go on back," he warned. "I reckon after what's happened, the less we see of each other the better."

"Huh?" Major Reynolds grunted. "What's got into you?"

Grady waited for him then. "I thought that girl was following me and I didn't want to see her."

"If this is what the settlements are like, I don't blame you for coming back." His friend chuckled. "Do pretty gals trail you around here? Matter of fact, that one wouldn't have to follow me far. She strikes me as the right sort."

They had reached the trees back of the hotel. Grady loosed the rope that picketed his horse. "I'm surprised you still think so. You're the one who warned me against her."

"Me? What are you talking about?"

"At Spy Butte. You said she told you where to find me."

"I warned you against a girl but this isn't the one, Grady."

"What are you saying?"

"The girl who betrayed you had yellow hair. It wasn't Letty."

Grady didn't answer right away. He couldn't. Yellow hair! He felt dazed, as if Maj had struck him. "Here." He handed over the halter rope. "Take him to the wagon yard and get some oats in him, will you? I've got to see Letty."

He couldn't find her out front where the riders were gathering. He went inside. The front room was deserted but a lamp was burning on the desk. He picked it up, explored back to the kitchen, calling her name as he went, but there was no one there. "Letty!" he called sharply from the foot of the stairs. He had to see her. He couldn't remember what he'd said but he didn't want her hurt. Outside they were calling his name. The major was ready to ride. Grady continued up the stairs. The corridor was dark, every door shut, and there was no telltale light beneath any of them. "Letty," he called again, without result.

"Come on, Scott. We're waiting for you," the major shouted.

He walked heavily down the stairs, left the lamp on the desk. What's the difference? he thought. Nothing seemed to matter any more. Reynolds was waiting with his horse. He swung into the saddle.

They didn't ride hard. The major was thinking of the sixty miles ahead and set a gait they could hold. He wanted to know all about the Scalp Creek Breaks and kept Grady at his side to answer questions. "I think I know Rowden now. He won't leave that herd behind if he can help it. What's his best way out?"

"Down the valley would be easiest, of course, but now that we're closing in he couldn't make it. He's smart enough to know that. There's an old Comanche trail across the hills. Rough going but he might try it."

Jones nodded. "I think he will. That's why I aim to circle around, cut off his escape and hit him from that side. That will drive him this way of course. Where are the cowmen?"

Grady told him of the meeting place on Spy Butte. "There will be about thirty good men there. They promised to wait while I took Pakebusch in and got in touch with you. If I don't show up by tomorrow they aim to head for Scalp Creek themselves."

"Keeping to the hills, I reckon, sweeping in from the north."

"That's the best cover for a surprise attack."

Major Jones planned his campaign to make use of this knowledge. He measured the distances in his mind, gauged the time and outlined his plan for Grady. "I'll cross the river at Lazy B headquarters, keep south of it till we hit the Breaks before I circle to get behind them. Allowing twelve hours, we should be close to our position by midday, but that's not allowing for the rough country up yonder nor for slow going to keep under cover. Give me two hours extra for that.

"I'm sending you to Spy Butte to join your friends. Their plan's good. Don't change it, except that I'm depending on them to close this way out. Be sure I have time to get in position. Then we'll close in all at once, get the Rowden gang and the cattle too."

"I understand. Two hours after midday." Grady angled his horse northward toward Spy Butte.

By sunup he'd left the valley floor. Hills mounded his path here. Off north they scalloped the horizon. This was near the path he'd ridden with Pakebusch. His eyes turned sharp at sight of buzzards wheeling. He checked his horse to watch as their numbers grew. They drifted in lazy circles. It was a sign he'd been taught to investigate, but this morning his errand was too urgent. He started on, then changed his mind. It wasn't more than half a mile out of his way. He had plenty of time.

Carl felt no pain when he opened his eyes. He didn't remember what had happened. This was much like many another camp where he'd awakened lately. He lay quiet, listened. No one else was stirring yet. He felt tired. It would be good to drowse a little longer. Still, it must be late. He squinted at the sun, saw its position. That puzzled him. He tried to rise.

The flame went right through his body, like the stab of a branding iron. He fell back, clutching at his shirt. His hand came away wet. He stared at his fingers and saw that they were red.

Then he remembered.

He gritted his teeth against the dizziness. By turning only his head he could peer around him. Over there, about a hundred yards away, his horse grazed, reins dangling. Almost within reach of his hand, his pistol lay gleaming in the sun. There was no sign of Pete Falkner. Carl wondered how long he'd been gone.

He tried to think what to do. One thing was sure, he couldn't stay here. He was far off the familiar valley trail. It might be months before a rider came this way again. He wondered how badly he was hurt and stared again at his horse, thankful for those trailing reins that had kept the animal here. Still he seemed a long way off, when he remembered how it hurt to move.

Carl rested a little before making the attempt. He stirred cautiously, twisting first onto his side. The pain seared him again. He gasped, wanted to stop, but was afraid to rest. The longer I put it off the weaker I'll be, he decided. He reached his knees, found he could get no farther. When he stared at the horse now, the distance seemed to have grown.

I've got to reach him . . . I've got to, he kept repeating as he started to crawl. I can reach a stirrup, pull myself up by that.

The movement started his wound bleeding again. He pressed his hand against it, tried to hold back the flow. That didn't help. The pain dragged at him; it made his progress slow. The throb had become a hammer now, pounding in his ears. He kept moving, pulling himself along the ground, his eyes fixed on his mount.

So near now. The horse raised its head, ears cocked suspiciously. Carl inched closer; he raised his arm.

The bronc snorted, pranced away. This was something the animal didn't understand. He moved only a few feet but to the pain-racked boy the distance seemed vast.

Again he crept close; again the animal wheeled and eluded him.

It's the crawling that spooks him, Carl decided. If I can just get on my feet, he won't dodge. Having thought out each move carefully, he drew his legs up under him for the effort, his hands clenched in the grass for balance.

He choked back the agony, forced himself upward until he gradually reached his feet. The horse stood watchful, but didn't move. I was right, Carl exulted. Only a step or two now. He stretched out his arm, staggered forward—one step—two. He couldn't force his strength further; he knew he was going to fall. He clutched for the dangling reins. as he tottered. Then everything went black.

When he opened his eyes again it was nearly dusk. He was no longer alone. I'm glad you found me, he thought. His eyes were blurred with fever. He stared through a haze of pain at the silent figures which ringed him. Why didn't they help him? Why didn't someone say something?"

"Help me," he groaned. "Help me."

The circle stirred at sound of his voice. Great wings flapped noisily. In their first launching, the thin whistle of air through their feathered arms sounded like the creak of rusty hinges.

"Buzzards!" Carl croaked. "Buzzards! They think I'm already dead!" He wondered about it himself, before he drifted off into unconsciousness again.

Grady was glad he'd turned when, around the next hill, he saw a saddled pony grazing. He broke into a canter then, forgot his caution and rode in a straight line for the guiding birds. They scattered at his approach. He found Carl.

The boy was unconscious but his pulse still fluttered faintly. He'd lost a lot of blood. Grady pulled back the crusted shirt for a look at the wound. It was near the center of the body with a perforation at the back where the bullet had gone on through. So far so good. He pressed his ear against it to listen. There was no telltale foam as Carl breathed, no sound of bubbling air. Too low for the lungs, he decided. He's got a chance. A body wound was hard to bandage. Grady used his knife on his blanket, cut out two pads for front and back. The rest he cut in strips, knotted them together, wound them tight around Carl's body to hold the dressings in place. It worried him that Carl didn't open his eyes during all this.

The horse was skittish. It swerved at his approach, so he roped it and lashed Carl, face down, across the saddle. Then Grady headed for Spy Butte.

The rannies swore when they recognized Carl. They'd liked this boy. "Another score to settle," said Soames.

"He's not dead yet. I think he's got a chance, if we can get him to Ma," Grady explained. He looked at Peg.

"I was countin' on bein' in at the finish of this, Grady."

"That would be too late for Carl. I'd take him in myself, but I'm the one who scouted out the Breaks. I'll be needed."

Peg threw a saddle over his horse. "I'd best get started then. This young'un' larned me to like some Germans, right much."

Rowden's dun horse had played out. He'd shifted mounts. Pete Falkner, a lighter and better horseman, kept pace easily. He had spotted smoke over Spy Butte, pointed it out. "*Mire, jefe—humo.* These *vaqueros* grow careless. That is where we will find Charlie Springer."

"Not now," Rowden warned.

"No, we will keep out of sight *ahora* but they have shown me where to come. I will be back."

They turned south to avoid the mountain and reached the Breaks unseen. They found seven of Pete's riders in camp there, uneasy since Charlie Springer's party had failed to return. "We was about ready to high-tail it out of here," said Taos, a rawboned rider with a knife seam down his face. "We aimed to leave tonight if we didn't git word from you by then."

"Rustle up fresh horses," Rowden ordered. "We're going now and we're taking our herd with us. There's a nice split here for everybody if we move fast."

"*Pero* not yet, *jefe.* First we have business at Spy Butte. I am going back for Charlie Springer." Falkner told the others what had happened.

"There are only nine of us left," Rowden objected. "What chance would we have against the whole valley?"

"I counted the *hombres* who surprised Charlie," Pete retorted. "There were only nine of them. Just ordinary rannies. They would be no match for a gun-wise outfit like this."

"If we go back we'll lose the herd," the sheriff pointed out. He tried to measure the effect of that statement on this hard-faced circle. "There's a neat little fortune here. Shall we throw it away? Charlie lost a good gamble, that's all."

"*Oiga, amigos.* You know what it means to be caught—rope meat." Pete spoke quietly. "If you were one of those prisoners you would like to know Pete Falkner had not forgotten you—no? What is a herd of cattle? We will find more. But after a man's neck has been stretched——" He shrugged.

Rowden argued but he discovered Pete Falkner was the leader here. These were his men. Rowden suggested starting the herd, dropping out two men to keep it moving while the others turned back.

Pete vetoed that, too. "We will ride *juntamente*."

"That's it," Taos agreed. "We'll stick together."

Rowden didn't dare say more. He had to go along. Even if he could slip away undetected, he realized he didn't know the trail across the hills. He fumed at his helplessness, considered the venture brash, but now kept his thoughts to himself. Pete led the way, kept to the easy cover of the broken hills.

"They won't expect us from the north," he explained. "*Esconderemos* in the hills until dark. Then we will move in."

Grady led the way. This was the path he'd used when scouting the Breaks. Curly rode beside him. Behind them the column, warned against talk here, moved quietly. The sun was straight overhead. They wanted to be in position, overlooking the outlaw camp, before the Rangers made their move. This rugged country was lightly grazed, crowded with thickets. Curly pointed out how birds sheltered in the brush. Quail rose whirring at their approach. Their way progressed through a series of narrow valleys. At the head of each, the two leaders paused, studied the trail ahead before they entered.

Grady moved slowly around the shoulder of a hill at the head of such a boulder-strewn depression and halted to peer ahead. "It looks all right," he decided. "We're still several miles above their camp."

"No, wait." Curly pointed ahead where birds were rising. "Somethin's stirrin' 'em up. Let's bide our time a spell."

He left his horse to scramble up the hill. From there he could look down into the shallow saucer, peer over the brush. Grady knew by the caution of his return that he'd seen something.

"Hyar they come," he announced. "Nine of 'em. 'Pears to me like thar a-huntin' us." He studied the rugged pass. "Couldn't pick a likelier spot fer a meetin'. I'll beckon up the boys."

The cowmen left their horses behind, crawled into position. They lined the sloping ridge to wait. Each boulder sheltered a marksman. By the time they were ready the clatter of hoofs was audible.

Pete Falkner was shrewd. Taos was his best hand in rough country and was sent ahead to pick the way. He rode into the gap and stopped. The hills around him bristled with men but no one stirred. He didn't see them. It was the trail ahead that bothered him, for there he'd spotted grazing horses. Their empty saddles warned him. He knew he must be covered; he didn't dare betray his knowledge by peering around, and it was too late to turn back. There was a cedar brake not a hundred feet ahead. It offered cover. He started for it, careful of each deliberate movement. He'd draw fire if he showed alarm.

Pete hesitated. Taos had not signaled them but had ridden on. His riders started forward. "Wait for Taos' *señal*," Pete cautioned.

As he neared the cedar, Taos swerved toward it, dug in his spurs to crash his horse into the shelter. Curly's six gun already was leveled. He squeezed the trigger. The animal floundered through the green screen out of sight, left its lifeless rider dangling in the brush.

The blast of Curly's gun was followed by a volley from the ridge. It caught most of the outlaws in the open. Four went down in that first deadly hail. Pete reined back in the shelter of some boulders. His six gun spoke when he saw a careless movement along the hill ahead. One ranny less, he thought. Off to his right another gun chattered. He liked its sound. We are not all gone, he decided grimly, looking around to take stock. Two men had escaped. He could see them down the valley, riding hard. One was Rowden. He didn't recognize the other. He counted the bodies sprawled in the grass, summed up the odds. Just two of them left here. All the while his eyes were busy scanning the hill for movement. Twice he fired. It was time to get out but first he'd make that position unhealthy for any who watched.

He located his remaining companion by the sound of his guns, behind a near-by ledge of rock. "Time to go, *amigo*," he called softly. "Can you hear me? Are you ready?"

"I been ready a long time, Pete."

This time Pete used his Winchester, sprayed its lead up and down the slope. "Keep your head down, *muchacho*," he muttered. Then he brought the barrel down hard against his horse's flank, sent him racing down the trail. Lead whined around him. He knew when his companion went down. The horse shrilled when it was hit. Glancing back, he saw the rider roll free, regain his feet, then wilt when the bullets found him.

Pete thought he was going to make it. He was half the length of the valley away, beyond range of pistols now. Bullets had stopped their scream around him. Only a rifle could reach him.

He felt the shudder of his horse, knew he'd been hit. The animal floundered a few more steps before it went down. Pete pitched clear, landed on his shoulder and kept rolling to the shelter of an agrita clump. There were plenty of spare horses back at camp if he could reach it. He kept crawling, using all the cover he could find for another hundred yards. There a large thicket offered shelter. Once beyond it, he got to his feet and ran.

Soames was impatient with the delay. He wanted Rowden most of all and he had escaped. "Get the horses. Don't let 'em get away," he shouted.

Grady restrained him until after Pete broke cover. "No use exposing yourself. Don't worry. They won't get far."

The pursuit started after Pete's horse went down. Grady led it. "Remember Pete's mine," he said. "I've still got a score to settle. You go after the others."

There were two canyons at the end of this valley, each offering a trail. Curly forked to the left, led the column to intercept anyone trying to escape eastward. The other led toward the outlaw camp. Grady rode it alone.

"Don't bite off more'n you can chew," Curly warned. "Look out he don't dry-gulch you."

Grady didn't underestimate his opponent. A gun slinger of Pete's type could be more dangerous afoot and cornered than mounted and in flight. I'll swap him the first shot for the last one, he thought grimly. Just so I get the job finished. After that I wouldn't much care. He hadn't been able to shake the thought of Clee's duplicity all day.

He dismounted when he reached Falkner's inert horse, examined the saddle, found the mark he'd left there with his knife. This was the only evidence he lacked. The tapaderos already had been identified as Charlie Springer's. Now he knew the men who'd waited to shoot him down the night he escaped from the jail.

The next valley was a short one and it offered plenty of cover. Pete's anxious to get a horse. He'll go on through, Grady decided when he saw it. He turned west across a fold in the hills, found a parallel path and took it at a gallop. When he reached its end, he was sure he was in the lead. He tethered his horse in some scrub, made his way back toward the trail cautiously.

Rowden was on a strange horse; he wasn't familiar with this rough terrain. His breakneck pace was suited to neither. The animal was winded. Will dug in his spurs, forced it through the narrow pass at a gallop. There'd be fresh mounts back at camp. The floundering horse lost its footing on the rough trail, stumbled across some rocks, and slid to its knees, tossing its rider free before it toppled, head foremost, into the arroyo.

The fall bruised Rowden. He scrambled to his feet quickly enough, but when he tried to run, his leg gave way. It had been badly wrenched. He swore. It still was a couple of miles back to the camp corrals. He'd never make it now.

He dragged himself off the trail. There must be some place in this rough valley where he could hide. It was filled with scrubby thickets. He chose one of these, burrowed his way in. A branch caught on his sleeve and tore it. A brittle twig scraped across his cheek, drawing blood. He lunged on blindly, until he reached the heart of the tangle. When he stopped his panting sounded loud. He held his breath to listen. There was no sound. He had outdistanced pursuit.

His feeling of safety grew as he waited. Who would think to hunt him here? They'd watch the trails. Perhaps his hidden camp already had been found. If so, it had become a trap by now. No, this was best. Here he could wait until they'd given up the chase. After a few days of fruitless search, they'd decide he had escaped. By then his leg would be mended, too. It was a good thing his horse fell where it did.

He cursed Falkner for his folly. If it hadn't been for that foolhardy decision to rescue Charlie Springer they'd be far away by now, herding a fortune in beeves across Little Scalp pass. Oh, well, Falkner had paid for his mistake. Rowden was sure he hadn't survived that first murderous fire back yonder.

His lieutenants were gone. The valley had been bad medicine for them—all but him. He still had those bank deposits in St. Louis. They'd been growing all this time—of late, faster than ever. He'd always known the wisdom of getting his money out where he could reach it when a time like this came. Once this crisis was past, he'd make his way there. Why, he'd be a rich man, live in luxury. If Clee hadn't been such a fool—— He scowled at thought of her.

He heard the scrape of a boot and caught his breath. Someone was creeping past the screen of his thicket. He drew his six gun silently, peered through the greenery until he saw the man slipping past, still as a shadow.

He raised his arm, squinted along the barrel.

Pete's caution grew as he advanced. He paused at the draw, listened to the distant sound of horses. They'd be here, *muy pronto*. He was tempted to make his fight here. One man could do a lot of damage in a narrow pass. He decided against it. That was all right for a last stand, when there was no hope. He wasn't convinced of that yet.

He decided that they'd overtake him before he could reach the horses back at camp, though. He slipped silently down into the little valley. This was the best play. A horseman was easy to spot, but there was lots of cover in the Breaks for a lone man afoot.

Grady waited by the trail, sure Pete would come soon. How else would he reach a horse? The minutes dragged. Finally he realized what had happened. Falkner, fearful of a trap, had taken cover. But he's still here. I'll find him, Grady thought.

He raised his head cautiously, scanned the valley for movement. Less than a mile in length and only a quarter that in width, it was hedged in by bare ridges where a man would make an easy target. Its floor was strewn with boulders, though, and shaggy with thickets. Plenty of cover here.

Grady started forward, slid cautiously from boulder to shrub, exploring as he went. Twice he worked his way across the valley's width and found nothing. He stopped to listen, heard no sound, but not far distant he saw quail rising and remembered how that had betrayed the outlaw column. He watched the spot and was rewarded presently by the shiver of greenery in a thicket there. Someone was using its cover. He eased out and began a careful circle toward it.

Once located, his enemy wasn't hard to trace. The swaying of a branch, a mockingbird's scolding—each made its contribution. One time he glimpsed his prey, a shadow sliding swiftly behind a boulder, still too far to risk a shot. Grady set his course to intercept Falkner's, stalked him silently. His pistols were eased in their holsters now, and ready.

Rowden held his six gun steady. He was sure he knew the meaning of this skulking figure. Someone had picked up his trail. There was no telling who it was—the fellow's back still was turned. What did it matter?

Unconsciously he bared his teeth. They'll never take me—not alive, Rowden thought. He squeezed the trigger.

The gun's crash caught Grady offguard. It came from the heart of the live oak motte toward which he was moving. He dropped to the ground, gun ready. He'd heard no bullet's whine.

Rowden knew he hadn't missed. He saw his victim fall. If anyone else were near, that shot would bring them running. He listened, heard nothing. It was all right. There'd been only a single man on his trail. He wondered who it was. He stared out at the still form, face down in the brown grass, and his curiosity grew. He decided to see.

He was careless of sound now. Who could move quietly through this jungle? Snapping twigs marked his path. He stepped out into the sunlight and stooped to turn the body over. He grunted his surprise when he recognized Pete.

When Grady saw Rowden, he returned his six gun to its holster. He didn't want a prisoner, not this one. Pakebusch's story of Tom's helpless end was too sore in his mind. He wanted Rowden to go for his gun. Strangely, too, even in this guarded moment, Clee crowded his mind. These weren't the aching thoughts that had galled him all day, but were memories of the Clee who had saved him once from this man who had humiliated her. He stepped into the clear and his shadow fell across the body.

Rowden saw it and looked up. His body froze. Only his eyes moved, darting quickly right and left. Their panic died and they turned malevolent when he discovered Grady was alone and that his guns were in their holsters.

"In the back. From a dry-gulch. I might have guessed it was you, Rowden."

Grady stood with feet spread, leaning slightly forward, weight nicely balanced. His arms hung loosely at his sides. Rowden knew how to measure that stance. It had the menace of a tensed trigger spring.

He didn't try to rise. It was better this way, he thought, for here his crouched body half hid his right arm. By stretching his fingers he could touch the butt of his pistol. Its feel was reassuring.

"I wish this was you lying here, Scott. I got the wrong man."

He used the words to cover his cautious movement. His wrist edged downward. His fingers closed on the gun's grip.

Grady, watching his eyes, read the deadly purpose in those narrowing pupils. His hand flicked when Rowden's shoulder nudged forward.

There were two gun blasts, one an echo of the other. Grady's bullet toppled Rowden. The second, late, plowed a furrow in the flinty ground before it screamed off into the air harmlessly.

Having spied the two riders first, Peg came hobbling toward the corral to meet them.

"How's Carl?" Curly voiced the anxiety in both their minds.

"He's goin' to make it." Peg grinned, jerked a thumb toward the dining room. "Ma fixed him a bunk in thar, handy to the kitchen—so's she could get some chores out of Ohmie, I reckon. Shucks, it'd be worth a bullet, just to have the womenfolks make such a fuss over you. I never seed the beat of it. That gal cain't leave him alone long enough to peel taters. Good thing I'm hyar, or we'd never get any vittles on the table."

Ma grinned. She'd arrived in time to hear the last of Peg's complaint. "Sure, we've got to take good care of that young'un. Hell's bells, I want him up in time for the weddin', don't I?"

Grady laughed. "Have they set the date already?"

Ma shrugged. "They've been so busy, makin' moon eyes, I'm not sure they know it yet. But anybody with two eyes in his head can see that's the way it's meant to be, with that pair." Her smile faded. She turned serious. "That's the best hope there is for peace in this valley— young'uns like them. It's not so hard, hatin' somebody you don't know. But we know 'em both. Sure, they're German—good German. I reckon Carl takes after his father. Not a cowman in the valley doesn't like him, now he knows him, either.

"That's what we need here most, understandin'. It's Carl an' Ohmie, an' others like 'em, that will give us that. Then nobody will smoke up this valley again—ever."

Curly told the story of the final battle in the Breaks, the death of Rowden, the breaking up of his gang. Ma stayed on, worrying Grady for the details, after Curly followed Peg in to see Carl. Several times during his recital, her attention strayed. She kept glancing back toward the house.

"Clee'll want to hear this," she finally broke in. "Suppose you go tell her, Grady."

He hesitated. So Clee was still here. He'd wondered about that. When he thought of her, everything was confused. It would be better if he didn't see her again. The hurt of her betrayal stood between them. Why had she done it? Why had she saved him once—then turned against him later? Why? Why? All day he'd probed his mind with such questions. And yet he longed for the sight of her. It angered him, that persistent hunger for her. Hadn't he learned his lesson? He'd better get out of here.

Ma saw his hesitation. "What's wrong, son? 'T ain't Letty, is it?"

"No. I'd be better off if it was."

"That's just what you think."

"Clee doesn't want to face me. Not now."

Ma shook her head. "Sounds serious. 'T ain't like either one of you to fuss."

He kept his eyes on the distant corral and refused to be drawn out. "I reckon it's time for me to be movin' on. My job here's done."

"That's not you talkin', Grady. I never knew you to turn tail an' run before. Not from anything."

"Run?" His resentment flickered. Then his voice turned flat. "Maybe you're right. But some things haven't got an answer, Ma. When you strike questions like that, they're best left unasked."

"Even if they leave you all torn up inside?"

"Yes, even then."

"You've told me all I need to know. Nobody can hurt you like that unless you love 'em, son. When the pain's in your heart, you can't leave it behind, no matter how far you ride—nor how fast."

He tried to interrupt, but she stopped him. "Take Clee now. Lots of spunk in that filly. Far as I know she never shed a tear in her life till the other night. She came ridin' in from Spy Butte way, actin' 'bout like you do now. When I tried to get at the bottom of her trouble, she went all to pieces. All I could make out was, she was plumb sick with worry over you.

"Yes, an' she'd been hurt, too. Bad hurt. She wouldn't talk to me, but I could tell. Next morning she headed out for Spy Butte again. I watched her go an' was glad, 'cause I knew whatever the trouble was, she'd settled it in her own mind. The only thing that mattered was findin' you.'

"That's how she lost her mare. She ran into Pete Falkner an' he set her afoot. 'T wasn't losin' the horse she minded. What seemed to set her crazy was not bein' able to reach you. She's been hard to live with, ever since."

"What are you trying to tell me, Ma?"

"How do I know when I can't figure it out myself?" She brushed her palms together in disgust. "She traipses all over the country after you; now you're here in easy reach and how does she act?"

He looked toward the house, still hesitated. "I wish you were right, Ma, but——"

"Hell's bells! It's catchin'! Damned if you ain't as stubborn as she is, standin' here wastin' time. If I ever saw two folks achin' for each other it's you an' Clee." She gave him a shove. "Get on in there; it's high time you did somethin' about it."

He started toward the house.

"Grady!"

"Yes, Ma?"

"Start fresh, son. Plenty of time for those questions later."

He heard her snort, "Hell's bells," again as she strode off toward the kitchen.

Grady opened the door hesitantly and squared his shoulders before he went in. Clee was waiting for him. All the torment that had bothered him that day was in her face, too. He saw it, forgot his own doubts.

"Grady, you've come back."

"What could keep me away from you, Clee? What could keep me away?"

NORTHERN
TRAIL USED BY C
SCALP CREEK BREAKS
SCALP CREEK
SPY BUTTE
Forked W Range
APACHE
RIVER
15 MILES
18 MILES
La
FORKED W HEADQUARTERS
APACHE
16
APACHE VALLEY
20 MILES
28 MILES
Snake on a Rock Range
SNAKE ON A ROCK HEADQUARTERS
SOUTHERN HILLS